POLAROGRAPHY
Second Edition

By I. M. Kolthoff and James J. Lingane

VOLUME I:
  Theoretical Principles
  Instrumentation and Technique

VOLUME II:
  Inorganic Polarography
  Organic Polarography
    (with the collaboration of S. Wawzonek)
  Biological Applications
  Amperometric Titrations

PROFESSOR JAROSLAV HEYROVSKY

Originator of Polarographic Analysis
to whom this book is dedicated

POLAROGRAPHY

Second completely revised
and augmented edition

In Two Volumes

I. M. KOLTHOFF

*Professor and Head of Division
of Analytical Chemistry
University of Minnesota
Minneapolis, Minnesota*

JAMES J. LINGANE

*Professor of Chemistry
Harvard University
Cambridge, Massachusetts*

VOLUME I

Theoretical Principles

Instrumentation and Technique

INTERSCIENCE PUBLISHERS

a division of John Wiley & Sons, Inc., New York · London · Sydney

Preface to the Second Edition

In the dozen years since the first edition of this book appeared, the polarographic literature has tripled in size and the current rate of growth exceeds 200 journal articles per year. The advances in both factual knowledge and theoretical interpretation presented by these new contributions have been so extensive that it was necessary to reorganize completely and rewrite most of the original chapters—and to write several new ones—in preparing this revision.

Among the new chapters are Chapter V, in which general characteristics of nonaqueous solvent media are summarized, Chapter VI, which discusses some unusual phenomena associated with the diffusion current, and Chapter XV, in which the characteristics of limiting currents that depend on reaction rates—"kinetic currents"—are described. The new Chapter XVIII, which summarizes important experimental factors that must be considered in polarographic measurements and operations and techniques commonly used, has been added to orient the beginner and assist him in getting started in practical polarographic analysis. The chapters in Part Three on the polarographic chemistry of the elements, and those in Part Four on the polarography of carbon compounds, have been so drastically revised and reorganized that they are virtually new.

Although the increased size necessitated division into two volumes, we have adhered to the same general plan and aims described in the following Preface to the First Edition. The present Volume I is concerned with theoretical principles, practical fundamentals, instrumentation, and methodology. Volume II comprises the polarographic chemistry of the elements and selected practical analytical procedures for their determination, the polarography of organic substances, biological applications, and amperometric titrations. Author and subject indexes are at the end of Volume II.

Although insight into certain aspects of polarographic theory has deepened in recent years, some other aspects still lack satisfactory interpretation and require much more fundamental study. For example the pioneering studies of R. Brdicka in Prague have greatly clarified the interpretation of limiting currents controlled by reaction rates, but certain quantitative aspects of the interpretation are still incomplete. Refinements in the interpretation of diffusion controlled currents have enhanced our ability to better control the many factors which influence the diffusion current in practical polarographic analysis, but there are still many puzzles. We are less ignorant than we were ten years ago about various kinds of catalytic processes that are observed with the dropping electrode. On the other hand, the cause of maxima in polarographic waves, and the functional mechanism of maximum suppressors, is still as good a subject for debate as ever. Much the same is true as regards the interpretation of polarographic waves resulting from irreversible reactions, and indeed the whole problem of the detailed mechanisms of electrode reactions remains a topic for further study. However, recent innovations in the methodology of attacking such problems, notably the increasing use of the cathode ray oscilloscope, give promise of accelerating their solution.

Symptomatic of the approach of polarography to practical maturity, the great majority of current publications describe applications to specific analytical problems. Because it was not feasible to discuss all these specialized applications critically, we selected for detailed description those practical procedures which seemed best to exemplify different tactical approaches to a particular kind of analytical problem, which we judged to be the most reliable and convenient of similar published procedures, and which appear to be most catholic in application. Other specialized applications may be located easily by consulting the bibliographies listed at the end of Chapter I.

The widespread adaptation of polarography to problems peculiar to the various fields of chemistry, and to related disciplines such as biology and geology, coupled with our limited competence outside our own fields, makes it increasingly difficult to present a complete critical account of the entire literature. We hope the time is near when textbooks in realms outside of analytical, inorganic, and physical chemistry will discuss specific polarographic applications in their special fields with sufficient thoroughness so that they will not have to be treated in a monograph on polarography. In this connection we are especially indebted to Professor Stanley Wawzonek of the University of Iowa, who contributed greatly to the major task of reorganizing the chapters on Organic Polarography in Part Four. Similarly, Dr. W. Stricks of the University of Minnesota gathered much information for the preparation of the enlarged Part Five on Biological Applications. We are also grateful to Dr. Clemens Auerbach for his assistance in combing the literature for the revision of Part Three on Inorganic Polarography.

We believe the literature coverage is reasonably complete up through 1950, but, except for a few cases, it has not been possible to include more recent references. Several good polarographic bibliographies are now available, and these are listed on pages 15–17 at the end of Chapter I. That of J. Heyrovsky, published as Part II of the Proceedings of 1st International Polarographic Congress, Prague, 1951, is the most recent and complete.

Minneapolis, Minnesota   I. M. KOLTHOFF
Cambridge, Massachusetts   JAMES J. LINGANE
February 15, 1952

From the Preface to the First Edition

When an electrolyte solution is electrolyzed in a cell consisting of a dropping mercury electrode and a second non-polarizible electrode it is possible to determine from the resulting current–voltage curve both the nature and concentration of the reducible or oxidizable substance, or substances, present. This is the essence of polarographic analysis, for whose invention and pioneer development we are indebted to Professor Jaroslav Heyrovsky and his colleagues at the Charles University in Prague.

Although the polarographic method has developed rapidly during the twenty years of its existence, and the literature in the field now comprises more than four hundred journal articles, no complete monograph on the subject has heretofore been published in the English language. Since interest in the method has been growing rapidly in this country during the last few years, and in view of the fact that most of the pertinent literature is scattered through foreign journals of relatively limited circulation, we have felt the need of a monograph in which the theoretical principles and practical applications of polarographic analysis would be correlated and systematized. It was to fill this need that the present book was written.

We have attempted to present a complete and critical account of the present status of polarographic analysis with the dropping mercury electrode, as well as related techniques with platinum microelectrodes, and the newly developed "amperometric titration" methods. For this purpose it has seemed most expedient to divide the book into the several parts indicated in the Table of Contents.

Part One consists of an outline of the general principles of polarography, and a brief résumé of its applications in the various branches of chemistry and allied fields.

This is followed in Part Two by twelve chapters that deal with those theoretical principles that are essential to the rational practical applications of the method. The characteristics of polarographic current-voltage curves are influenced by many different factors, and a thorough understanding of these is a *conditio sine qua non* in the successful use of the polarographic method. The treatment in these chapters probably goes beyond the immediate needs of the practical analytical chemist, but we feel that it is justified in view of the fact that the usefulness of the polarographic method extends beyond the realm of applied analytical chemistry, and it is proving to be a powerful tool in the solution of more abstract problems in chemistry and related fields. It can be applied advantageously to the study of electrode reactions, overvoltage, and the electrokinetic phenomena at a mercury-electrolyte solution interface; to the determination of

ix

diffusion coefficients of ions and uncharged molecules; as an analytical tool in the study of rates and equilibria of both inorganic and organic reactions; as a "pilot technique" to obtain information about optimum conditions in electrochemical preparative work; as a simple means of obtaining valuable information about the oxidation-reduction behavior of many inorganic and organic systems that are inaccessible to the classical methods: and in the study of the nature and dissociation constants of complex metal ions.

The apparatus and technique of polarographic analysis is discussed in the two chapters of Part Three.

Inorganic polarographic analysis is discussed in Part Four, which contains all the available data on the polarographic behavior of inorganic substances and the procedures that have been developed for the determination of the various elements. In Chapter XXV procedures that have been recommended for the analysis of common technical materials, such as steel, brass, other alloys, and ores, are described in sufficient detail to permit their application without recourse to the original literature.

Part Five comprises several chapters that deal with the polarographic behavior of organic compounds, and all known data are included.

Applications of the polarographic technique in biological chemistry are discussed in Part Six.

The use of platinum microelectrodes, as substitutes for the dropping electrode in polarographic analysis, is discussed in Part Seven.

Part Eight contains a discussion of the theory of the newly developed "amperometric titration" method, and its practical applications.

Throughout the book we have tried to maintain a critical attitude in the interpretation of the literature, and to assign proper credit to original sources of information. The literature has been covered completely up to about the middle of December, 1940. However, a few papers published on the continent of Europe during 1940 may have been overlooked because some journals have not been available on account of the war.

It is our hope that this book will stimulate the further development of polarographic analysis and its applications in the various branches of chemical science. Criticisms and suggestions for improvement will be welcomed.

We express our appreciation to Dr. Herbert A. Laitinen for helpful suggestions and constructive criticism, especially in the preparation of the manuscript of Chapter II.

Minneapolis, Minnesota   I. M. KOLTHOFF
Berkeley, California   JAMES J. LINGANE
March 15, 1941

Contents—Volume I

Contents — Volume II

Part One

THEORETICAL PRINCIPLES

CHAPTER I

Introduction

The polarographic method of chemical analysis, invented by Jaroslav Heyrovsky at the Charles University in Prague about 1920,[1] is based on the unique characteristics of the current–voltage curves obtained when solutions of electrooxidizable or electroreducible substances are electrolyzed in a cell in which one electrode consists of mercury falling dropwise from a fine bore capillary glass tube. From such current–voltage curves it is possible not only to identify but also simultaneously to determine the concentrations of several or all of the reducible or oxidizable substances present, *i. e.*, simultaneously to obtain a qualitative and quantitative analysis of a solution. In favorable cases as many as five or six substances, present in concentrations ranging from 10^{-6} to 0.01 M, can be identified from a single current–voltage curve. Its adaptability to very small concentrations, coupled with the fact that the volume of solution required for an analysis need be only a small fraction of a milliliter, places polarography among the most sensitive analytical techniques. In addition to the majority of the elements, the method is applicable to the determination of a wide variety of organic substances, and it can be applied to solutions in nonaqueous (but polar) solvents and even to molten salts.

In 1925 Heyrovsky and Shikata[2] invented an instrument—the polarograph—which records dropping electrode c.v. curves automatically in a small fraction of the time required to obtain them point by point manually. Thus Professor Heyrovsky and his collaborators not only established the theoretical foundations of polarographic analysis but also led the way in providing the automatic instrumentation that is essential to the exploitation of any physicochemical method in analytical practice.

The term *polarography* was coined by Heyrovsky to designate the determination of current–voltage (c.v.) curves with the dropping mercury electrode, especially when such "polarization curves" are automatically recorded. Kolthoff and Laitinen[3] advocated the more descriptive general

---

[1] J. Heyrovsky, *Chem. Listy*, **16**, 256 (1922).

[2] J. Heyrovsky and M. Shikata, *Rec. trav. chim.*, **44**, 496 (1925).

[3] I. M. Kolthoff and H. A. Laitinen, *Science*, **92**, 152 (1940).

3

name *voltammetry* to indicate that voltage and current are the two quantities measured, the former providing *qualitative* information on the nature of the electroactive substance present and the latter *quantitative* indication of its concentration.   The term voltammetry may also be used to include cases in which the c.v. curve is measured manually, or when platinum or other microelectrodes are used in place of the dropping electrode.   The designation *amperometric*, as in *amperometric titrations*, has come into use to indicate concentration measurements based on the measurement of electrolysis current at a constant potential of the indicator electrode.

1. CHARACTERISTICS OF CURRENT-VOLTAGE CURVES WITH PLATINUM INDICATOR ELECTRODES

Electrolysis is the occurrence of chemical reactions, under the influence of an electromotive force, at electrodes immersed in solutions.   Electrode reactions are characterized by the transfer of electrons between the electrode and substances in the solution.   This electron transfer tends to unbalance the equality of positive and negative ions in the solution at the electrode surface, and this tendency is counteracted—and electroneutrality of the solution maintained—by the oppositely directed movement of positive and negative ions through the solution to produce the "flow of current through the solution," which actually is measured by the rate of movement of electrons in the external circuit connecting the two electrodes.   The current is the result, not the cause, of the electrode reactions.   When the electrode reactions occur spontaneously on short-circuiting the two electrodes we speak of a "galvanic cell," but when the reactions are forced to occur by the imposition of an external electromotive force the cell is referred to as an "electrolysis cell."   In either case the reaction at one electrode involves the transfer of electrons from the electrode to substances in the solution (reduction), and an exactly equivalent electron transfer from substances in the solution to the electrode (oxidation) occurs at the other electrode.   Regardless of its relative polarity (+ or − sign with respect to the other electrode), the electrode at which reduction occurs is the *cathode*, and the electrode at which oxidation takes place is the *anode*.   The curve obtained by plotting the e.m.f. applied to a cell against the resulting current is the *current-voltage curve*.

To illustrate the principles of voltammetry consider the electrolysis apparatus shown schematically in Fig. I-1.   Suppose that the cell contains a very dilute solution of thallous chloride (say 0.001 M) in a relatively large concentration of potassium chloride (*e. g.*, 0.1 M).   Because oxygen is easily reducible, and its reduction current more or less masks the currents of other substances, the cell is provided with a gas delivery tube through which nitrogen or hydrogen is passed to remove dissolved air from the solution. E is a short length of platinum wire which serves as the indicator electrode. The other electrode D is a silver–silver chloride electrode whose area is large enough (several cm.^{2}) so that it retains a practically constant potential (remains "depolarized") when the relatively small electrolysis current flows. ABC is a potential divider, powered by a battery, by means of which an e.m.f. from zero up to the battery voltage may be applied to the cell.

Before electrolysis the cell may be represented by

$$Ag \mid AgCl(s), K^+, Tl^+, Cl^- \mid Pt$$

and the potential of the silver–silver chloride electrode is found to be considerably more positive (more oxidizing) than the potential of a metallic

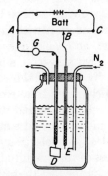

Fig. I-1. Electrolysis cell and platinum microelectrode.[5]

thallium electrode would be in this solution. The potential of the platinum indicator electrode in the oxygen-free thallous chloride–potassium chloride solution is indeterminate and variable, but it is more negative (more reducing) than that of the silver–silver chloride electrode. Consequently, if the cell were short-circuited practically no current would flow, because for this to occur a spontaneous cell reaction would have to take place involving the reduction of silver chloride to silver at the silver electrode and the oxidation of an equivalent amount of some substance at the platinum electrode. Since the solution does not contain any easily oxidized substance, and platinum itself is not oxidized under these conditions, the platinum electrode simply assumes the potential of the silver–silver chloride when the cell is short-circuited and no appreciable current passes. Under this condition the platinum electrode is said to be polarized, because its potential can be altered over a certain range without the occurrence at it of a continuous electrode reaction.

Actually a tiny current will flow *momentarily* when the above cell is short-circuited, corresponding to the change in charge density at the platinum electrode surface necessary to conform to the impressed potential. This "charging current" is analogous to the current which flows very briefly when a constant direct-current voltage is impressed on a condenser or capacitor. With an electrode of constant area the charging current flows for such an exceedingly short time that its influence on a direct-current measuring device is negligible, but it is significant with the dropping mercury electrode whose surface is continuously renewed (see Chap. IX). A current that flows continuously at an electrode of constant area at a constant potential necessarily must follow Faraday's Law, and it is with this "Faradaic current" that we are presently concerned.

The expressions "polarized electrode" and "depolarized electrode" should be clearly understood. An electrode is said to be polarized when it adopts the potential externally impressed on it with little or no change in the rate of the electrode reaction, *i. e.*, no change in current. The current may be zero, as in the example above, or it may have a finite value. This condition is recognized experimentally by the fact that the potential of a polarized electrode varies greatly with changing total e.m.f. applied to the cell, and if only one electrode of the cell is polarized its potential changes by the same amount as the change in the applied e.m.f.

At the other extreme an ideally depolarized electrode is one that retains a constant potential regardless of the magnitude of the current, and it can be recognized experimentally by the fact that its potential is not altered by changes in the total e.m.f. applied to the cell. Polarization and depolarization are, of course, only relative terms and in practice various degrees of polarization are encountered depending on experimental conditions. In the case under consideration the silver–silver chloride electrode in 0.1 M potassium chloride behaves very nearly as an ideal depolarized electrode, and thus retains a constant potential, when the current density is small (*ca.* 10^{-4} amp. per cm.^{2} or less). Imposition of an external e.m.f. to this electrode causes the reaction

$$Ag + Cl^- \rightleftharpoons AgCl + e$$

to proceed either to the right or to the left. The potential is governed by the concentration of chloride ion, and because this concentration is relatively large it changes only slightly with changes in current when the current density is small.

If the chloride ion concentration were very small in the above case, *e. g.*, 10^{-5} M, even a relatively small reduction current would increase the chloride ion concentration markedly, and thus the potential of the silver–silver chloride electrode would change considerably to correspond to the change in chloride ion concentration *at the electrode surface*. This behavior, observed at an electrode which is reversible in the thermodynamic sense, is commonly called "concentration polarization," and it is the chief phenomenon on which polarography depends. The term "chemical polarization" is sometimes used to characterize instances in which an electrode does not respond rapidly to changes in the concentration of potential-determining ions at its surface.[4]

Suppose now that an e.m.f. is applied to the cell in Fig. I-1 in such a direction that the platinum electrode is made negative with respect to the

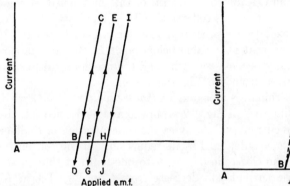

Fig. I-2. Current–voltage curves without polarization.[5]

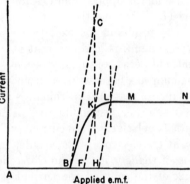

Fig. I-3. Current–voltage curves with concentration polarization.[5]

silver–silver chloride electrode. The solution is well stirred to minimize changes in the thallous ion concentration at the surface of the platinum microelectrode. The current–voltage curve obtained in this somewhat idealized case is indicated by *ABC* in Fig. I-2. From *A* to *B* the current remains practically zero. When the potential of the platinum electrode has

---

[4] Justifiably or not, the term "polarization" is commonly associated with "irreversibility." If one defines a polarized electrode as one whose actual potential differs from the potential calculated according to the Nernst equation, then "concentration polarization" becomes nonexistent *provided the calculated potential is based on concentrations or activities of the potential-determining substances at the electrode surface rather than in the body of the solution*. The experimental definition adopted in the above text entails no commitment regarding the reversibility or irreversibility of the reaction at a polarized electrode.

[5] I. M. Kolthoff, in *Frontiers in Chemistry*, Vol. VII. Interscience, New York, 1949.

been made equal to the potential of a thallium electrode in the thallous chloride solution (point B), further increase of the applied e.m.f. causes the reduction of thallous ion at the platinum electrode, $Tl^+ + e = Tl$, and correspondingly the current increases rapidly. In other words, at point B and beyond the platinum microelectrode is depolarized by the reduction of thallous ion. With increasing applied e.m.f. the current increases linearly in accordance with Ohm's Law, the slope of the line being inversely proportional to the cell resistance. If, after point C has been reached, the applied e.m.f. is decreased, the current will retrace the line CB only until point B is reached, which is the reversible potential of the thallium–thallous ion couple against the silver–silver chloride electrode. Further decrease in the applied e.m.f. leads to a reversal of the direction of current flow (BD), because the spontaneous cell reaction $Tl + AgCl \rightleftharpoons Tl^+ + Ag + Cl^-$ results in the oxidation of thallium from the microelectrode. If applied e.m.f. is held constant at a value below point B, this anodic current will decay and finally become zero when all the previously deposited thallium has been stripped from the microelectrode.

Suppose that the experiment is repeated *but that the solution is not stirred*. If an e.m.f. corresponding to C in Fig. I-2 is applied and held constant, the initially relatively large current will decay as the concentration of thallous ion at the electrode surface is depleted by its reduction. If the concentration of thallous ion at the electrode decreases to one-tenth of that in the bulk of the solution the current will decrease from C in Fig. I-3 to K, where the thallium-plated electrode is in equilibrium with the ten-fold decreased concentration of thallous ion at the electrode surface. The current eventually drops to a steady state value that is determined by the rate of diffusion of thallous ion from the bulk of the solution to the electrode surface. The number of thallium ions diffusing from the bulk of the solution to the electrode is equal to the number that is deposited when the steady state is reached. Similarly, point L in Fig. I-3 corresponds to a concentration of thallous ions at the electrode surface which is 0.01 of that in the bulk of the solution. As the potential of the small electrode is made more and more negative, the concentration of thallous ions at the electrode surface is continually decreased, until at point M the concentration at the electrode surface is negligibly small in comparison with that in the bulk of the solution. A further increase in the applied e.m.f. from M to N can no longer appreciably decrease the thallous ion concentration at the electrode surface. The microelectrode is then in a state of virtually complete concentration polarization, and the current can no longer increase because it is determined by the rate of diffusion of thallous ion from the bulk of the solution to a region of practically zero concentration.

The region MN is therefore called a *diffusion current* region. Because the rate of diffusion is proportional to the difference in concentration in the two regions between which diffusion occurs, *the diffusion current is proportional to the concentration of thallous ion* in the bulk of the solution. This proportionality is the basis of quantitative determinations from c.v. curves.

In the above experiments a relatively large concentration (compared to the concentration of thallous chloride) of nonreducible electrolyte (potassium chloride) was added to the solution to eliminate electrical migration of thallous ion. A nonreducible electrolyte added to an electrolysis solution in polarography is called a "supporting electrolyte." In the present example, the rate of electrical migration of thallous ion depends on its relative concentration as compared to that of potassium chloride, and on the transference numbers of thallous and potassium ions. When the concentration of the supporting electrolyte is much greater than that of the thallous chloride the transference number of thallous ions is reduced practically to zero, and the current through the solution is carried very nearly entirely by the ions of the supporting electrolyte. The transfer of thallous ion to the cathode then takes place solely by diffusion, and the limiting current is called "diffusion current," because it is entirely diffusion controlled. If the electrical transference of the thallous ion is not completely eliminated the limiting current is greater than the diffusion current, the difference between the two being called the *migration current*. Characteristics of the migration current are discussed in Chapter VII.

Chapter XIX deals with voltammetry with the stationary and rotated platinum electrodes. From a practical viewpoint the rotated electrode is preferable to the stationary one, because it yields steady state currents immediately, while with the stationary electrodes the general practice is to wait a few minutes before each current measurement until a steady state is obtained. The rotated electrode is particularly useful in the measurement of very small concentrations of electroreducible substances, and finds important analytical applications in amperometric titrations (see Chap. XLVII).

Even when dealing with reversible electrode reactions the c.v. curves with the platinum microelectrode hardly ever correspond to the theoretical ones, because of chemical polarization phenomena. This is not so with the dropping mercury electrode.

The applicability of a metal wire electrode to electroreduction is much more limited than that of the dropping electrode, because hydrogen ion is relatively easily reduced at solid metal electrodes, while the hydrogen overvoltage at the dropping electrode is very large. Thus, the determination of such ions as the alkali and alkaline earth metal ions, of aluminum, etc. is excluded at wire electrodes, whereas these ions can be determined polaro-graphically with the dropping electrode as indicator electrode. For quanti-tative studies of electroreduction the dropping electrode therefore has a very wide field of application, in both inorganic and organic chemistry.

Use of the dropping mercury electrode at the anodic side is more limited than that of the platinum microelectrode. Mercury is intermediate between the noble and base metals and goes into solution at a relatively positive potential. On the other hand, noble metal electrodes are limited on the anodic side by the oxidation of hydroxyl ions to oxygen

$$2OH^- \rightarrow \tfrac{1}{2}O_2 + H_2O + 2e$$

Another advantage of the dropping electrode over metal wire electrodes is that the surface of the former is constantly renewed. The surface of wire electrodes easily becomes contaminated, and it may change its area during the electrodeposition of metals.

2. CURRENT-VOLTAGE CURVES WITH THE DROPPING MERCURY ELECTRODE

The dropping electrode is shown schematically in Fig. I-4. It consists essentially of a capillary glass tube supplied with mercury from a reservoir. The capillary diameter (ca. 0.03 to 0.05 mm.) and the height of the reser-voir are adjusted so that mercury issues dropwise from the tip at a rate of about 3 sec. per drop. The maximum diameter of the drops is of the order of 0.5 mm. Because the electrolysis current seldom exceeds about 50 micro-amp. (5×10^{-5} amp.), a sensitive current-measuring technique is required, and a long period galvanometer is commonly used.

Since oxygen is reduced at the dropping electrode (d.e.) at a relatively positive potential its reduction current masks the currents of most other substances. Consequently it is usually desirable to remove dissolved air from the test solution by bubbling an inert gas (nitrogen, hydrogen, or carbon dioxide) through the solution before the electrolysis.

Fig. I-5 shows a typical cathodic c.v. curve obtained with an air-free solution of 1.3 millimolar zinc sulfate in 0.1 M potassium chloride. The current-determining cathode reaction is the reduction of zinc ion to form a very dilute zinc amalgam on the surface of the mercury drops

$$Zn^{++} + 2e + Hg \rightleftharpoons Zn(Hg)$$

This "polarographic wave" qualitatively resembles the c.v. curve obtained with a platinum microelectrode. The limiting current is diffusion con-trolled and directly proportional to the concentration of zinc ion.

The periodic change in area as each mercury drop grows and falls causes the current to oscillate between a minimum value close to zero and a maximum value at the instant each drop falls.   It is usual practice to employ a

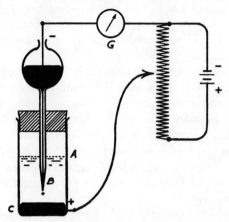

Fig. I-4. Schematic apparatus for polarographic analysis.

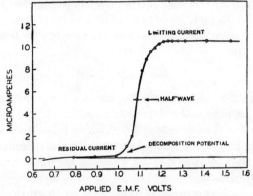

Fig. I-5. Typical current–voltage curve obtained with the dropping electrode, with an air-free solution of 0.0013 M ZnSO$_4$ in 0.1 N KCl.

galvanometer or other current-measuring device whose period is several times greater than the drop time so that the apparent oscillations amount to only about 5 per cent of the total current, and the average of the oscillations is measured.   With a properly functioning d.e. the oscillations are so uniform that their average value can be measured easily and accurately.

The current (average of the oscillations) observed with the d.e. becomes steady immediately at each new setting of the applied e.m.f.   This favorable characteristic is due to the fact that a fresh electrode surface is continuously exposed by the growing drops; the phenomena at a given drop are duplicated exactly at its successor.   Consequently the current is solely a function of the applied e.m.f., and is independent of the previous history of the electrolysis.   A c.v. curve obtained with continuously increasing applied e.m.f. usually will be retraced exactly if the applied e.m.f. is gradually decreased.

Because the electrolysis current is so small the total quantity of electrode reaction during an electrolysis is infinitesimally small, so that the same solution can be electrolyzed repeatedly with no change in the c.v. curve, i. e., without significantly altering the composition of the solution.   For example, a 1 millimolar solution of a reducible substance produces a limiting current of the order of 5 microamp., and if 10 ml. of solution is electrolyzed it follows from Faraday's Law that the electrolysis would have to be prolonged for over an hour to decrease the concentration of the reducible substance by 1 per cent.

Because of the high overvoltage of hydrogen on a mercury surface the dropping electrode can be polarized to a much more negative potential than a platinum microelectrode before the final unlimited increase in current is observed.   In fact, when neutral potassium chloride is employed as supporting electrolyte the final current increase results from reduction of potassium ion

$$K^+ + e + Hg \rightleftharpoons K(Hg)$$

rather than reduction of hydrogen ion, because the formation of the amalgam so greatly decreases the reduction potentials of the alkali metal ions that they are reduced more easily than hydrogen ion from neutral or alkaline media.   By employing neutral or basic tetraalkylammonium salts as supporting electrolytes, well-defined waves of the alkali metal ions can be obtained with the d.e.

Although the cathodic range of the d.e. is much greater than that of a platinum microelectrode its anodic range is more limited.   On anodic polarization the current will finally increase without limit when the potential is made sufficiently positive so that the mercury itself is oxidized

$$2Hg \rightleftharpoons Hg_2^{++} + 2e$$

The potential at which this occurs depends on whether or not the solution contains substances which form insoluble salts or stable complexes with mercury, and it ranges from -0.6 v. vs. the saturated calomel electrode in an alkaline sulfide solution to an upper or anodic limit of about $+0.4$ v.

vs. the saturated calomel electrode (S.C.E.). Anodic waves with well-developed limiting currents can be obtained with many substances that are oxidized more easily than mercury itself or that form slightly soluble or slightly dissociated compounds with mercury.

When several reducible or oxidizable substances are present each will produce its own wave provided the reduction or oxidation potentials differ by at least 0.15 v. It is thus possible simultaneously to detect and determine several substances from a single c.v. curve.

Since the "decomposition potential" is not an exactly definable quantity, and because it varies with concentration, it has become standard practice to report polarographic reduction or oxidation potentials as the potential at the midpoint of a polarographic wave where the current is equal to one-half its limiting value. This half-wave potential has exact thermodynamic significance and is closely related to the ordinary standard potential of the electrode reaction. The half-wave potential is usually independent of the concentration of the reducible or oxidizable substance. Half-wave potentials are most commonly quoted with reference to the saturated calomel electrode.

Half-wave potentials, like ordinary standard potentials, are functions of the molecular state of the reducible or oxidizable substance, and thus can be altered by complexation, pH changes, etc. This is often taken advantage of to separate overlapping waves. For example, in a potassium chloride supporting electrolyte the waves of thallous ion and lead ion are practically coincident, but in a potassium hydroxide solution the two waves are well separated due to the facts that the half-wave potential of the hydrogen plumbite ion is 0.35 v. more negative than that of simple lead ion and that thallous ion does not complex with hydroxide ion so that its half-wave potential remains unchanged. In acid media the half-wave potentials of fumaric acid and its isomer maleic acid are so nearly alike that only a single reduction wave is observed with mixtures of the acids; in neutral or alkaline medium, however, the wave of maleate ion is several tenths of a volt in advance of that of fumarate ion. To a very great extent research in practical polarographic analysis consists of systematic investigations of the influence of supporting electrolyte composition on half-wave potentials and other wave characteristics.

3. SCOPE OF POLAROGRAPHY

Since so many diverse types of substances are subject to electrolytic reduction or oxidation the potential scope of polarographic analysis is very broad. In the field of inorganic analysis it has been applied to the determination of nearly all the elements. Reliable procedures are available for the analysis of most common types of alloys, and in many instances these methods are not only more rapid but also more reliable than classical techniques. The determination of zinc in copper-base alloys, of sodium in aluminum alloys, or of traces of cadmium in zinc and zinc compounds are only a few examples of analytical situations in which the polarographic method excels classical methods. The determination of oxygen in gases and solutions is another uniquely valuable application of polarographic analysis.

Under usual analytical conditions the accuracy of the polarographic method is of the order of ± 1 per cent in the concentration range from about 10^{-2} down to about 10^{-4} molar, and of the order of ± 5 per cent between 10^{-4} and 10^{-5} molar. By observing certain precautions it is possible in favorable cases to obtain somewhat greater accuracy. The lower limit of polarographic detection is in the neighborhood of 10^{-6} molar. In view of the small concentrations involved and the small volumes of solutions that can be used, the precision and sensitivity of polarography compare very favorably with other microanalytical methods.

A great variety of organic compounds, including various aldehydes and ketones, unsaturated acids, nitro and nitroso compounds, azo and diazo compounds, halogenated compounds, quinones of various types, peroxides, and many others, are reducible at the dropping electrode. Consequently polarographic analysis has become a very valuable analytical tool in organic chemistry and related fields such as biology and biochemistry.

Aside from practical analysis, polarography provides a fruitful means of studying oxidation-reduction chemistry in solution, and many such applications have been and are being made. It is well suited to following rates of reactions in kinetic studies. Polarography has enriched the general field of electrochemistry by serving as a reliable and convenient pilot technique to establish optimum conditions for electrolytic preparation of both inorganic and organic compounds, and it is a valuable technique in studies of overvoltage, rates of electrode reactions, and electrocapillary phenomena at a mercury–electrolyte solution interface. Because in one way or another polarography utilizes virtually all of the known principles of electrochemistry, it provides a new viewpoint which has led to better understanding of many electrochemical phenomena.

Polarographic analysis is not limited to aqueous solutions, and can be applied to solutions in certain nonaqueous solvents. The essential condition is that the solvent be sufficiently polar so that ionic (conducting) solutions can be prepared. The use of nonaqueous solvents is particularly necessary with many water-insoluble organic substances.   It is even possible to obtain polarographic waves in molten salt media.

A new electrometric titration technique—amperometric titration—has developed as a branch of polarography. Amperometric titration is based on the measurement, at a constant potential of the dropping electrode or rotated platinum microelectrode, of the change of the diffusion current of a reducible or oxidizable substance when it is titrated with an appropriate reagent. The method is particularly useful for titrating relatively small concentrations of substances, and it is being used to advantage in many cases where reversible indicator electrodes are not available for titration by the classical potentiometric method.

Polarographic analysis is a complex subject that is far more simple on paper than in actual practice. The limiting current and other wave characteristics are influenced by a great many factors, and the effect of each of these must be recognized and controlled. Anyone who attempts to apply polarography to a practical analytical problem without first taking the time to learn the fundamental theory of the method is simply inviting failure. No amount of elegant equipment can compensate for lack of fundamental knowledge. We do not mean to imply that routine polarographic analyses cannot be performed by technicians of limited training, but this should be done under supervision of a chemist well versed in the theoretical and practical fundamentals of polarography.

4. POLAROGRAPHIC LITERATURE

The remarkably rapid growth of polarography is indicated by the histogram[6] in Fig. I-6, which shows the number of polarographic publications per year. At the time of this writing (January, 1951) the total number of published research papers in polarography exceeded 2200 and the current publication rate approximated 200 papers per year.

The bulk of the polarographic literature up to about 1935 appeared in *Collections of the Czechoslovak Chemical Communications*. The same journal contains a complete bibliography of polarographic papers which is kept up to date by Heyrovsky through periodic additions.[7]

A bibliography of 1078 titles up to 1945 is available from E. H. Sargent and Co., Chicago; and the Leeds and Northrup Co., Philadelphia, has recently made available a bibliography of 2208 titles which covers the

---

[6] J. J. Lingane, *Anal. Chem.*, **23**, 86 (1951).

[7] J. Heyrovsky, *Collection Czechoslov. Chem. Communs.*, **10**, 153 (1938); **11**, 98, 667 (1939); **12**, 156 (1947).

literature up through 1949, Bibliography E-90 (1).   These two bibliographies are especially useful because they include both author and subject indexes in addition to the usual chronological sequence.   A comprehensive bibliography of 2175 titles up through 1949 has also been published by Semerano.[8]

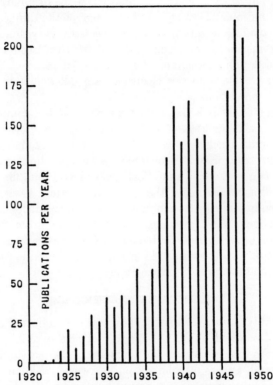

Fig. I-6. Rate of growth of polarographic literature.[6]

Following is a list of monographs devoted to polarographic analysis:

1. J. Heyrovsky, *Polarographie*, Springer, Vienna, 1941.   Reproduced by J. W. Edwards, Ann Arbor, Mich., 1944.

2. H. Hohn, *Chemische Analysen mit dem Polarographen*, Springer, Berlin, 1937.

3. O. H. Müller, *Polarographic Method of Analysis*, published by *Journal of Chemical Education*, Easton, Pa., 2nd ed., 1951.

4. G. Semerano, *Il Polarografa sua Teoria e Applicazioni*, A. Draghi, Padova, 1933.

[8] G. Semerano, *Bibliografia Polarografica* 1922-1949, Consiglio Nazionale Delle Ricerche, Centro Di Studio Per La Polarografia, Padova.

5. M. von Stackelberg, *Polarographische Arbeitsmethoden*, W. de Gruyter and Co., Berlin, 1950.

6. J. Heyrovsky, *Polarographisches Praktikum*, Springer, Berlin, 1948.

7. I. Vavruch, *Polarographic Maxima in Theory and Practice*, State Printing Office, Prague, 1949.

Sections on polarography will also be found in the following treatises:

1. W. Böttger, *Physikalische Methoden der analytischen Chemie*, Akadem. Verlags-gesellschaft, Leipzig, 1936. Section on *Polarographie* by J. Heyrovsky.

2. A. Weissberger, *Physical Methods of Organic Chemistry*, 2nd ed., Vol. I, Part 1, Interscience, New York, 1949. Section on *Polarography* by O. H. Müller.

3. W. G. Berl, *Physical Methods in Chemical Analysis*, Vol. II, Academic Press, New York, 1951. Section on *Polarographic Analysis and Amperometric Titrations* by J. Heyrovsky.

4. I. M. Kolthoff and H. A. Laitinen, *pH and Electrotitrations*, Wiley, New York, 1941.

CHAPTER II

Theory of Diffusion Currents

1. INTRODUCTION

The limiting current obtained with the dropping mercury electrode, and under certain conditions with solid microelectrodes, is caused by the extreme state of concentration polarization which results from the depletion of the concentration of the electroreducible or electrooxidizable substance at the electrode surface by the electrode reaction. When a limiting current is reached the reducible or oxidizable substance is reduced or oxidized as rapidly as it reaches the electrode surface, and its concentration at the electrode surface remains constant at a value that is negligibly small compared to the concentration in the body of the solution. Under these conditions the current resulting from the electrode reaction is independent, within certain limits, of the applied e.m.f., and is governed solely by the rate of supply of the reducible or oxidizable substance to the electrode surface from the surrounding solution.

In the most general case reducible or oxidizable *ions* are supplied to the depleted region at the electrode surface by two forces: (1) a diffusive force, proportional to the concentration gradient at the electrode surface, and (2) an electrical force, proportional to the electrical potential difference between the surface and the solution. Reducible or oxidizable ions are, therefore, supplied to the electrode surface partly by diffusion and partly by electrical migration, so that the limiting current can be regarded as the sum of a "diffusion current" and a "migration current."

The current through an electrolyte solution is carried impartially by all the ions present, regardless of whether or not all the ions take part in the electrode reactions. The fraction of the total current carried by any particular species of ion depends primarily on its relative concentration in the solution, and to a lesser degree on its charge and intrinsic mobility; in other words, on its transference number in the particular solution in question. When a large excess of an indifferent salt, *i. e.*, a salt whose ions do not participate in the electrode reaction is added to a solution containing a relatively small concentration of the reducible or oxidizable ions, the current through the solution will be carried practically entirely by the large excess of indifferent ions, *i. e.*, the transference number of the reducible

18

or oxidizable ions is reduced practically to zero. Under these conditions the electrical forces on the reducible ions are nullified, the migration component of the limiting current is practically completely eliminated, and the limiting current becomes solely a diffusion current.

In the case of reducible or oxidizable *uncharged* substances diffusion usually plays the predominant role in governing the limiting current, even when the ionic concentration of the solution is small, because uncharged molecules are not subject to electrical migration in the same sense as ions. However, in the case of dipolar uncharged molecules that possess a permanent electric moment, or that can acquire an induced electric moment, there will be a certain amount of electrical migration when the ionic concentration of the solution is small. The electric field at a microelectrode is not homogeneous, that is, the electrical intensity is not a linear function of the distance from the electrode surface, but increases rapidly close to the electrode. In such a field dipolar uncharged molecules will not only become oriented, but will also undergo movement toward the electrode, due to the fact that the electrical intensity (*i. e.*, the gradient of the electrical potential) is greater at the front of the molecule than at its back. However, when a large excess of an indifferent salt is present in the solution the electrical intensity near the electrode is reduced to such a small value that orientation and directed motion of dipolar molecules is eliminated. Hence, just as in the case of reducible ions, the limiting current of an uncharged substance is solely a diffusion current when the solution contains a relatively large concentration of an indifferent salt.

Since it is of such fundamental importance to an adequate understanding and appreciation of diffusion currents, the theory of diffusion will be discussed in some detail in the following pages, together with the methods of calculating diffusion currents at various types of microelectrodes. The diffusion at plane and spherical solid microelectrodes will be discussed first, because it is much simpler than the theory of diffusion at the dropping mercury electrode.

2. LINEAR DIFFUSION AND LINEAR DIFFUSION CURRENTS

Diffusion may be defined as the directed movement of a substance in either a solid, liquid, or gaseous medium, under the influence of forces that arise from differences in concentration of the substance in various parts of the medium. The direction of diffusion is from regions of larger to smaller concentration, and its rate is proportional to the magnitude of the concentration differences, and to certain characteristic properties of the diffusing substance and the medium.

The simplest diffusion process is one which takes place in only a single direction, and this is termed linear diffusion. Consider a linear diffusion cylinder as shown in Fig. II-1, in which the diffusion is proceeding upward in the negative x-direction. The number of moles of the diffusing substance that diffuse across a given cross-sectional plane of area A cm.^{2} in the infinitesimal interval of time dt is proportional to the concentration gradient $\partial C/\partial x$ at the plane in question, and is expressible by

$$dN = DA \frac{\partial C}{\partial x} dt \qquad (1)$$

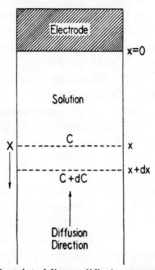

Fig. II-1. Restricted linear diffusion to a flat electrode.

The proportionality constant D is the "diffusion coefficient," and it is evidently numerically equal to the number of moles of substance that diffuse across unit area in unit time when the concentration gradient is unity. This relation was first recognized and annunciated by Fick[1] and it is usually referred to as Fick's First Law. D has the dimensions of length squared divided by time, and it is usually expressed in the units cm.^{2} day^{-1} or cm.^{2} sec.$^{-1}$.

It is often convenient to consider the number of moles of substance that diffuse through a unit area in unit time, and this is called the unit flow or flux. The flux at a plane at a distance x from the origin, designated by f_x, is evidently given by

$$f_{x,t} = \frac{dN}{A \, dt} = D \frac{\partial C}{\partial x} \qquad (2)$$

[1] A. Fick, *Pogg. Ann.*, **94**, 59 (1855).

Since the concentration, and the concentration gradient, at a given plane decrease with time as the diffusion proceeds, the flux decreases correspondingly.   Hence eq. 2 is only valid at a given plane at a given instant (instantaneous flux), and this condition is denoted by the subscripts x and t.

In order to calculate the total amount of material that will diffuse across a given plane in a finite interval of time it is necessary to have a knowledge of the change in concentration with time at the plane in question; that is, it is necessary to know C both as a function of time and distance x.   The change in concentration with time between two planes separated by the infinitesimal distance dx is obviously equal to the difference between the number of moles which enter across the plane at $x + dx$ and the number which leave across the plane at x, divided by the volume $A\,dx$ enclosed between the planes; that is

$$\frac{\partial C}{\partial t} = \frac{f_{x+dx} - f_x}{dx} \tag{3}$$

since A is equal to unity when we speak of the flux.   We also have

$$f_{x+dx} = f_x + \frac{\partial f_x}{\partial x} dx \tag{4}$$

and since from eq. 2

$$\frac{\partial f_x}{\partial x} = D\,\frac{\partial^2 C}{\partial x^2} \tag{5}$$

we find from eq. 3 that the change in concentration with time at a given plane at a given instant is given by

$$\frac{\partial C}{\partial t} = D\,\frac{\partial^2 C}{\partial x^2} \tag{6}$$

This is the fundamental differential equation for linear diffusion, and it is sometimes referred to as Fick's Second Law.   In order to obtain an expression for C as a function of x and t it is necessary to integrate this equation, and the integration requires a specification of the initial and boundary conditions; that is, the concentration at the plane in question at zero time, the method of establishing the diffusion layer, and the restrictions imposed by the geometry of the diffusion field.

In the present discussion we are interested in linear diffusion up to a plane microelectrode.   We shall suppose that this electrode is situated at the top of the diffusion cell at $x = 0$ (see Fig. II-1), so that the density gradients which arise from the depletion in concentration of the diffusing substance near the surface of the electrode, as a result of the electrode reaction, will preserve rather than disturb the concentration gradient. We shall also suppose that the diffusion cell represented in Fig. II-1 is immersed in a larger body of the same solution in which there is a second nonpolarizable electrode, so that the whole arrangement constitutes an electrolysis cell. The concentration of the reducible or oxidizable substance is initially uniform throughout the cell, and the diffusion field is established by applying an e.m.f. to the cell of such magnitude that the diffusion current is obtained.

Since the diffusion current is governed by the flux *at the electrode surface* the problem at hand is to obtain an expression for the concentration gradient at any instant at $x = 0$, from which, by means of eq. 2, the flux, and hence the current, can be computed. At the instant the e.m.f. is applied $(t = 0)$, the concentration at the electrode surface (designated by C_0) is equal to that in the body of the solution (designated by C). After the e.m.f. is applied C_0 is rapidly decreased by the electrode reaction, and becomes negligibly small compared to the concentration in the body of the solution. The initial and boundary conditions in this type of experiment are therefore

$$C_0 = C \qquad \text{when} \qquad t = 0$$

and

$$C_0 \ll C \qquad \text{or} \qquad C_0 = 0, \qquad \text{when} \qquad t > 0$$

Under these conditions the solution of eq. 6 is

$$C_{x,t} = C \frac{2}{\sqrt{\pi}} \int_0^{x/2\sqrt{Dt}} e^{-y^2} \, dy \tag{7}$$

where $C_{x,t}$ is the concentration of the diffusing substance at a distance x from the electrode at the time t, C is the initial uniform concentration, and y is an integration variable.

The quantity $2/\sqrt{\pi} \int_0^z e^{-y^2} \, dy$ is the familiar "error function" and it has been evaluated for various values of z, which in the present case is simply the numerical value of the quantity $x/2\sqrt{Dt}$. Values of this function for various values of z are given in Table II-1. It will be noted that the value of the function rapidly approaches unity as a limit, and hence the integral itself rapidly approaches $\sqrt{\pi}/2$, with increasing values of z.

The value of the integral in eq. 7 varies from zero when the upper limit is zero, to $\sqrt{\pi}/2$ when the upper limit is indefinitely great. Therefore, eq. 7 is consistent with the known initial and boundary conditions, because when $t = 0$, eq. 7 predicts that $C_{x,t}$ will be equal to C, whereas when $t > 0$ and $x = 0$ it predicts that $C_{x,t}$ will be equal to zero.

In Fig. II-2 are shown curves, calculated by means of eq. 7, for the quantity $C_{x,t}/C$ (i. e., the fraction of the initial concentration at any plane) plotted as a function of the distance from the electrode for various values of the time of diffusion for a substance having a diffusion coefficient of

TABLE II-1[a]

VALUES OF THE FUNCTION $2/\sqrt{\pi} \int_0^z e^{-y^2} dy$ FOR VARIOUS VALUES OF z

z	$\dfrac{2}{\sqrt{\pi}} \int_0^z e^{-y^2}\, dy$	z	$\dfrac{2}{\sqrt{\pi}} \int_0^z e^{-y^2}\, dy$
0	0	1.3	0.93401
0.1	0.11246	1.4	0.95229
0.2	0.22270	1.5	0.96611
0.3	0.32863	1.6	0.97635
0.4	0.42839	1.7	0.98379
0.5	0.52050	1.8	0.98909
0.6	0.60386	1.9	0.99279
0.7	0.67780	2.0	0.99532
0.8	0.74210	2.2	0.99814
0.9	0.79691	2.4	0.99931
1.0	0.84270	2.6	0.99976
1.1	0.88021	2.8	0.99992
1.2	0.91031	3.0	0.99998
		∞	1

[a] From J. Jeans, *The Dynamical Theory of Gases*, 4th ed., London, 1925, p. 438.

1×10^{-5} cm.^{2} sec.$^{-1}$, which is a usual value. Each curve represents the concentration as a function of distance from the electrode at a given instant. The concentration gradient at any point is given by the slope of the concentration–distance curve at that point, and it will be noted that the concentration gradient has a maximum value at $x = 0$ at any given time. The concentration gradient at the electrode surface is very large for very small values of the time, but gradually decreases with increasing time, and finally approaches zero as t approaches infinity. Therefore, the flux at the electrode surface, being proportional to the concentration gradient, also decreases continuously with time and approaches zero as the time of diffusion becomes very great.

In the type of experiment that we are considering, the diffusion current is governed by the flux of the electroreducible or electrooxidizable substance, and hence by its concentration gradient, at the electrode surface where $x = 0$. The current at any instant is given by

$$i_t = nF_y Af_{x=0,\ t} = nF_y AD \left(\frac{\partial C}{\partial x}\right)_{x=0,\ t} \tag{8}$$

where n is the number of faradays of electricity required per mole of electrode reaction, F_y is the faraday (96,500 coulombs), and A is the area of the electrode in cm.^{2}. This gives the current in amperes when C is expressed in terms of moles per cm.^{3}, and x is expressed in cm. By differ-

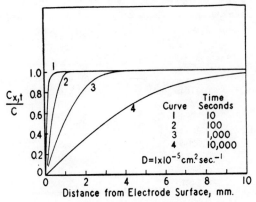

Fig. II-2. Concentration–distance curves as a function of the diffusion time in linear diffusion.

entiating eq. 7, under the condition that $x = 0$, we obtain

$$\left(\frac{\partial C}{\partial x}\right)_{x=0} = \frac{C}{\sqrt{\pi Dt}} \tag{9}$$

and hence

$$i_t = nF_y CA \sqrt{\frac{D}{\pi t}} \tag{10}$$

This is the equation for the instantaneous current at any time t after the e.m.f. is applied.[2-4] According to this equation the current should decrease continuously with time at a constant value of the applied e.m.f.,

[2] H. A. Laitinen and I. M. Kolthoff, *J. Am. Chem. Soc.*, **61**, 3344 (1939).

[3] F. G. Cottrell, *Z. physik. Chem.*, **42**, 385 (1902).

[4] D. MacGillavry and E. K. Rideal, *Rec. trav. chim.*, **56**, 1013 (1937).

and should approach zero as the time becomes very great.   It will also be noted that the product $i\sqrt{t}$ should be constant and independent of the time.

Laitinen and Kolthoff tested eq. 10 in the oxidation of ferrocyanide ion, the reduction of ferricyanide ion, and the discharge of silver ion, in solutions containing an excess of an indifferent salt to eliminate the migration current.   They used platinum microelectrodes of the forms shown in Fig. II-3, in an H-cell of the type shown in Fig. XVII-2 of Chapter XVII. A large silver–silver chloride electrode was used as the second electrode of the cell.   Air was removed from the solutions with nitrogen, because oxygen is easily reduced at a platinum electrode.   The experiments were run by applying a constant potential to the microelectrode, corresponding to the limiting current section of the current–voltage curves, and the resulting

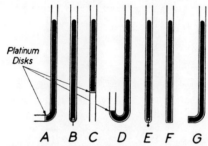

Platinum
Disks

A   B   C   D   E   F   G

Fig. II-3. Various forms of platinum microelectrodes.

current was measured with a calibrated galvanometer at various times after the e.m.f. was applied.

A typical set of data obtained by Laitinen and Kolthoff for the current–time curve of the oxidation of ferrocyanide ion is shown in Table II-2. These data were obtained with electrode C of Fig. II-3, i. e., with upward linear diffusion.   The corrected values of the current given in the third column of the table were obtained by determining the current–time curve of the pure, air-free 0.1 N potassium chloride solution alone without any ferrocyanide present, and subtracting the resulting small currents found after various intervals of time from the observed currents when ferrocyanide ion was present.

As predicted by eq. 10 the current was inversely proportional to the square root of the time, as shown by the constancy of the values of $i\sqrt{t}$ in the last column.   These data constitute convincing proof of the validity of the foregoing theory of linear diffusion.

It should be realized that the foregoing theory is strictly applicable only when the diffusion is truly linear, and when the diffusion cell is sufficiently long so that the concentration gradient does not extend all the way to its end during the time of an experiment. In the experiments of Laitinen and Kolthoff these conditions were satisfied by the glass mantle extending from the electrode as shown in Fig. II-3. The glass mantle was

TABLE II-2

CHANGE OF THE DIFFUSION CURRENT WITH TIME IN THE ELECTROLYSIS OF 0.00488 M
POTASSIUM FERROCYANIDE IN 0.1 N POTASSIUM CHLORIDE

Data obtained by Laitinen and Kolthoff using electrode C of Fig. II-3. Potential of the microelectrode maintained constant at +0.70 v. with respect to the Ag/AgCl, 0.1 N KCl electrode, 25° C. Area of the electrode was 0.1016 cm.².

t, sec.	i, microamp.		$i\sqrt{t}$, microamp. sec.$^{1/2}$
	Obs.	Corr.	
110	6.90	6.85	71.8
120	6.62	6.57	71.9
150	5.92	5.88	71.7
180	5.41	5.37	72.1
210	5.02	4.99	72.3
240	4.70	4.67	72.3
300	4.19	4.16	72.1
360	3.82	3.80	72.1
420	3.54	3.52	72.1
540	3.13	3.11	72.2
600	2.98	2.96	72.4
660	2.83	2.81	72.3
780	2.61	2.59	72.3
900	2.43	2.42	72.6
1200	2.10	2.09	72.4
Av..			72.3

sufficiently long (ca. 3 cm.) so that the concentration gradient did not extend entirely to its open end during the course of an experiment.

In order to calculate the theoretical current–time curve from eq. 10, it is necessary to know the diffusion coefficient of the reducible or oxidizable ions. Lingane and Kolthoff[5] have shown that the effective diffusion coefficient of the reducible or oxidizable ions in the presence of an excess of an indifferent salt can be calculated with satisfactory accuracy from the relation

$$D = \frac{RT\lambda_i^0}{zF_y^2} = 2.67 \times 10^{-7} \frac{\lambda_i^0}{z} \text{ cm.}^2 \text{ sec.}^{-1} \tag{11}$$

[5] J. J. Lingane and I. M. Kolthoff, J. Am. Chem. Soc., 61, 825 (1939).

where the numerical factor is valid at 25° C.   In this equation, which is derived and discussed in detail in Chapter III, λ_i^0 is the equivalent conductance of the ion at infinite dilution, and z is its charge without regard to sign.   The equivalent conductance of the ferrocyanide ion at infinite dilution and 25° C. is 110.5,[6] and hence the diffusion coefficient of ferrocyanide ion is calculated from eq. 11 to be 0.74×10^{-5} cm.[2] sec.[-1].

For the 4.88×10^{-3} M potassium ferrocyanide solution used by Laitinen and Kolthoff to obtain the data in Table II-2, C is equal to 4.88×10^{-6} mole per cm.[3], n is equal to 1 in the oxidation of ferrocyanide ion, A is equal to 0.1016 cm.[2], and hence from eq. 10 the theoretical value of the quantity

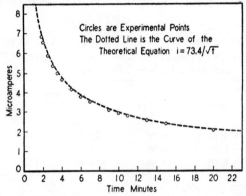

Fig. II-4. Comparison of theoretical current–time curve with observed values in the oxidation of ferrocyanide ion at a linear diffusion microelectrode.

$i\sqrt{t}$ is

$$i\sqrt{t} = \frac{96500 \times 4.88 \times 10^{-6}(0.74 \times 10^{-5})^{1/2} \times 0.1016}{(3.14)^{1/2}}$$

$$= 73.4 \times 10^{-6} \text{ amp. sec.}^{1/2}$$

$$= 73.4 \text{ microamp. sec.}^{1/2}$$

From the data in Table II-2 the average observed value of $i\sqrt{t}$ is 72.3 microamp. sec.[1/2], in good agreement with the theoretical value.   The good agreement between theory and experiment is further demonstrated in Fig. II-4 where the circles are experimental points (Table II-2), and the broken curve is the theoretical current–time curve calculated according to the theoretical equation $i_t = 73.4/\sqrt{t}$.

Laitinen and Kolthoff (loc. cit.) also studied the current–time curves of

[6] E. Swift, Jr., J. Am. Chem. Soc., 60, 728 (1938).

the oxidation of ferrocyanide ion using electrode D of Fig. II-3. With this electrode, in which the diffusion is linear but in a *downward* direction, they found that the observed current was much greater than that predicted from eq. 10 and, furthermore, it fluctuated irregularly. They showed that this erratic behavior is due to the fact that the density of a dilute solution of potassium ferrocyanide (the diffusing material) is slightly greater than that of a solution of the same concentration of potassium ferricyanide (the oxidation product near the electrode surface). Unless the direction of diffusion is such that the less dense solution lies above the denser solution (electrode C in the oxidation of ferrocyanide ions) convection currents arise due to density gradients, and the resultant stirring disturbs the concentra-

TABLE II-3

COMPARISON OF OBSERVED AND THEORETICAL VALUES OF $i\sqrt{t}$

Electrode C used for ferrocyanide and silver ions, and electrode D used for ferricyanide ion at 25° C. Area of electrode = 0.1016 cm.².

Ion	C, mmole/ liter	D, cm.² sec.$^{-1}$ × 10^5 (calcd.)	$i\sqrt{t}$, microamp. sec.$^{1/2}$		Difference per cent
			Obs.	Calcd.	
Fe(CN)$_6^{-4}$	4.88	0.74	72.3[a]	73.4	−1.5
Fe(CN)$_6^{-3}$	5.01	0.89	80.4[a]	82.8	−2.9
Ag$^+$	5.00	1.69	115.4[b]	113.7	+1.5

[a] In 0.1 N potassium chloride.
[b] In 0.1 N potassium nitrate.

tion gradient and causes a greater supply of material to reach the electrode than by diffusion alone (electrode D in the oxidation of ferrocyanide ions).

On the other hand, in the reduction of ferricyanide ion Laitinen and Kolthoff found that electrode D gave theoretical results, whereas with electrode C the current was abnormally large and fluctuated erratically. These results are just the opposite of those obtained in the oxidation of ferrocyanide ion, and were to be expected, because the density gradients act in the opposite direction in the reduction of ferricyanide ion.

The data obtained by Laitinen and Kolthoff in the oxidation of ferrocyanide ion, and the reduction of ferricyanide and silver ions, are summarized in Table II-3, in which the experimentally observed values of the quantity $i\sqrt{t}$ are compared with the theoretical values calculated from eq. 10. Electrode C was used in the cases of ferrocyanide and silver ions, and electrode D in the case of ferricyanide ion. The data show good agreement between the observed and calculated values in all three cases.

The experiments of Laitinen and Kolthoff demonstrate that the measurement of linear diffusion currents constitutes a method of determining the diffusion coefficients of electroreducible and electrooxidizable ions that is simpler and more rapid than, and apparently at least as accurate as, classical methods.

3. TEMPERATURE COEFFICIENT OF LINEAR DIFFUSION CURRENTS

For a given linear diffusion electrode the quantity $i\sqrt{t}$ can be expressed in terms of the equivalent conductance of the diffusing ions and the absolute temperature by combining eqs. 10 and 11:

$$i\sqrt{t} = k(\lambda_i^0 T)^{1/2} \tag{12}$$

where T is the absolute temperature. By differentiating this equation with respect to temperature, and dividing the left side of the resulting differential equation by $i\sqrt{t}$ and the right side by $k(\lambda^0 T)^{1/2}$, the temperature coefficient of the quantity $i\sqrt{t}$ at the temperature T is found to be

$$\frac{1}{i\sqrt{t}} \cdot \frac{d(i\sqrt{t})}{dT} = \frac{1}{2}\left(\frac{1}{T} + \frac{1}{\lambda^0} \cdot \frac{d\lambda^0}{dT}\right) \tag{13}$$

Laitinen and Kolthoff calculated temperature coefficients of $i\sqrt{t}$ by means of this equation and compared the calculated values with experimentally measured values over the temperature range from 25° to 35° C., with the results shown in Table II-4. The observed temperature coefficients are in good agreement with the theoretical values in all three cases.

TABLE II-4

TEMPERATURE COEFFICIENT OF THE QUANTITY $i\sqrt{t}$ IN LINEAR DIFFUSION

Ion	$\frac{1}{\lambda^0}\frac{d\lambda^0}{dT}$, deg.$^{-1}$	$\frac{1}{i\sqrt{t}} \cdot \frac{d(i\sqrt{t})}{dT}$, deg.$^{-1}$	
		Calcd.	Obs.
$Fe(CN)_6^{-4}$	0.0195	0.0114	0.0101
$Fe(CN)_6^{-3}$	0.0185	0.0109	0.0118
Ag^+	0.0200	0.0116	0.0116

The temperature coefficient of the linear diffusion current itself, i. e., $(1/i)(di/dT)$, will be the same as the temperature coefficient of $i\sqrt{t}$ for a given value of t. It is seen from the data in Table II-4 that the temperature coefficient ranges from $+1$ to $+1.2$ per cent per degree for the three cases studied.

4. SYMMETRICAL SPHERICAL DIFFUSION

In symmetrical spherical diffusion the diffusing substance diffuses toward the center of a sphere along its radii. Consider a solid spherical electrode immersed in a solution of an electroreducible or electrooxidizable substance which is diffusing to, and undergoing reaction at, the electrode. The diffusion field in this case is a spherical shell surrounding the electrode as shown in Fig. II-5. Distance measured radially from the center of the spherical electrode is designated by r, and the radius of the electrode is designated by r_0.

Consider an infinitesimally thin shell of thickness dr at a distance r from the center of the electrode as shown in Fig. II-5. The area of the spheri-

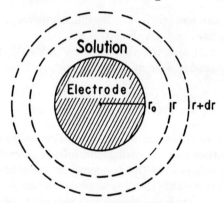

Fig. II-5. Symmetrical spherical diffusion to a solid spherical electrode.

cal surface at r is equal to $4\pi r^2$, and the number of moles dN_r that diffuse across this surface in the time dt is given by the following expression, analogous to Fick's First Law,

$$dN_r = 4\pi r^2 D \left(\frac{\partial C}{\partial r}\right)_r dt \tag{14}$$

and the flux at r is

$$f_r = \frac{dN_r}{4\pi r^2 dt} = D \left(\frac{\partial C}{\partial r}\right)_r \tag{15}$$

Similarly, the area of the spherical surface at $r + dr$ is $4\pi(r + dr)^2$, and the number of moles that diffuse across this surface in the time dt is

$$dN_{r+dr} = 4\pi(r + dr)^2 D \left(\frac{\partial C}{\partial r}\right)_{r+dr} dt \tag{16}$$

and

$$f_{r+dr} = D \left(\frac{\partial C}{\partial r}\right)_{r+dr} \tag{17}$$

The concentration gradient at $r + dr$ is related to that at r by

$$\left(\frac{\partial C}{\partial r}\right)_{r+dr} = \left(\frac{\partial C}{\partial r}\right)_{r} + \frac{\partial}{\partial r}\left(\frac{\partial C}{\partial r}\right) dr \tag{18}$$

and hence eq. 16 may be written as

$$dN_{r+dr} = 4\pi(r + dr)^2 D \, dt \left[\left(\frac{\partial C}{\partial r}\right)_{r} + \left(\frac{\partial^2 C}{\partial r^2}\right) dr\right] \tag{19}$$

or in the expanded form

$$dN_{r+dr} = 4\pi D \, dt \left[r^2 \left(\frac{\partial C}{\partial r}\right) + 2r \left(\frac{\partial C}{\partial r}\right) dr \right.$$
$$\left. + r^2 \left(\frac{\partial^2 C}{\partial r^2}\right) dr + \left(\frac{\partial C}{\partial r} + 2r \frac{\partial^2 C}{\partial r^2}\right) (dr)^2 + \frac{\partial^2 C}{\partial r^2} (dr)^3 \right] \tag{20}$$

The last two terms, containing infinitesimals of the second and third orders, may be neglected, and hence eq. 20 becomes

$$dN_{r+dr} = 4\pi D \, dt \left[r^2 \left(\frac{\partial C}{\partial r}\right) + 2r \left(\frac{\partial C}{\partial r}\right) dr + r^2 \left(\frac{\partial^2 C}{\partial r^\circ}\right) dr \right] \tag{21}$$

The change in concentration in the spherical shell in the time dt is evidently equal to the difference between the number of moles which enter the shell at $r + dr$ and the number which leave at r, divided by the volume of the shell which is $4\pi r^2 dr$, that is

$$dC = \frac{dN_{r+dr} - dN_r}{4\pi r^2 \, dr} \tag{22}$$

Therefore, the rate of change of the concentration with time at a given value of r and a given time t is

$$\frac{\partial C}{\partial t} = \frac{dN_{r+dr} - dN_r}{4\pi r^2 \, dr \, dt} \tag{23}$$

By substituting the relations expressed by eqs. 14 and 21 into eq. 23, and simplifying, we obtain

$$\frac{\partial C}{\partial t} = D \left[\frac{\partial^2 C}{\partial r^2} + \frac{2}{r}\left(\frac{\partial C}{\partial r}\right)\right] \tag{24}$$

This is the fundamental differential equation describing symmetrical spherical diffusion up to a stationary spherical electrode. Since the concentration at any point in the diffusion shell decreases continuously with time $\partial C/\partial t$ is a negative quantity.

Equation 24 for spherical diffusion is the analogue of eq. 6 for linear diffusion, but it differs formally from eq. 6 by the term $(2/r)(\partial C/\partial r)$, due to the fact that in spherical diffusion the area of the diffusion field increases with increasing distance from the surface of the electrode.

As in the case of linear diffusion, in order to calculate the total flow through a given shell of infinitesimal thickness during a finite time it is necessary to integrate eq. 24, and the particular solution to be used will depend on the initial and boundary conditions. In the present case, the concentration is uniform before the e.m.f. is applied and equal to C, but as soon as the electrode reaction is initiated the concentration at the electrode surface, designated by C_0, becomes negligibly small compared to C. The initial and boundary conditions are therefore

$$C_0 = C \qquad \text{when} \qquad t = 0$$

and

$$C_0 \ll C, \qquad \text{or} \qquad C_0 = 0, \qquad \text{when} \qquad t > 0$$

Under these particular conditions the solution of eq. 24 becomes

$$C_{r,t} = C\left(1 - \frac{r_0}{r}\right) + \frac{2Cr_0}{r\sqrt{\pi}} \int_0^{(r-r_0)/(2\sqrt{Dt})} e^{-y^2}\, dy \qquad (25)$$

This solution has been given by MacGillavry and Rideal (*loc. cit.*), and in a slightly different form by Lederer.[7]

For a given constant value of r the value of the integral, and hence the whole last term in eq. 25, approaches zero as the time approaches infinity, and hence

$$\lim_{t \to \infty} C_r = C\left(1 - \frac{r_0}{r}\right) = \text{a constant} \qquad (26)$$

In other words, with increasing time of diffusion the concentration at any given point in the diffusion field gradually approaches a constant value, and the concentration–distance curve becomes independent of the time. Under these conditions a *steady state* is said to exist. The constant con-

---

[7] E. L. Lederer, *Kolloid-Z.*, **44**, 108 (1928); **46**, 169 (1928).

centration in the steady state is, of course, a function of r as shown by eq. 26, and varies from zero at the electrode surface $(r = r_0)$ to C at a large distance from the electrode $(r \gg r_0$, and $r_0/r \to 0)$. This is an important fundamental difference between symmetrical spherical diffusion and linear diffusion, in which latter case a steady state is theoretically unattainable.

The current at any instant is governed by the flux at the electrode surface, i.e., by the concentration gradient at $r = r_0$. By differentiating eq. 25 we find that the concentration gradient at the electrode surface at any time t is given by

$$\left(\frac{\partial C}{\partial r}\right)_{r=r_0,\,t} = C\left(\frac{1}{r_0} + \frac{1}{\sqrt{\pi Dt}}\right) = \frac{f_{r=r_0}}{D} \qquad (27)$$

The instantaneous value of the resulting current is, therefore,

$$i_t = nF_y \cdot 4\pi r_0^2 \cdot f_{r=r_0} = nF_y ADC\left(\frac{1}{r_0} + \frac{1}{\sqrt{\pi Dt}}\right) \qquad (28)$$

where A is the area of the spherical electrode, equal to $4\pi r_0^2$. This equation is of the form

$$i_t = k_1 + \frac{k_2}{\sqrt{t}} \qquad (29)$$

from which it is evident that a constant value of i should be obtained when t becomes large and a steady state exists.

By comparing eq. 28 with the corresponding equation for the instantaneous linear diffusion current (eq. 10), it is apparent that for spherical and linear diffusion to electrodes of equal area, and with the same diffusing substance at the same concentration, the theoretical currents at any time differ by the constant amount $nF_y ADC/r_0$, which is the steady-state current in spherical diffusion.

Unfortunately, an experimental test of eq. 28 is impossible, because density gradients are produced near the surface of the spherical electrode and the resulting convection currents cause a stirring effect which destroys the concentration gradient. As a result of this stirring the flux of the diffusing substance at the electrode surface, and hence the current, is considerably greater than if diffusion alone were the controlling factor. Laitinen and Kolthoff (loc. cit.) attempted a test of eq. 28 in the oxidation of ferrocyanide ion, at a spherical platinum microelectrode, and they found currents considerably larger than those predicted by eq. 28. They tried to prevent stirring due to density gradients by adding agar to the solution so as to form a stiff gel, but even in this case the observed currents were too large, indicating that the stirring effect was still operative in the semisolid gel.

5. UNSYMMETRICAL DIFFUSION AND DIFFUSION CURRENTS WITH PLATI-NUM WIRE MICROELECTRODES

It is possible to obtain reproducible current–voltage curves with platinum wire microelectrodes, consisting simply of a short length of platinum wire sealed into the end of a glass tube as shown by electrode B in Fig. II-4. The diffusion at such an electrode is unsymmetrical, and not subject to exact mathematical interpretation, but such microelectrodes are, nevertheless, useful in practical work.

Laitinen and Kolthoff[8] made a thorough experimental study of current–voltage and current–time curves, with platinum wire microelectrodes. They found that the current decreases rapidly with time shortly after the e.m.f. is applied, but a constant current results after two or three minutes. They found that the steady-state current was more reproducible than that obtained with spherical platinum microelectrodes. Apparently the stirring produced by the density gradients at a wire microelectrode is more uniform than at any other type of unshielded microelectrode. Due to the fact that reproducible currents are readily obtained, this simple wire type microelectrode is more suitable than any other type of solid microelectrode for practical analytical purposes (see Chap. XIX).

6. DIFFUSION AT THE DROPPING MERCURY ELECTRODE. THE ILKOVIC EQUATION

Diffusion at a dropping mercury electrode is spherically symmetrical, but due to the periodic growth and fall of the mercury drops the area of the diffusion field changes continuously during the life of a drop. Hence the problem of diffusion to the dropping electrode is more complicated than symmetrical spherical diffusion to a solid spherical electrode, or to a stationary mercury drop electrode. In the case of the dropping electrode the diffusion takes place in a medium that is moving with respect to the center of the drop, in a direction opposite to the direction of diffusion.

In order to appreciate the physical nature of the problem, it is instructive to contrast the diffusion at a dropping mercury electrode with linear diffusion up to a *moving* flat electrode. We have seen that the fundamental differential equation which describes linear diffusion to a stationary flat

---

[8] H. A. Laitinen and I. M. Kolthoff, *J. Am. Chem. Soc.*, **61**, 3344 (1939); *Nature*, **144**, 549 (1939).

electrode is

$$\frac{\partial C}{\partial t} = D \frac{\partial^2 C}{\partial x^2} \tag{6}$$

where the distance x is measured from the surface of the stationary flat electrode (see Fig. II-1). Suppose that the flat electrode is moving with a velocity v in the positive x-direction (opposite to direction of diffusion). Since the solution is virtually incompressible, a given diffusion plane in the solution will also move with the same velocity, and in the same direction, as the electrode. The area of the diffusion field obviously will remain constant. It is evident, therefore, if we retain the convention of measuring the distance x from the surface of the moving flat electrode, that the diffusion situation will not be altered by the uniform movement of the electrode, and hence eq. 6 will still apply. In other words, due to the incompressibility of the solution, and the fact that the area of the diffusion field remains constant, the physical nature of linear diffusion to a moving flat electrode is exactly the same as that to a stationary flat electrode, and the mathematical description of the diffusion is identical in the two cases.

On the other hand, this is no longer true in the case of symmetrical spherical diffusion to an *expanding* spherical electrode (the dropping electrode), because, due to the expansion of the growing mercury drops, the area of the diffusion field *at a given distance from the surface of the dropping electrode* increases continuously with time during the life of each drop. Therefore, the equations that describe diffusion to the dropping electrode differ from those for stationary spherical diffusion by terms which describe the increase in the area of the diffusion field with time.

Ilkovic[9] was the first to solve the complex problem of diffusion to the dropping electrode, and to derive an equation for the resulting current. The Ilkovic equation was rederived by MacGillavry and Rideal,[10] who obtained the same final expression for the diffusion current. The following discussion is based mainly on that of MacGillavry and Rideal.

We have seen that the fundamental differential equation for symmetrical spherical diffusion is

$$\frac{\partial C}{\partial t} = D \left[\frac{\partial^2 C}{\partial r^2} + \frac{2}{r} \left(\frac{\partial C}{\partial r} \right) \right] \tag{24}$$

---

[9] D. Ilkovic, *Collection Czechoslov. Chem. Communs.*, **6**, 498 (1934); *J. chim. phys.*, **35**, 129 (1938).

[10] D. MacGillavry and E. K. Rideal, *Rec. trav. chim.*, **56**, 1013 (1937).

in which r is radial distance measured on a *fixed* coordinate system whose origin is at the center of the spherical electrode. In order to apply this equation to diffusion at the dropping electrode the fixed coordinate r must be replaced by a *moving* coordinate, ρ, to take into account the increase in area of the diffusion field during the growth of the mercury drops. MacGillavry and Rideal defined the moving coordinate ρ as the radius of a hypothetical sphere whose volume is the same as the volume enclosed between the surface of the growing mercury drop and a spherical surface of radius slightly larger than the radius of the drop; that is

$$\tfrac{4}{3}\pi r^3 - \tfrac{4}{3}\pi r_0^3 = \tfrac{4}{3}\pi \rho^3 \tag{30}$$

or

$$\rho^3 = r^3 - r_0^3 \tag{31}$$

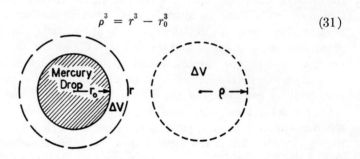

$$\Delta V = \tfrac{4}{3}\pi r^3 - \tfrac{4}{3}\pi r_0^3 = \tfrac{4}{3}\pi \rho^3$$

Fig. II-6. Diffusion to the dropping electrode and definition of ρ (drawn to correct scale).

where r is the radial distance from a point in the solution to the center of the drop, and r_0 is the radius of the drop at any instant. This definition of ρ is represented pictorially in Fig. II-6, which has been drawn to correct scale.

If we assume that the mercury drop is truly spherical, then its volume at any time t measured from the beginning of its formation is

$$V = \tfrac{4}{3}\pi r_0^3 = \frac{mt}{d} = \alpha t \tag{32}$$

where m is the weight of mercury flowing from the capillary per second, and d is the density of mercury. The proportionality constant α is the volume of mercury flowing from the capillary per second. It will be shown later that with a given capillary, and a constant pressure on the dropping mercury, m and α are virtually constant and independent of the interfacial tension at the mercury–solution interface; that is, m and α are practically independent of the potential of the dropping electrode. It is evident that the volume of the drop is directly proportional to its age, but its radius increases with the cube root of its age:

$$r_0^3 = \frac{3\alpha}{4\pi}\, t = \gamma t \tag{33}$$

In view of these relations, and eq. 31, ρ can be expressed as a function of the age of the drop by

$$\rho^3 = r^3 - \gamma t \tag{34}$$

The flux of the diffusing substance at a given instant and a given value of r is

$$f_r = D\,\frac{\partial C}{\partial r} = D\,\frac{\partial C}{\partial \rho}\cdot\frac{\partial \rho}{\partial r} \tag{35}$$

From eq. 34, for a given value of t, we have

$$\frac{\partial \rho}{\partial r} = \frac{r^2}{\rho^2} \tag{36}$$

and hence eq. 35 becomes

$$f_r = \frac{Dr^2}{\rho^2}\cdot\frac{\partial C}{\partial \rho} = \frac{dN}{A_r\,dt} \tag{37}$$

where A_r is the area of the diffusion field at r at any instant, and dN is the number of moles that diffuse through A_r in the time dt. By differentiating eq. 37 we obtain

$$\frac{\partial f_r}{\partial r} = D\left[\frac{r^2}{\rho^2}\cdot\frac{\partial^2 C}{\partial \rho^2}\cdot\frac{\partial \rho}{\partial r} + \frac{\partial C}{\partial \rho}\left(\frac{2r}{\rho^2} - \frac{2r^2}{\rho^3}\cdot\frac{\partial \rho}{\partial r}\right)\right] \tag{38}$$

Now in terms of the flux of the diffusing substance eq. 24 may be written

$$\frac{\partial C}{\partial t} = \frac{\partial f_r}{\partial r} + \frac{2}{r}f_r \tag{39}$$

By substituting the foregoing relations for f_r and $\partial f_r/\partial r$ into this equation, and simplifying, we obtain

$$\frac{\partial C}{\partial t} = \frac{Dr^4}{\rho^5}\left[\rho\,\frac{\partial^2 C}{\partial \rho^2} + \frac{2(\rho^3 - \gamma t)}{(\rho^3 + \gamma t)}\cdot\frac{\partial C}{\partial \rho}\right] \tag{40}$$

We are interested in the region very close to the surface of the dropping electrode, and since in this region r is only slightly greater than r_0, it follows that ρ^3 is very much smaller than γt. When $\rho^3 \ll \gamma t$, we have

$$\frac{\rho^3 - \gamma t}{\rho^3 + \gamma t} \cong -1$$

and

$$r^4 = (\gamma t)^{4/3}$$

Therefore, for this region very near to the surface of the dropping electrode eq. 40 becomes

$$\frac{\partial C}{\partial t} = \frac{D(\gamma t)^{4/3}}{\rho^5} \left[\rho \frac{\partial^2 C}{\partial \rho^2} - 2 \frac{\partial C}{\partial \rho} \right] \tag{41}$$

In order to obtain a solution of this equation it is convenient to perform a substitution of variables to simplify the algebra. Let

$$x = \rho^3 \qquad \text{and} \qquad y = t^{7/3}$$

Then

$$\frac{dx}{d\rho} = 3\rho^2 \qquad \text{and} \qquad \frac{d^2 x}{d\rho^2} = 6\rho$$

and

$$\frac{dy}{dt} = \tfrac{7}{3} t^{4/3}$$

In terms of these new variables, we have

$$\frac{\partial C}{\partial t} = \frac{\partial C}{\partial y} \cdot \frac{dy}{dt} = \tfrac{7}{3} t^{4/3} \frac{\partial C}{\partial x} \tag{42}$$

$$\frac{\partial C}{\partial \rho} = \frac{\partial C}{\partial x} \cdot \frac{dx}{d\rho} = 3\rho^2 \cdot \frac{\partial C}{\partial x} \tag{43}$$

$$\frac{\partial^2 C}{\partial \rho^2} = \frac{\partial C}{\partial x} \cdot \frac{d^2 x}{d\rho^2} + \frac{\partial^2 C}{\partial x^2} \cdot \left(\frac{dx}{d\rho} \right)^2 \tag{44a}$$

$$\frac{\partial^2 C}{\partial \rho^2} = 6\rho \frac{\partial C}{\partial x} + 9\rho^4 \frac{\partial^2 C}{\partial x^2} \tag{44b}$$

Substituting the relations expressed by eqs. 42, 43, and 44 into eq. 41 leads to

$$\frac{\partial C}{\partial y} = \tfrac{27}{7}\gamma^{4/3} D \frac{\partial^2 C}{\partial x^2} = m \frac{\partial^2 C}{\partial x^2} \tag{45}$$

where

$$m = \tfrac{27}{7}\gamma^{4/3} D$$

A solution of eq. 45 is

$$C = K + B \cdot \frac{2}{\sqrt{\pi}} \int_0^{x/2\sqrt{my}} e^{-q^2}\, dq \tag{46}$$

where K and B are constants.

The initial and boundary conditions of the diffusion at the dropping electrode are

$$C_0 = C \qquad \text{when} \qquad t = 0$$

and

$$C_0 \ll C, \qquad \text{or} \qquad C_0 = 0, \qquad \text{when} \qquad t > 0$$

where C is the concentration in the body of the solution, and C_0 the concentration at the surface of the mercury drops. When $t > 0$, $\rho = 0$, and since $x = \rho^3$, x is also equal to zero. Hence, when $t > 0$ the upper limit of the integral in eq. 46, and the integral itself, become equal to zero (Table II-1). Since C_0 is also equal to zero when $t > 0$, it follows that K in eq. 46 must be equal to zero. On the other hand, when $t = 0$, since $y = t^{7/3}$, the upper limit of the integral becomes infinity, and the value of the integral becomes $\sqrt{\pi}/2$ (Table II-1). Since C_0 is equal to C when $t = 0$, it follows that the constant B is equal simply to C. Hence eq. 46 becomes

$$C_0 = \frac{2C}{\sqrt{\pi}} \int_0^{x/2\sqrt{my}} e^{-q^2}\, dq \tag{47}$$

Since $x = \rho^3$, $y = t^{7/3}$, and $m = \tfrac{27}{7}\gamma^{4/3} D$,

$$\frac{x}{2\sqrt{my}} = \frac{1}{6}\sqrt{\frac{7\gamma}{3D}} \cdot \frac{\rho^3}{(\gamma t)^{7/6}} = s \tag{48}$$

and hence eq. 47 may be written

$$C_0 = \frac{2C}{\sqrt{\pi}} \int_0^s e^{-q^2}\, dq \qquad (49)$$

The resulting current at any instant during the life of a drop is governed by the flux of the diffusing substance at the surface of the drop ($\rho = 0$), and is given by

$$i_t = 4\pi r_0^2\, nF_y(f_r)_{\rho=0} \qquad (50)$$

From eq. 37

$$f_r = \frac{Dr^2}{\rho^2} \frac{\partial C}{\partial \rho} \qquad (37)$$

By differentiating eq. 49 with respect to ρ, we obtain

$$\frac{\partial C}{\partial \rho} = \frac{2C}{\sqrt{\pi}} \cdot \frac{\partial s}{\partial \rho} \cdot \frac{\partial}{\partial s} \left(\int_0^s e^{-q^2}\, dq \right) \qquad (51)$$

or in view of eq. 48

$$\frac{\partial C}{\partial \rho} = \frac{Ce^{-s^2}}{\sqrt{\pi}} \left(\frac{7\gamma}{3D} \right)^{1/2} \frac{\rho^2}{(\gamma t)^{7/6}} \qquad (52)$$

Therefore

$$f_r = \frac{Dr^2}{\rho^2} \cdot \frac{\partial C}{\partial \rho} = \frac{DCr^2}{(\gamma t)^{7/6}} \left(\frac{7\gamma}{3\pi D} \right)^{1/2} e^{-s^2} \qquad (53)$$

When $\rho = 0$,

$$e^{-s^2} = e^0 = 1, \qquad \text{and} \qquad r = r_0 = (\gamma t)^{1/3}$$

Hence from eq. 53, the flux at the surface of the drops is given by

$$(f_r)_{\rho=0} = \frac{DC}{(\gamma t)^{1/2}} \left(\frac{7\gamma}{3\pi D} \right)^{1/2} = \frac{D^{1/2}C}{t^{1/2}} \left(\frac{7}{3\pi} \right)^{1/2} \qquad (54)$$

and the expression for the current (eq. 50) becomes

$$i_t = 4 \left(\frac{7\pi}{3} \right)^{1/2} nF_y D^{1/2} C \gamma^{2/3} t^{1/6} \qquad (55)$$

Since

$$\gamma = \frac{3\alpha}{4\pi} = \frac{3m}{4\pi d} \qquad (56)$$

where m is the weight of mercury flowing from the capillary per second, and d is the density of mercury (13.6 g. cm.$^{-3}$), eq. 55 becomes

$$i_t = 0.732\ nF_yD^{1/2}Cm^{2/3}t^{1/6} \tag{57}$$

where 0.732 is simply a combination of the numerical constants. It should be emphasized that this is the theoretical equation for the current *at any instant* t during the life of a mercury drop. This relation was originally derived by Ilkovic (*loc. cit.*).

Equation 57 gives the current in amperes when F_y is expressed in coulombs, D in the units cm.^{2} sec.$^{-1}$, C in terms of moles per cm.^{3}, m in the units g. sec.$^{-1}$, and t in seconds. It is more convenient to express the current in microamperes (1 microamp. $= 10^{-6}$ amp.), the concentration in

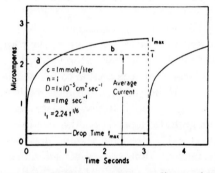

Fig. II-7. Theoretical current–time curve according to the Ilkovic equation during the formation of an individual mercury drop at the dropping electrode.

terms of millimoles per liter, and m as mg. sec.$^{-1}$, and on this basis, when the numerical value of F_y (96,500 coulombs) is introduced into eq. 57, we have

$$i_t = 706nD^{1/2}Cm^{2/3}t^{1/6} \text{ microamperes} \tag{58}$$

The foregoing equations predict that the current should increase with the sixth root of the time during the life of a drop and hence the current–time curve for an individual drop should be a sixth-order parabola. The theoretical current–time curve for a single drop calculated by means of eq. 58, for a substance whose diffusion coefficient is 1×10^{-5} cm.^{2} sec.$^{-1}$, a concentration of 1 millimole per liter, and a value for m of 1 mg. sec.$^{-1}$, and a value for n of 1, is shown in Fig. II-7. The area under the current–time curve of a single drop is equal to the *quantity* of electricity, in microcoulombs, associated with each drop.

In the previous cases of linear diffusion and spherical diffusion to stationary electrodes, we have seen that the current *decreases* with time after the e.m.f. is applied, because the concentration gradient at the electrode surface decreases with time. In the case of the dropping electrode, the *increase* of the current with time is due to the fact that the decrease of the concentration gradient at the drop surface is more than compensated by the increase in area of the diffusion field during the life of a drop. The decrease in current due to the decreasing concentration gradient at the drop surface is *inversely* proportional to the square root, or the three-sixths power, of the time. On the other hand, the increase in current due to the increasing area of the drop is directly proportional to the two-thirds, or four-sixths, power of the time. The cumulative result of these two opposing factors is an increase in current according to the one-sixth power of the time.

With an ordinary D'Arsonval galvanometer, which is the type usually used to measure current in polarographic work, the complete current–time curves of the individual drops are not observable, because the inertia of the moving coil is so large that it is unable to follow the complete periodic change in the current. Hence with an ordinary galvanometer the indicating device (pointer or light beam) simply oscillates over a relatively small amplitude, whose magnitude depends on the particular characteristics of the instrument that is used. However, Ilkovic[11] has shown that it is possible to obtain complete current–time curves of individual drops by using a torsion string galvanometer of very short period (0.01 to 0.02 sec.).[12] The current–time curves obtained by Ilkovic had the theoretical shape predicted by the foregoing equations when conditions were such that maxima in the current–voltage curves were eliminated, and when the applied e.m.f. was of such magnitude that a well-defined limiting current was obtained.

The *average* current during the life of a drop is defined as the hypothetical *constant* current which, flowing for a length of time equal to the drop time, would produce the same quantity of electricity as the quantity actually associated with each drop. The average current, $\bar{\imath}$, is defined by

$$\bar{\imath} = \frac{1}{t_{max.}} \int_0^{t_{max.}} i_t \, dt \qquad (59)$$

[11] D. Ilkovic, *Collection Czechoslov. Chem. Communs.*, **8**, 13 (1936).

[12] Torsion string galvanometers with a period of 0.01 sec. can be purchased from the firm of P. J. Kipp und Zonen, Delft, Holland.

where $t_{max.}$ is the drop time. In view of eq. 58

$$\bar{i} = \frac{706nD^{1/2}Cm^{2/3}}{t_{max.}} \int_0^{t_{max.}} t^{1/6}\,dt \tag{60}$$

By performing the indicated integration we finally obtain

$$\bar{i} = 607nD^{1/2}Cm^{2/3}t_{max.}^{1/6} \tag{61}$$

This is the equation for the average current which is usually referred to as the "Ilkovic equation."

It is evident from eq. 58 that the *maximum* current during the life of a drop, at the instant the drop falls, is given by

$$i_{max.} = 706nD^{1/2}Cm^{2/3}t_{max.}^{1/6} \tag{62}$$

By comparing this equation with eq. 60 or eq. 61 it is seen that

$$\bar{i} = \tfrac{6}{7}i_{max.} \tag{63}$$

According to the foregoing relations both the maximum current and the average current are directly proportional to the concentration of the electroactive substance. In practice the average current is measured with a galvanometer or other current-measuring device whose period is long compared to the drop time. Under this condition the galvanometer oscillations are much smaller than the true change in current during the life of each mercury drop, and the average of the galvanometer oscillations corresponds closely to the true average current.[13] With other types of recording devices this may or may not be true, depending on the "equation of motion" of the device.

The diffusion currents obtained with the dropping mercury electrode are perfectly reproducible. During the relatively short life of the mercury drops the concentration gradient around the dropping electrode does not have time to extend very far into the solution, and hence the diffusion layer around the drops is much thinner than that at a stationary spherical microelectrode. In an ingenious series of experiments Antweiler[14] utilized the gradient of refractive index produced by the concentration gradient as a means of photographing the diffusion layer around the mercury drops. His photographs show that the thickness of the normal diffusion layer (maxima

---

[13] J. K. Taylor, R. E. Smith, and I. L. Cooter, *J. Research Natl. Bureau Standards*, **42**, 387 (1949).

[14] H. J. Antweiler, *Z. Elektrochem.*, **44**, 719, 831, 888 (1938).

eliminated) is only of the order of 0.05 mm. The diffusion layer is so thin that there is no appreciable stirring effect due to density gradients, as there is in the case of solid spherical electrodes.

7. MODIFIED EQUATION FOR THE DROPPING ELECTRODE DIFFUSION CURRENT

Lingane and Loveridge[15] pointed out that although the derivation of the Ilkovic equation begins with the postulate of symmetrical spherical diffusion the simplifications introduced in the intermediate mathematical operations are equivalent to neglect of the curvature of the electrode surface.

That the final Ilkovic equation (eq. 61) neglects the curvature of the electrode surface is demonstrated by the fact that an equation of identical form follows directly from the equation for the linear diffusion current at a *plane* electrode (eq. 10) by simply expressing the area at any instant as a function of m and t. Assuming that the mercury drops are spherical the area A at any instant t during the drop life is

$$A = (4\pi)^{1/3}3^{2/3}m^{2/3}t^{2/3}d^{-2/3} \qquad (64)$$

where d is the density of mercury. When this relation is substituted into eq. 10, and the various quantities are expressed in the customary units, it follows that at 25°

$$i_t = 464nCD^{1/2}m^{2/3}t^{1/6} \qquad (65)$$

Correspondingly the average current during the drop life is

$$i_d = \frac{1}{t} \int_0^t i_t \, dt = 397nD^{1/2}Cm^{2/3}t^{1/6} \qquad (66)$$

This equation is identical *in form* with the Ilkovic equation (eq. 61) and differs from it only in the value of the numerical constant. Furthermore, if the constant 397 is multiplied by $\sqrt{7/3}$ the "Ilkovic constant" 607 is obtained.

This seemingly arbitrary procedure has theoretical significance because the factor $\sqrt{7/3}$ represents the fact that the expansion of the electrode surface counteracts the decay of the concentration gradient at the electrode surface and correspondingly increases the diffusion current. This effect is distinct from the mere increase in the area of the diffusion field which is adequately taken into account by the A term in the preceding equations. The physical significance of the $\sqrt{7/3}$ can be appreciated by visualizing

[15] J. J. Lingane and B. A. Loveridge, *J. Am. Chem. Soc.*, **72**, 438 (1950).

the situation at a plane electrode whose area is increasing. As the electrode surface expands the extent of the field from which the reducible substance can diffuse to the electrode increases, and only this is represented by the A term. In addition, because the electrode surface expands relatively undepleted electrolyte is brought into contact with the electrode and consequently the concentration gradient at the electrode is larger that it would have been after the same duration of electrolysis at an electrode of constant area equal to the instantaneous area of the expanding electrode. This is the effect represented by the $\sqrt{7/3}$ factor.

Because the Ilkovic equation follows so directly from the equation for linear diffuson to a plane electrode provided that the $\sqrt{7/3}$ factor is introduced Lingane and Loveridge assumed that a more nearly correct equation for the dropping electrode diffusion current which would take into account the curvature of the electrode surface should be obtainable by an analogous procedure starting with the equation for the diffusion current at a *stationary spherical* electrode (eq. 28). Introducing $\sqrt{7/3}$ into the second term of eq. 28 leads to

$$i_t = nFADC \left(\frac{1}{r} + \sqrt{\frac{7}{3\pi Dt}} \right) \tag{67}$$

where r is the area of the mercury drop at any instant which may be expressed as a function of m and t by

$$r = (3mt/4\pi d)^{1/3} \tag{68}$$

Substituting this relation and the relation for the instantaneous area given by eq. 64 into eq. 67 leads to

$$i_t = 709nD^{1/2}Cm^{2/3}t^{1/6} + 31{,}560nDCm^{1/3}t^{1/3} \tag{69}$$

Integration over the drop life yields for the average current

$$i_d = 607nD^{1/2}Cm^{2/3}t^{1/6} \left(1 + \frac{39D^{1/2}t^{1/6}}{m^{1/3}} \right) \tag{70}$$

This equation differs from the Ilkovic equation by the term $1 + 39 D^{1/2}t^{1/3}m^{-1/3}$ which represents the influence of the electrode curvature. The numerical value of this term evidently depends on the particular substance (D) and on the characteristics of the particular dropping electrode (m and t), and it is of the order of 1.1.

An equation identical with eq. 70, except that the constant in the second term is 17 instead of 39, has been derived independently by Strehlow and von Stackelberg.[16]   Their derivation follows the general pattern of Ilkovic's original derivation and that of MacGillavry and Rideal but retains in the intermediate mathematical operations those terms, neglected in the original derivations, which represent the curvature of the electrode surface. Kambara and Tachi,[17] apparently unaware of the previous derivations, later derived an equation identical with eq. 70, including the constant 39. Experimental tests of these relations are discussed in Chapter IV.

---

[16] H. Strehlow and M. von Stackelberg, *Z. Elektrochem.*, **54,** 51 (1950).

[17] T. Kambara and I. Tachi, *Proceedings International Polarographic Congress,* Prague, Feb. 1951, Part I, p. 126.

CHAPTER III

Evaluation of Diffusion Coefficients

1. GENERAL REMARKS

Diffusion currents obtained with either the dropping mercury electrode or platinum microelectrodes are proportional to the square root of the diffusion coefficient of the electroreducible or electrooxidizable substance. A knowledge of numerical values of diffusion coefficients of various substances is therefore essential for practical applications of the diffusion current equations.

The available experimental data in the literature on diffusion coefficients are very scanty, and in most cases of doubtful accuracy.[1] This is particularly true as regards the diffusion coefficient of ions. There are practically no reliable experimental data available for the diffusion coefficients of individual ions under the conditions extant in polarographic work; *i. e.*, in solutions containing relatively large concentrations of indifferent salts. Fortunately, however, it is possible to calculate ionic diffusion coefficients from ionic conductance data, and the diffusion coefficients of uncharged molecules of high molecular weight can be computed from their molecular weights. These methods will be discussed in the following pages.

It should be emphasized at this point that the methods to be described are strictly applicable only to *ideal* ions and molecules. The diffusion coefficients of actual ions and molecules vary with the concentration of the diffusing substance and with the ionic strength of the solution. Hence the equations that will be discussed should be regarded as limiting relations, strictly valid only at infinite dilution. The exact interpretation of the change of the diffusion coefficient with varying concentration and ionic strength is a difficult problem, which has not yet been completely solved. Although a complete account of this problem would be beyond the scope of the present discussion, a few examples will be cited to demonstrate the magnitude of the effect, and to give the reader an approximate idea of the errors involved in the application of the limiting equations. Fortunately,

---

[1] For reviews of experimental methods used to measure diffusion coefficients see, J. Williams and L. Cady, *Chem. Revs.*, **14**, 171 (1934); and J. Duclaux, *Diffusion dans les Liquides*, Actualités Scientifiques et Industrielles, No. 349, Paris, 1936.

the divergence of most substances from ideal behavior is not so great as to invalidate completely the application of the limiting equations to actual solutions, and these equations are of invaluable service in the interpretation of diffusion current data.

2. RELATION BETWEEN THE DIFFUSION COEFFICIENT AND THE MOBILITY OF DIFFUSING MOLECULES AND IONS

The velocity acquired by a molecule or ion moving through a solution is proportional to the force causing the movement. The velocity produced by a unit force is called the *mobility*. The mobility is independent of the nature of the force, whether it is an electrical force, as in conductance measurements, or an osmotic force, as in diffusion. This fact makes possible the calculation of the "diffusion mobility," and the diffusion coefficient, of an ion from its mobility measured by conductance methods.

Representing the velocity by v, the force by φ, and the mobility by δ, we have the relation

$$v = \delta\varphi \tag{1}$$

The dimensions of δ are those of velocity divided by force, or cm./sec./dyne in c.g.s. units. On the assumption that the resistance to motion is due entirely to friction, the reciprocal of δ is sometimes referred to as the *frictional coefficient*.

In order to derive the relation between the diffusion coefficient and the mobility of diffusing molecules or ions, let us consider a diffusion field of area equal to A cm.^{2}, in which either ions or uncharged molecules are diffusing. Let C be the molecular concentration (number of molecules or ions per cm.^{3}), and v the velocity of the diffusing molecules, at a given plane in the diffusion field at a given instant. The number of molecules or ions, dn, which diffuse across this plane in the infinitesimal interval of time dt is given by

$$dn = CvA \, dt \tag{2}$$

The flux of the diffusing particles is equal to

$$f = \frac{dn}{A \, dt} = Cv \text{ (molecules/cm.}^2\text{/sec.)} \tag{3}$$

or, in terms of the mobility of the diffusing molecules and the force acting on them,

$$f = C\delta\varphi \tag{4}$$

where φ is the force on the molecules or ions which causes them to diffuse.

The various diffusing molecules do not, of course, all have the same velocity; the velocities of the individual molecules vary from relatively very large to very small values in a manner analogous to the distribution of molecular velocities in gases. However, just as we speak of the average velocity of gas molecules, we will regard the v in the foregoing equations as the average velocity of the diffusing molecules or ions. Similarly, the force φ will be regarded as the average force acting on each diffusing molecule.

The force causing diffusion arises from differences in concentration in the diffusion field, and it is most conveniently expressed in terms of the gradient of the chemical potential of the diffusing molecules or ions (gradient of the partial molar free energy at constant temperature and pressure). The molar chemical potential, μ, of an *ideal* substance in a solution is related to its concentration by the equation

$$\mu = k + RT \ln C \tag{5}$$

where R is the molar gas constant, T is the absolute temperature, and k is a constant, the standard chemical potential, which is a function of the temperature and pressure but is independent of the concentration. The diffusive force on a mole of ideal diffusing molecules at a given plane is equal to the gradient of the chemical potential, $\partial\mu/\partial x$, at the plane in question. Hence the average force on each diffusing molecule is expressible by

$$\varphi = \frac{1}{K}\frac{\partial\mu}{\partial x} = \frac{RT}{KC}\frac{\partial C}{\partial x} \tag{6}$$

where K is Avogadro's number (6.03×10^{23} molecules per mole). For an excellent detailed discussion of the justification of this concept the reader may consult a paper of Onsager and Fuoss.[2]

By combining eqs. 4 and 6 we obtain

$$f = C\delta\varphi = \frac{RT\delta}{K}\frac{\partial C}{\partial x} \tag{7}$$

The flux is independently expressable by the empirical law of Fick:

$$f = D\frac{\partial C}{\partial x} \tag{8}$$

which is also the *definition* of the diffusion coefficient D. By comparing

[2] L. Onsager and R. M. Fuoss, *J. Phys. Chem.*, **36**, 2689–2778 (1932).

eqs. 7 and 8, it is evident that the diffusion coefficient of *ideal* molecules or ions is related to their mobility by

$$D = \frac{RT}{K} \delta \tag{9}$$

The diffusion coefficient has the dimensions of length squared divided by time, and it is usually expressed in the units cm.^{2} sec.$^{-1}$ or cm.^{2} day^{-1} The numerical value of D is independent of the units in which the concentration and the flux are expressed.

It should be realized that the diffusion coefficient and the mobility are not characteristic properties of the diffusing molecules alone, but they also depend on the properties of the solvent medium. Every diffusion process is strictly an *interdiffusion* of "solute" and "solvent" molecules, and hence D is a characteristic property of the whole system.

3. INDIVIDUAL IONIC DIFFUSION COEFFICIENTS

Equation 9 will apply to ideal ions, *provided conditions are such that the ion in question is free to diffuse independently of other ions.* In other words, eq. 9 can be regarded as the definition of what we may term the characteristic or individual diffusion coefficient of a single species of ideal ion when the electrical restrictions ordinarily imposed by its charge are removed.

It is a well-known fact that there is an electrical potential gradient (diffusion potential) in the diffusion field when a salt is diffusing between two different concentrations. The diffusion potential arises from the tendency of the intrinsically more mobile ions to outrun the slower ions of opposite charge, but after it is established it acts in such a way that the faster ions are retarded and the slower ions accelerated until they both migrate at the same net rate (electroneutrality of diffusion). The ions are constrained to diffuse at the same rate by virtue of the fact that the total force on the more mobile ions is less than that on the slower ions of opposite sign.

The total force on a single diffusing ion is the sum of a diffusive force, proportional to the concentration gradient, and an additional electrical force due to the diffusion potential gradient. If we represent the diffusion potential gradient by $\partial E/\partial x$, the average total force on a single ideal ion is equal to

$$\frac{RT}{KC} \frac{\partial C}{\partial x} \pm \frac{zF_y}{K} \frac{\partial E}{\partial x}$$

where z is the charge of the ion without regard to sign. (The sign before the second term is positive for positive ions, and negative for negative ions.) In the diffusion of a single salt the concentration force will be the same on both the positive and negative ions (*vide infra*), but the electrical forces are oppositely directed. The *total* forces on the positive and negative ions differ, due to the balancing effect of the diffusion potential gradient, by an amount just sufficient to counteract any difference in the ion mobilities, and the positive and negative ions diffuse at the same rate.

In order that a single species of ion may diffuse independently of other ions according to its characteristic diffusion coefficient the electrical force (diffusion potential) must be eliminated. Experimentally, this can be accomplished, more or less completely, by having a large excess of some indifferent salt present *at a uniform concentration throughout the diffusion field*. By choosing an indifferent salt whose ions have as nearly as possible the same mobilities, *e. g.*, potassium chloride, and by having the concentration of the added salt much larger than that of the diffusing ions, the diffusion potential—and hence the electrical force on the diffusing ions—is practically completely eliminated. Under these conditions, which are the conditions under which polarographic diffusion currents are measured, the positive and negative ions of the diffusing salt diffuse independently of each other according to their individual diffusion coefficients.

In order to calculate the characteristic diffusion coefficient of an ideal ion by means of eq. 9, we make use of the fact that the equivalent conductance of an ion at infinite dilution, *i. e.*, in the absence of interionic forces, is a direct measure of its mobility. We have the well-known relation[3]

$$u = \frac{\lambda^0}{F_y} \qquad (10)$$

where u is the velocity acquired by the ion under *unit potential gradient*, λ^0 is the equivalent conductance of the ion at infinite dilution (ohm^{-1} cm.^{2} equiv.$^{-1}$), and F_y is the faraday (96,500 coulombs when the potential gradient is expressed in ordinary volts). When the potential gradient is unity, the force on an ion of charge z is numerically equal to ze, where e is the unit electronic charge (4.80×10^{-10} e.s.u.). In ordinary electrical units, e is equal simply to F_y/K, or 1.60×10^{-19} coulomb. Hence the mobility of an ion at infinite dilution is given by

$$\delta_i^0 = \frac{u}{ze} = \frac{\lambda^0}{zeF_y} = \frac{K\lambda^0}{zF_y^2} \qquad (11)$$

---

[3] See, for example, M. Dole, *Experimental and Theoretical Electrochemistry*, New York, 1935.

By substituting this expression for the mobility into eq. 9 we find that the characteristic diffusion coefficient of an ion at infinite dilution is given by

$$D_i^0 = \frac{RT}{K} \delta_i^0 = \frac{RT}{zF_y^2} \lambda^0 \tag{12}$$

This relation was derived originally by Nernst,[4] and it is exact at infinite dilution.

When the numerical values, $R = 8.317$ volt-coulombs per degree, $F_y = 96,500$ coulombs, and $T = 298°$ K., are substituted into eq. 12, we obtain

$$D_i^0 = 2.67 \times 10^{-7} \frac{\lambda^0}{z}, \text{ cm.}^2 \text{ sec.}^{-1} \text{ at } 25° \text{ C.} \tag{13}$$

For convenient reference the diffusion coefficients at $25°$ C. of a number of common ions at infinite dilution in aqueous solution, calculated by means of this equation, are given in Table III-1.

TABLE III-1

DIFFUSION COEFFICIENTS OF VARIOUS IONS AT INFINITE DILUTION AT 25°C.

Ion	λ^0 ohm^{-1} cm.^{2}	D^0 cm.^{2} sec.$^{-1}$ $\times 10^5$	Ion	λ^0, ohm.$^{-1}$ cm.^{2}	D^0, cm.^{2} sec.$^{-1}$ $\times 10^5$
H$^+$	350	9.34	OH$^-$	196	5.23
Li$^+$	39	1.04	Cl$^-$	76	2.03
K$^+$	74	1.98	NO$_3^-$	72	1.92
Na$^+$	50.5	1.35	CH$_3$COO$^-$	41	1.09
Cs$^+$	79	2.11	IO$_3^-$	41	1.09
Tl$^+$	75	2.00	BrO$_3^-$	54	1.44
Pb^{++}	73	0.98	SO$_4^{--}$	81	1.08
Cd^{++}	54	0.72	CrO$_4^{--}$	80	1.07
Zn^{++}	54	0.72	Fe(CN)$_6^{---}$	100	0.89
Cu^{++}	54	0.72	Fe(CN)$_6^{----}$	110.5	0.74
Ni^{++}	52	0.69			

4. TEMPERATURE COEFFICIENT OF IONIC DIFFUSION COEFFICIENTS

The effect of temperature on ionic diffusion coefficients can be readily computed with the aid of eq. 12. By differentiating eq. 12 we obtain

$$\frac{\partial D_i^0}{\partial T} = \frac{RT}{zF_y^2} \frac{\partial \lambda^0}{\partial T} + \frac{R\lambda^0}{zF_y^2} \tag{14}$$

[4] W. Nernst, Z. physik. Chem., 2, 613 (1888).

and hence the temperature coefficient of D_i^0 is given by

$$\frac{1}{D_i^0}\frac{\partial D_i^0}{\partial T} = \frac{1}{\lambda^0}\frac{\partial \lambda^0}{\partial T} + \frac{1}{T} \tag{15}$$

This relation, in conjunction with the Ilkovic equation for the diffusion current, is useful for calculating the influence of temperature on the diffusion current, and for correlating diffusion currents obtained at different temperatures.

Since the temperature coefficient of the equivalent conductance of most ions is approximately 0.02 deg.$^{-1}$ ($+2$ per cent per degree), and since at ordinary temperatures $1/T$ is only about 0.0033 deg.$^{-1}$, the temperature coefficient of D_i^0 is chiefly determined by—and is practically equal to—the temperature coefficient of the equivalent conductance. Hence, the temperature coefficient of D_i^0 for most ions is in the neighborhood of 2 per cent per degree.

5. DIFFUSION COEFFICIENT OF A SALT

In connection with the discussion of the migration current in a later chapter it is necessary to employ the diffusion coefficient of a salt. The method of computing this quantity from the characteristic diffusion coefficients of the constituent ions of the salt will now be described.

Consider the diffusion of a single pure salt, which we shall assume is completely dissociated into ideal ions. As already explained, the constituent positive and negative ions are constrained by the diffusion potential to diffuse at the same rate, and this rate is proportional to what we shall refer to as the diffusion coefficient of the salt. Let C be the molecular concentration (number of molecules per cm.^{3}) of the salt, C_+ and C_- be the concentrations (number of ions per cm.^{3}) of the positive and negative ions, and ν_+ and ν_- the number of positive and negative ions of charge z_+ and z_- formed by the dissociation of one molecule of the salt. The flux of positive ions will be

$$f_+ = C_+ \, \delta_+^0 \, \varphi_+ = \nu_+ \, C \, \delta_+^0 \, \varphi_+ \tag{16}$$

and that of the negative ions is

$$f_- = C_- \, \delta_-^0 \, \varphi_- = \nu_- \, C \, \delta_-^0 \, \varphi_- \tag{17}$$

where φ_+ and φ_- are the average *total* forces on a positive and a negative ion, respectively, and δ_+^0 and δ_-^0 are the characteristic mobilities of the positive and negative ions (eq. 11). The average *total* forces on each ion are

$$\varphi_+ = \frac{RT}{K}\frac{\partial \ln C_+}{\partial x} + \frac{z_+ F_y}{K}\frac{\partial E}{\partial x} \tag{18}$$

and

$$\varphi_- = \frac{RT}{K}\frac{\partial \ln C_-}{\partial x} - \frac{z_- F_y}{K}\frac{\partial E}{\partial x} \tag{19}$$

The first terms in these equations are the osmotic forces, and the second terms the electrical forces due to the diffusion potential gradient $\partial E/\partial x$, on the diffusing ions. The osmotic forces on the positive and negative ions are equal, because

$$\frac{\partial \ln C_+}{\partial x} = \frac{\partial(\nu_+ C)}{\nu_+ C\, \partial x} = \frac{\partial C}{C\, \partial x} = \frac{\partial \ln C}{\partial x} \tag{20}$$

and similarly

$$\frac{\partial \ln C_-}{\partial x} = \frac{\partial(\nu_- C)}{\nu_- C\, \partial x} = \frac{\partial C}{C\, \partial x} = \frac{\partial \ln C}{\partial x} \tag{21}$$

Hence the *difference* in the total forces on the two ions is given by

$$\varphi_+ - \varphi_- = (z_+ + z_-)\frac{F_y}{K}\frac{\partial E}{\partial x} \tag{22}$$

Since there is electroneutrality of diffusion, the flux of positive charge is equal to the flux of negative charge; that is,

$$z_+ f_+ = z_- f_-, \qquad \text{or} \qquad \frac{f_+}{\nu_+} = \frac{f_-}{\nu_-} \tag{23}$$

By making use of this fact, and combining eqs. 16, 17, 18, 19, 20, and 21 with eq. 23, we find that the diffusion potential gradient at the plane in question is given by

$$\frac{\partial E}{\partial x} = \left(\frac{\delta_-^0 - \delta_+^0}{z_+ \delta_+^0 + z_- \delta_-^0}\right)\frac{RT}{F_y}\frac{\partial \ln C}{\partial x} \tag{24}$$

By substituting this expression for the diffusion potential gradient into the foregoing equations for the flux of positive and negative ions, we obtain

$$f_+ = \frac{\nu_+ RT}{K}\frac{\partial C}{\partial x}\left[\frac{\delta_+^0 \delta_-^0 (z_+ + z_-)}{z_+ \delta_+^0 + z_- \delta_-^0}\right] \tag{25}$$

and

$$f_- = \frac{\nu_- RT}{K} \frac{\partial C}{\partial x} \left[\frac{\delta_+^0 \delta_-^0 (z_+ + z_-)}{z_+ \delta_+^0 + z_- \delta_-^0} \right] \qquad (26)$$

The flux of the salt (molecules of salt per cm.^{2} per second) can be expressed in terms of the flux of either the positive or negative ions, since we have the relation

$$f_{\text{salt}} = \frac{f_+}{\nu_+} = \frac{f_-}{\nu_-} \qquad (27)$$

Hence, from either eq. 25 or 26 and eq. 27, we find

$$f_{\text{salt}} = \frac{RT}{K} \frac{\partial C}{\partial x} \left[\frac{\delta_+^0 \delta_-^0 (z_+ + z_-)}{z_+ \delta_+^0 + z_- \delta_-^0} \right] \qquad (28)$$

The flux of the salt is also independently expressible by Fick's Law

$$f_{\text{salt}} = D_{\text{salt}}^0 \frac{\partial C}{\partial x} \qquad (29)$$

By comparing eqs. 28 and 29 it is evident that

$$D_{\text{salt}}^0 = \frac{RT}{K} \left[\frac{\delta_+^0 \delta_-^0 (z_+ + z_-)}{z_+ \delta_+^0 + z_- \delta_-^0} \right] \qquad (30)$$

In view of eq. 11, the diffusion coefficient of a salt at infinite dilution can be expressed in terms of the equivalent conductances of its ions at infinite dilution by

$$D_{\text{salt}}^0 = \frac{RT}{F_y^2} \left(\frac{\lambda_+^0 \lambda_-^0}{\lambda_-^0 + \lambda_+^0} \right) \left(\frac{1}{z_+} + \frac{1}{z_-} \right) \qquad (31)$$

In terms of the characteristic diffusion coefficients, D_+^0 and D_-^0, of its ions as given by eq. 12, and in Table III-1, the expression for the diffusion coefficient of an ideal salt becomes

$$D_{\text{salt}}^0 = \frac{D_+^0 D_-^0 (z_+ + z_-)}{z_+ D_+^0 + z_- D_-^0} \qquad (32)$$

It should be emphasized that the foregoing relations are strictly valid only for a completely dissociated salt whose ions behave as ideal solutes or for an actual salt only at infinite dilution. Although the application of these relations is thus limited, they are nevertheless very useful in the interpretation of limiting currents in ion reductions or oxidations at the dropping electrode when no foreign salt is present in the solution.

For a more complete discussion of the foregoing relations the reader is referred to the papers of Haskell,[5] Planck,[6] Hermans,[7] and Onsager and Fuoss.[8]

6. THE DIFFUSION COEFFICIENT OF UNCHARGED SUBSTANCES. THE STOKES-EINSTEIN DIFFUSION EQUATION

We have seen that the diffusion coefficient is related to the mobility of the diffusing molecules by

$$D = \frac{RT}{K} \delta \tag{9}$$

In the case of large spherical molecules, which are much larger than the molecules of the solvent medium, the mobility can be computed from the radius of the molecules, r, and the viscosity coefficient of the solvent, η, by means of Stokes' Law,

$$\delta = \frac{1}{6\pi\eta r} \tag{33}$$

It must be realized that this relation is only valid when the moving particles or molecules are spherical and very much larger than the molecules of the solvent medium, i. e., when the medium is continuous with respect to the diffusing molecules, so that the retarding forces are entirely frictional in nature and proportional to the bulk viscosity of the solution. It can be applied, for example, to spherical colloid particles, and to certain types of large molecules in ordinary solvent media, but it is not valid for small molecules or ions, or for nonspherical molecules. In the case of nonspherical particles the shape factor $6\pi r$ must be modified.[9]

[5] R. Haskell, *Phys. Revs.*, **27**, 145 (1908).

[6] M. Planck, *Wied. Ann.*, **39**, 161, 561 (1890); *Sitzber. preuss. Akad. Wiss.*, 285 (1927); 9 (1929); 367 (1930); and 113 (1931).

[7] J. J. Hermans, *Diffusion of Electrolytes*, Leyden, 1937; *Rec. trav. chim.*, **56**, 635 (1937).

[8] L. Onsager and R. M. Fuoss, *J. Phys. Chem.*, **36**, 2689–2778 (1932).

[9] A good discussion of the Stokes' relation and its limitations may be found in H. S. Taylor, *Treatise on Physical Chemistry*, New York, 1936, pp. 183, 1026, and 1584.

By combining eqs. 9 and 33 we obtain

$$D = \frac{RT}{K} \cdot \frac{1}{6\pi\eta r} \tag{34}$$

which is known as the Stokes-Einstein equation.[10] This relation has been frequently employed for determining the size of colloidal particles and the size of large molecules and large ions from measurements of their diffusion velocity.[11-16]

In order to apply this relation to problems in polarography it is necessary to know the radius, r, of the molecules or ions in question. If we are dealing with large spherical molecules which do not polymerize in solution, or undergo solvation, and whose molar volume in solution is the same as in the pure state, then the radius r can be computed from the molecular weight M and the density d of the substance in the pure state by means of the relation

$$M = \tfrac{4}{3}\pi r^3 K d \tag{35}$$

where K is Avogadro's number. By combining eqs. 34 and 35 we obtain

$$D = \frac{RT}{K} \frac{(4\pi K d)^{1/3}}{6\pi\eta(3M)^{1/3}} \tag{36a}$$

When we introduce the numerical values, $R = 8.315 \times 10^7$ ergs deg.$^{-1}$, $T = 298°$ K. (25° C.), and $K = 6.03 \times 10^{23}$, and combine all the numerical constants into a single term, we have

$$D = \frac{2.96 \times 10^{-7}}{\eta(V_m)^{1/3}} \text{ cm.}^2 \text{ sec.}^{-1} \text{ at } 25° \text{ C.} \tag{36b}$$

where V_m is the apparent molar volume of the substance in the pure solid state (mol. wt./density). The viscosity coefficient of pure water at 25° is 8.93×10^{-3} dyne sec. cm.$^{-2}$, and hence at *infinite dilution* in aqueous

[10] A. Einstein, *Ann. Physik*, (4) **17**, 549 (1905); **19**, 371 (1906); *Z. Elektrochem.*, **14**, 235 (1908).

[11] J. Williams and L. Cady, *Chem. Revs.*, **14**, 171 (1934).

[12] G. Hartley and D. Runnicles, *Proc. Roy. Soc. London*, **168**, 420 (1938).

[13] J. McBain and T. Liu, *J. Am. Chem. Soc.*, **53**, 59 (1931).

[14] M. Laing-McBain, *J. Am. Chem. Soc.*, **55**, 545 (1933).

[15] G. Jander and K. Weitendorf, *Angew. Chem.*, **47**, 197 (1934).

[16] E. Cohen and H. Bruins, *Z. physik. Chem.*, **103**, 404 (1923).

solutions at 25°

$$D_0 = \frac{3.32 \times 10^{-5}}{(V_m)^{1/3}} \text{ cm.}^2 \text{ sec.}^{-1} \tag{36c}$$

Multiplication of D by the factor 86,400 sec. day^{-1} converts the units of D from cm.^{2} sec.$^{-1}$ to cm.^{2} day^{-1}.

Friedman and Carpenter[17] investigated the limits of validity of eq. 36, with respect to the magnitude of the molar volume, and they found that it was valid as a limiting law at infinite dilution for substances whose molecular weight is as small as 180. This is demonstrated by their data for dextrose (mol. wt. = 180) which are reproduced graphically in Fig. III-1.

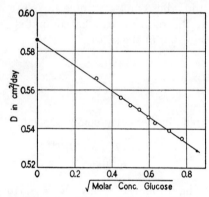

Fig. III-1. Diffusion coefficient of dextrose at 25° C. as a function of concentration.[17]

In this figure the experimentally measured diffiusion coefficient of dextrose at various concentrations is plotted against the square root of the molar concentration; the open circles are experimental points, and the solid circle on the ordinate is the value of D calculated by means of eq. 36. It will be noted that the experimental points fall on a straight line, and the extrapolated value of D at infinite dilution coincides with the value calculated from eq. 36.

Friedman and Carpenter found the same type of linear relation between the diffusion coefficient and concentration for various other substances (sucrose, maltose, lactose, mannitol, and salicin). In all these cases the decrease of the diffusion coefficient with increasing concentration could be satisfactorily represented by a simple linear equation of the form

$$D_c = D_0 - AC^{1/2} \tag{37}$$

---

[17] L. Friedman and P. G. Carpenter, *J. Am. Chem. Soc.*, **61**, 1745 (1939).

where D_0 is the diffusion coefficient at infinite dilution, and A is a constant which is different for different substances and different solvent media.

It is evident from these results that the Stokes-Einstein diffusion equation, in the form given by eq. 36c employing the viscosity of the pure solvent, is only valid at infinite dilution. It might be thought that the Stokes-Einstein relation could be applied to finite concentrations by employing the viscosity of the solution in place of that of the pure solvent, but in the case of dextrose, and presumably also in the case of most neutral molecules, this leads to a large overcorrection; in other words, the diffusion coefficient of dextrose does not decrease as rapidly with increasing concentration as the increase in viscosity would indicate.

When the Stokes-Einstein diffusion equation is not applicable, due to the small size of the neutral molecules in question, an approximate value for the diffusion coefficient of a neutral molecule can be obtained by assuming that it is the same as that of a large ion (usually an organic ion) of a size and structure closely comparable to that of the neutral molecule. For example, it is logical to assume that the diffusion coefficient of the nitrobenzene molecule at infinite dilution will be practically the same as that of the benzoate ion at infinite dilution, and the diffusion coefficient of the latter can be computed from the equivalent conductance of the benzoate ion by means of eq. 12. Similarly the diffusion coefficient of the nitronaphthalene molecule (I) should be virtually the same as that of the

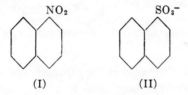

(I)   (II)

corresponding naphthalene sulfonate ion (II). Although this comparison method cannot be very exact, especially if the "comparison ion" is appreciably hydrated, it should nevertheless be useful when no other method of evaluating the diffusion coefficient is available.

7. THE DIFFUSION COEFFICIENT AS A FUNCTION OF THE CONCENTRATION OF THE DIFFUSING SUBSTANCE AND THE IONIC STRENGTH

The diffusion coefficients of both electrolytes and neutral molecules are dependent on the concentration of the diffusing substance and on the ionic strength of the medium. The diffusion coefficients of neutral molecules decrease continuously with increasing concentration (see Fig. III-1), and usually to a greater extent than those of electrolytes. After an initial decrease, the diffusion coefficients of electrolytes often increase again with increasing ionic strength, so that the diffusion coefficient–concentration curve displays a flat minimum. This typical behavior is exemplified in Fig. III-2, in which the ratio of the diffusion coefficient of potassium chloride at a concentration C to that at infinite dilution, D_c/D_0, is plotted against the molar concentration. For the sake of comparison similar plots of the conductance ratio Λ_c/Λ_0 and the activity coefficient γ of potassium chloride are included. The diffusion coefficient data have been taken from the paper of McBain and Dawson.[18]

It will be noted that, compared to the change in the conductance ratio and the activity coefficient, the variation of D with concentration is rela-

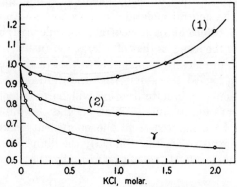

Fig. III-2. Effect of concentration on the diffusion coefficient, equivalent conductance, and activity coefficient of potassium chloride at 25° C. (1) D_c/D_o. (2) Λ_c/Λ_o.

tively small. Minima also occur in the diffusion coefficient–concentration curves of other valence-type salts, such as magnesium chloride and magnesium nitrate,[19] and cadmium and magnesium sulfates.[20] Such minima appear to be characteristic of electrolyte solutions, since they are not observed in the diffusion coefficient–concentration curves of uncharged substances.

In general the change in the apparent diffusion coefficient of a substance with changing concentration is due to two effects: (1) a change in the effective "osmotic force" of diffusion from its ideal value at a given concentration, due to the deviation of the diffusing molecules or ions from

[18] J. McBain and C. Dawson, *Proc. Roy. Soc. London*, **A148**, 32 (1935).

[19] L. Öholm, *Finska Kemistsamfundets Medd.*, **45**, 71 (1936).

[20] D. P. Davies, *Phil. Mag.*, (7) **15**, 489 (1933).

ideal behavior; and (2) a change in the mobility of the molecules or ions with changing concentration and ionic strength. Strictly speaking, the first factor does not change the true diffusion coefficient, but only the apparent diffusion coefficient that one calculates from experimental data using equations that have been derived on the assumption that the driving force of diffusion is directly proportional to a concentration gradient; this factor disappears when the driving force is correctly expressed in terms of an activity gradient. The evaluation of the second factor, which does change the true diffusion coefficient, is a difficult problem which has not yet been completely solved, and which would be beyond the scope of this book to discuss. For readers interested in this problem we recommend the papers of Onsager and Fuoss,[21] Van Rysselberghe,[22] and Gordon.[23]

8. POLAROGRAPHIC DIFFUSION COEFFICIENTS

We have seen in the preceding sections that it is possible to compute the characteristic diffusion coefficients of ions, salts, and certain neutral molecules, but that the relations involved are strictly correct only at infinite dilution. Any correction for changing concentration and changing ionic strength that we would attempt to make on the basis of the present incomplete knowledge of this problem would be of very doubtful validity. Hence it is better, for the present at least, to employ the infinite dilution or ideal values of D in polarographic work. This conclusion is justified by the reasonably good agreement between observed diffusion currents and those calculated using the Ilkovic equation and infinite dilution values of diffusion coefficients, which are discussed in a following chapter.

On the other hand, it is important to realize that the diffusion coefficient will be altered when the molecular or ionic state of an electroreducible substance is changed, for instance, by complex formation. For this reason, the diffusion current observed with an aquo metal ion differs appreciably from that found when the ion is present in a different complex form, such as a tartrate, cyanide, ammonia, thiocyanate, or citrate complex. It should also be mentioned in this connection that lyophilic colloids—such as gelatin or methyl cellulose—which are often added to the solution for the purpose of suppressing maxima, may combine to a certain extent with certain metal ions and change their effective diffusion coefficient. For instance, Kolthoff and Lingane[24] found that the diffusion current of lead ion, and

---

[21] L. Onsager and R. M. Fuoss, *J. Phys. Chem.*, **36**, 2689–2778 (1932).

[22] P. Van Rysselberghe, *J. Am. Chem. Soc.*, **60**, 2326 (1938).

[23] A. R. Gordon, *J. Chem. Phys.*, **5**, 522 (1937).

[24] I. M. Kolthoff and J. J. Lingane, *Chem. Revs.*, **24**, 1–94 (1939).

certain other heavy metal ions, is decreased markedly by adding relatively small amounts of gelatin to the solution. The change in viscosity caused by the addition of the gelatin was only partly responsible for the decrease in the diffusion current, and it appeared to be chiefly due to complex formation between the metal ions and gelatin.

It is also to be expected that the diffusion coefficients of reducible or oxidizable weak organic acids and bases will be influenced by the pH of the solution, when the mobilities of the corresponding anions and cations are different from those of the undissociated molecules.

These effects are usually of more importance in practical polarographic work than the effect of ionic strength on the diffusion coefficients.

From the physicochemical viewpoint it is of interest to mention that the dropping electrode is very suitable for the measurement of diffusion coefficients of reducible and oxidizable substances, and for studying the effect of complex formation and the effect of the solvent medium on the diffusion coefficient. Linear diffusion electrodes of the type described in Chapter II, are even better suited to such measurements than the dropping electrode.

The chief application of diffusion coefficient data in polarographic work is for the evaluation of the n-value of an electrode reaction by use of the Ilkovic equation. For this purpose highly exact values of diffusion coefficients are not usually required because it is only necessary to differentiate between small integral values of n. It is a fortunate circumstance, in this connection, that the diffusion current is proportional to the square root of D, so that a given error in D itself is greatly minimized in the application of the Ilkovic equation.

We strongly urge workers in the field of polarography to calculate diffusion coefficients from observed diffusion currents, whenever this is possible, and to report such data in the literature. This will greatly facilitate the attainment of a systematized knowledge of the effect of complex formation, the nature of the solvent, etc. on diffusion coefficients.

CHAPTER IV

Factors That Govern the Diffusion Current

1. INTRODUCTORY REMARKS

The theoretical equation for the diffusion current obtained with a dropping mercury electrode, which was first derived by Ilkovic, is

$$i_d = 607nD^{1/2}Cm^{2/3}t^{1/6} \tag{1a}$$

where i_d is the *average* current in microamperes during the life of a drop, n is the number of faradays of electricity required per mole of the electrode reaction, D is the diffusion coefficient of the reducible or oxidizable substance in the units cm.^{2} sec.$^{-1}$, C is its concentration in millimoles per liter, m is the rate of flow of mercury from the dropping electrode capillary expressed in the units mg. sec.$^{-1}$, and t is the drop time in seconds.

Because it neglects the curvature of the electrode surface the Ilkovic equation cannot be expected to be strictly valid. The following equation derived independently by Lingane and Loveridge[1] and by Strehlow and von Stackelberg[2] takes into account the curvature of the electrode surface (term in parenthesis)

$$i_d = 607nD^{1/2}Cm^{2/3}t^{1/6} \left(1 + \frac{AD^{1/2}t^{1/6}}{m^{1/3}} \right) \tag{1b}$$

According to Lingane and Loveridge the theoretical value of the constant A is 39, but Strehlow and von Stackelberg assign to it the value 17. The derivations of these equations have been discussed in Chapter II, and in this chapter they will be utilized to interpret the effect of each of the various factors that govern the diffusion current.

Both equations predict a linear relation between the diffusion current and concentration, which, of course, is the most important relation in practical polarography.

---

[1] J. J. Lingane and B. A. Loveridge, *J. Am. Chem. Soc.*, **72**, 438 (1950).
[2] H. Strehlow and M. von Stackelberg, *Z. Elektrochem.*, **54**, 51 (1950).

2. MEASUREMENT OF DIFFUSION CURRENTS AND CORRECTION FOR THE RESIDUAL CURRENT

In measuring the diffusion current the *average* of the galvanometer or recorder oscillations should be measured, rather than the maximum or minimum "throw." The magnitude of the observed oscillations, which are due to the periodic growth and fall of the mercury drops, depends on the ratio of galvanometer period to drop time. Since the type of galvanometer usually employed does not respond rapidly enough to follow the true change in current during the life of each mercury drop, the maximum or minimum of the observed oscillations does not correspond to the true maximum or minimum current. On the other hand, when the oscillations are not too large their average doubtless does coincide with the true average current to which the Ilkovic equation refers. This is demonstrated schematically in

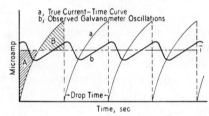

Fig. IV-1. Schematic comparison of true current–time curves and observed galvanometer oscillations.

Fig. IV-1, in which the curves *a* represent the actual current–time curves during the life of individual drops (Chap. II). and the solid curve *b* represents the observed galvanometer oscillations. The true (integrated) average current $\bar{i}$ is represented by the horizontal line drawn in such a way that the shaded area *A* is equal to the shaded area *B*.

Lingane and Loveridge[3] found in the case of lead ion in 1 *N* potassium chloride that the average of the galvanometer oscillations was constant to ±0.15 per cent when the drop time was 2.9 sec. and the galvanometer period was varied (by a damping shunt) from 3 to 11.2 sec. In these experiments the oscillations ranged from 13 to 5 per cent of the average value. Other recording devices may or may not show the same constancy as a galvanometer.

It has been shown in a previous chapter that a small residual current, due to a capacity or charging current plus a small faradaic current resulting from traces of accidental impurities in the solution, is observed before the decomposition potential is reached. In order to obtain the true diffusion

---

[3] J. J. Lingane and B. A. Loveridge, *J. Am. Chem. Soc.*, **66**, 1425 (1944).

current of a substance it is obvious that a correction must be made for this residual current, and this correction becomes increasingly more important the smaller the concentration of the reducible substance, i. e., the smaller the total diffusion current.

When the polarogram of the solution shows only a single wave the most reliable and satisfactory method of evaluating the true diffusion current is as follows.[4] The residual current is determined in a separate experiment by obtaining the polarogram of the supporting electrolyte solution alone, and the value of the residual current so obtained is then subtracted from the total diffusion current of the substance in question. This method is

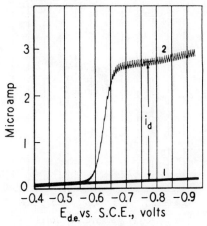

Fig. IV-2. Exact method of measuring a diffusion current: (1) residual current of an air-free, 0.1 N potassium chloride solution; (2) the same solution containing 5 × 10^{-4} M CdCl$_2$. The true diffusion current of the cadmium ion is indicated by i_d.

illustrated in Fig. IV-2, in which the current–voltage curves have been photographically recorded by means of a polarograph. Curve 1 is the polarogram (residual current) of an air-free 0.1 N potassium chloride solution which contained 2 × 10^{-5} M sodium methyl red as a maximum suppressor, and curve 2 is the polarogram of the same solution containing 5 × 10^{-4} M cadmium chloride. The true diffusion current of the cadmium ion is indicated by i_d, and the horizontal line is the "galvanometer zero line."

It is evident from Fig. IV-2 that the correction for the residual current becomes larger the more negative the reduction potential of the substance in question. It is also obvious that the residual current must be determined

---

[4] J. J. Lingane and I. M. Kolthoff, J. Am. Chem. Soc., **61**, 825 (1939).

under identically the same conditions that prevail when the polarogram of the substance itself is obtained.

The *apparent* diffusion currents of very small concentrations of reducible substances often increase markedly with increasing applied e.m.f., as in Fig. IV-2. In many cases this is due to the increase of the residual current with increasing applied e.m.f., and when the proper correction is applied for the residual current the corrected diffusion current is found to be practically constant. There are instances, however, in which this correction does not produce a constant limiting current, indicating that the limiting current is not entirely diffusion controlled. Even in such cases, it is usually

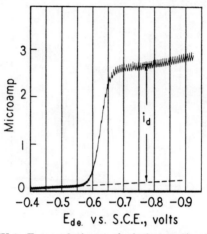

Fig. IV-3. Extrapolation method of correcting for the residual current: $5 \times 10^{-4}\,M$ CdCl$_2$ in 0.1 N KCl.

found that the limiting current is strictly proportional to concentration when care is taken to measure the current at exactly the same potential with the different concentrations.

Since the residual current usually increases practically linearly with the applied e.m.f., it is sometimes possible to correct adequately for it by simply extrapolating the residual current section of the curve beyond the decomposition potential, and measuring the distance between this extrapolated line and the total diffusion current, as shown in Fig. IV-3. Alternatively, the limiting current may be extrapolated *backward*, and a measurement made of the vertical distance between the extrapolation and the residual current just preceding the wave. When the slope of the residual current preceding the wave is the same as that of the limiting current plateau these two methods yield identical results.

The extrapolation method is useful when the polarogram in question comprises several waves, as shown in Fig. IV-4. In this polarogram the diffusion current of the manganous ion can be measured by simply extrapolating the diffusion current of the preceding wave of the cobaltous ion beyond the decomposition potential of the manganous ion as indicated, and measuring the distance between this extrapolated line and the total diffusion current.

When the half-wave potentials of two substances are close together, so that a well-defined diffusion current of the more easily reducible substance is not obtained before the reduction of the second substance starts, the measurement of both diffusion currents becomes difficult. This is demon-

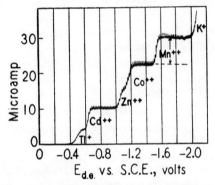

Fig. IV-4. Polarogram of a solution containing several metal ions each at a concentration of approximately 0.001 M in 0.1 N KCl containing 0.01 per cent gelatin.

strated by the waves of zinc and cobaltous ions in Fig. IV-4, which are too close together to permit an unambiguous evaluation of the two diffusion currents. Various empirical graphical methods have been proposed[5-9] for measuring poorly defined diffusion currents. Taylor[10] has described a

[5] J. Heyrovsky, "Polarographie," in W. Boettger, Die physikalischen Methoden der chemischen Analyse, Leipzig, 1936 (Vol. 2, pp. 260–322).

[6] H. Hohn, Chemische Analysen mit dem Polarographen, Berlin, 1937; Z. Elektrochem., 43, 127 (1937).

[7] J. Maas, De Polarografische Methode met de druppelende Kwikelectrode ten Dienste van het pharmaceutisch Onderzoek, Amsterdam, 1937.

[8] G. T. Borcherdt, V. W. Meloche, and H. Adkins, J. Am. Chem. Soc., 59, 2171 (1937).

[9] R. H. Müller and J. F. Petras, J. Am. Chem. Soc., 60, 2990 (1938).

[10] J. K. Taylor, Ind. Eng. Chem., Anal. Ed., 19, 368, 478 (1947).

useful mechanical device to facilitate the graphical measurement of wave heights, and has discussed some of the precautions that should be observed in empirical, comparative methods.

3. LINEAR RELATION BETWEEN THE DIFFUSION CURRENT AND CONCENTRATION

According to the Ilkovic equation, with all other factors constant

$$i_d = kC \tag{2}$$

where k is a constant defined by eq. 1. This relation is the foundation of quantitative polarographic analysis and its general validity is well established.

The precision of the linear relation between i_d and C under favorable conditions is exemplified by the data in Table IV-1 obtained by Meites and Meites.[11] In this case i_d/C is constant to ±0.2 per cent over a 630-fold range of cadmium ion concentration.

TABLE IV-1

LINEAR RELATION BETWEEN DIFFUSION CURRENT AND CONCENTRATION

The data were obtained at 25° with cadmium ion in a supporting electrolyte composed of 0.1 M each of potassium chloride and hydrochloric acid. Diffusion currents were measured at −1.00 v. $vs.$ S.C.E. and the values listed have been corrected for the residual current of the supporting electrolyte alone. $t = 2.47$ sec.; $m = 3.299$ mg. sec.$^{-1}$, $m^{2/3}t^{1/6} = 2.577$ mg.$^{2/3}$ sec.$^{-1/2}$.

Cd^{++}, millimolar	i_d , microamp.	i_d/C
0.01935	0.178	9.20
0.0554	0.507	9.15
0.1245	1.146	9.20
0.1847	1.700	9.20
0.2392	2.202	9.21
1.614	14.79	9.16
4.221	38.87	9.21
6.667	61.25	9.19
12.19	112.0	9.19
Av...9.19 ± 0.015		

Certain investigators, notably Maas (*loc. cit.*), Hamamoto,[12] and Than-

---

[11] L. Meites and T. Meites, *J. Am. Chem. Soc.*, **72**, 3689 (1950).

[12] E. Hamamoto, *Collection Czechoslov. Chem. Communs.*, **5**, 427 (1933).

heiser and Maassen,[13] have claimed that the diffusion currents of certain metal ions at very small concentrations are greater than corresponds to strict linear proportionality with the concentration. It is significant that these authors all used empirical graphical methods for measuring the diffusion currents. Maas claimed such anomalous behavior in the discharge of cadmium ion with potassium chloride as supporting electrolyte. However, the data in Table IV-1 leave no doubt of the strict proportionality between i_d and C in this same case when the proper correction is made for the residual current.

Thanheiser and Maassen reported that the diffusion current of $Cu(NH_3)_4^{++}$ ion in ammoniacal medium was relatively too large at very small concentrations. However, data which we have obtained under identically the same conditions employed by Thanheiser and Maassen show that this anomaly disappears after proper correction is made for the residual current.

There are instances, particularly when the limiting current is not diffusion controlled but is governed by the actual rate of the electrode reaction, in which the limiting current is not a linear function of concentration even when correction is applied for the residual current. For example, the cadmium tartrate complex present in an alkaline tartrate solution produces an abnormally small limiting current, and the ratio i_d/C decreases markedly with increasing concentration of cadmium.[14] Hence, in an unknown case it is always necessary to verify the relation between i_d and C.

Maas[15] has shown that the linear relation between i_d and C may fail when the drop time is too short, and he recommended a drop time between 4 and 6 sec. This has been verified by Lingane and Loveridge,[16] and Buckley and Taylor,[17] who demonstrated that the drop time should not be much smaller than about 2 sec. With very rapid drop rates there is appreciable stirring of the solution which disturbs the diffusion layer and produces an abnormally large current. Although eq. 2 is obeyed with very long drop times, the oscillations become inconveniently large when the ratio of galvanometer or recorder period to drop time is much less than about 2. As a general rule the optimum range of drop time is 3 to 6 sec.

[13] G. Thanheiser and G. Maassen, *Mitt. Kaiser-Wilhelm-Inst. Eisenforsch. Düsseldorf*, **19**, 27 (1937). G. Maassen, *Angew. Chem.*, **50**, 375 (1937).

[14] J. J. Lingane, *Ind. Eng. Chem., Anal. Ed.*, **15**, 583 (1943).

[15] J. Maas, *De Polarografische Methode met de druppelende Kwikelectrode ten Dienste van het Pharmaceutisch Onderzoek*, Dissertation, Amsterdam, 1937; *Collection Czechoslov. Chem. Communs.*, **10**, 42 (1938).

[16] J. J. Lingane and B. A. Loveridge, *J. Am. Chem. Soc.*, **66**, 1425 (1944).

[17] F. Buckley and J. K. Taylor, *J. Research Natl. Bur. Standards*, **34**, 97 (1945).

4. INFLUENCE OF CAPILLARY CHARACTERISTICS ON THE DIFFUSION CURRENT. THE DIFFUSION CURRENT CONSTANT

On the basis of the Ilkovic equation the diffusion current constant was originally defined[18] as

$$I = 607nD^{1/2} = \frac{i_d}{Cm^{2/3}t^{1/6}} \tag{3}$$

which predicts that $i_d/Cm^{2/3}t^{1/6}$ should be independent of the characteristics m and t of the dropping electrode capillary. On the other hand, from eq. 1b

$$I_1 = \frac{i_d}{Cm^{2/3}t^{1/6}} = 607nD^{1/2}\left(1 + \frac{39D^{1/2}t^{1/6}}{m^{1/3}}\right) \tag{3a}$$

which predicts that, instead of being independent of capillary characteristics, the quantity $i_d/Cm^{2/3}t^{1/6}$ should increase linearly with increasing values of the ratio $t^{1/6}/m^{1/3}$. The diffusion current "constant" predicted by the Ilkovic equation is a hypothetical limiting value corresponding to a value of zero for the quantity $39D^{1/2}t^{1/6}/m^{1/3}$, and from eq. 3a the true diffusion current constant is

$$I = \frac{i_d}{Cm^{2/3}t^{1/6}\left(1 + \frac{39D^{1/2}t^{1/6}}{m^{1/3}}\right)} = 607nD^{1/2} \tag{3b}$$

When diffusion currents of a given substance obtained under otherwise identical conditions with different dropping electrodes are compared, eq. 3 is adequate in those instances where the characteristics m and t are not greatly different. If the $m^{2/3}t^{1/6}$ values of the two electrodes are both in the usual range between about 1 and 3 mg.$^{2/3}$sec.$^{-1/2}$, and do not differ from each other by more than 0.5 mg.$^{2/3}$sec.$^{-1/2}$, the I-values according to eqs. 3 and 3a ordinarily will agree to 2 per cent or better. When the $m^{2/3}t^{1/6}$ values differ by more than 0.5 unit the more exact eq. 3b should be used. Equation 3b should also be employed in evaluating diffusion coefficients from observed diffusion currents.

A rigorous test of eqs. 3 and 3a has been carried out by Lingane and Loveridge[19] who employed a large number of different capillaries with drop times from less than 1 sec. to 9 sec. and m values from 0.9 to 16 mg. sec.$^{-1}$. They used lead ion in 1 N potassium chloride and tetrammino zinc

---

[18] J. J. Lingane, *Ind. Eng. Chem., Anal. Ed.*, **15**, 588 (1943).

[19] J. J. Lingane and B. A. Loveridge, *J. Am. Chem. Soc.*, **66**, 1425 (1944).

[20] *Ibid.*, **68**, 395 (1946).

ion in 1 M ammonium chloride–1 M ammonia as test substances. The solutions contained 0.01 per cent gelatin as a maximum suppressor. The diffusion currents were measured by three independent techniques: (*a*) measurement with a potentiometer of the iR drop across a standard resistance in series with the cell; (*b*) measurement in terms of the deflection of a calibrated galvanometer; and (*c*) measurement with a commercial photo-

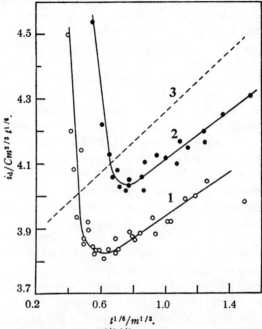

Fig. IV-5. Variation of $i_d/Cm^{2/3}t^{1/6}$ with capillary characteristics: (*1*) lead ion in 1 M potassium chloride containing 0.01 per cent gelatin; (*2*) tetramminozinc ion in 1 M ammonium chloride–1 M ammonia containing 0.01 per cent gelatin; (*3*) theoretical line for lead ion according to eq. 3a.[21]

graphically recording polarograph (Sargent-Heyrovsky Model XI). The results of the different methods of measurement were in good agreement. All known precautions were observed, and in particular the m and t values of each capillary were measured at the same time that the diffusion current was measured. The results obtained are shown graphically in Fig. IV-5, in which the quantity $i_d/(Cm^{2/3}t^{1/6})$ is plotted against $t^{1/6}/m^{1/3}$.

The rapid increase of $i_d/Cm^{2/3}t^{1/6}$ at values of $t^{1/6}/m^{1/3}$ less than about 0.6 (corresponding to drop times smaller than about 1.5 sec.) is caused by

[21] *Ibid.*, **72,** 438 (1950).

stirring produced by the rapidly forming drops, with consequent convective transfer of the reducible ion to the electrode surface and disruption of the diffusion layer. Because the current is no longer diffusion controlled when the drop time is less than about 1.5 sec. it is evident that the use of very short drop times can lead to large errors.

The linear increase of $i_d/Cm^{2/3}t^{1/6}$ at values of $t^{1/6}/m^{1/3}$ above about 0.7 demonstrates the inadequacy of the original Ilkovic equation (eq. 3) and confirms eq. 3a. The broken line is the theoretical line for lead ion according to eq. 3a and its slope agrees well with the slope of the observed lead ion line. Because the actual diffusion coefficient of lead ion in 1 M potassium chloride is not known, the theoretical line was drawn by employing the diffusion coefficient of lead ion *at infinite dilution*, which from the equivalent conductance of lead ion at infinite dilution (73 ohm^{-1} cm.^{2}) is 0.98 × 10^{-5} cm.^{2} sec.$^{-1}$ at 25°. The observed diffusion current of lead ion is 8 per cent smaller than the ideal infinite dilution value predicted by eq. 3a. This indicates that the actual diffusion coefficient of lead ion in 1 M potassium chloride is about 16 per cent smaller than the ideal infinite dilution value, which is entirely logical.

The diffusion current of lead ion predicted by the original Ilkovic equation (3.80 microamp. at $Cm^{2/3}t^{1/6} = 1$) happens to agree more closely with the observed value than that predicted by eq. 3a, but this simply reflects a compensation of errors. The neglect of the curvature of the electrode surface very nearly compensates for the fact that the actual diffusion coefficient is smaller than the infinite dilution value.

Data which produce curves of the same general shape as those in Fig. IV-5 have also been obtained by Buckley and Taylor[22] with nickel, cadmium, and thallous ions in 0.1 N potassium chloride and bismuthyl ion in 1 N nitric acid. Their curves do not show the minima observed by Lingane and Loveridge, because the measurements were not sufficiently precise, but they do show the same very rapid increase of $i_d/(Cm^{2/3}t^{1/6})$ at small drop times.

Buckley and Taylor[22] found that gelatin (added as a maximum suppressor) has a very pronounced effect on the critical drop time below which the Ilkovic equation fails. Without gelatin the Ilkovic equation began to fail even with drop times as large as 3 to 4 sec. As gelatin was added in amounts up to about 0.008 per cent the critical drop time decreased to the neighborhood of 1.5 sec. The beneficial effect of gelatin appears to be related to its action in suppressing maxima. Other maximum suppressors probably exert a similar effect.

[22] F. Buckley and J. K. Taylor, *J. Research Natl. Bur. Standards*, **34**, 97 (1945).

Strehlow and von Stackelberg[23] have presented data, obtained with thallous ion and cadmium ion in 0.1 M potassium chloride containing 0.01 per cent gelatin, which also verify the correctness of the form of eq. 1b. These investigators used a value of 17 instead of 39 for the constant in the second term in parenthesis. However, the precision of their measurements, especially with cadmium ion, is such that a definite conclusion as to whether the data correspond best to a value of 17 or 39 for this constant does not seem justified. It is evident from Fig. IV-5 that a value of 17 is definitely much too small to fit the data of Lingane and Loveridge. In the experiments of Strehlow and von Stackelberg the ratio of the concentration of supporting electrolyte to that of the reducible ion was rather small—50 in the case of thallous ion and only 23 with cadmium ion— and hence the limiting currents they observed may have included a significant contribution from electrical migration. It should also be noted that values of $i_d/Cm^{2/3}t^{1/6}$ only slightly to the right of the minimum (Fig. IV-5) will tend to be too large because of the beginning of the stirring effect and this tends to make the observed slope too small. In other words, in deciding on the best straight line relatively little weight should be given to points near the minimum.

Meites and Meites[24] recently determined the $i_d/Cm^{2/3}t^{1/6}$ values of silver ion and cadmium ion in 0.1 M potassium nitrate, ferricyanide ion in 0.1 M potassium chloride, and iodate ion in 0.1 M potassium chloride–0.1 M hydrochloric acid, with 0.009 per cent gelatin present in all cases. Their data show much better agreement with the theoretical constant 39 proposed by Lingane and Loveridge than with the value 17 proposed by Strehlow and von Stackelberg over a range of drop times from about 1.5 to 6 sec. In the cases they studied Meites and Meites concluded that the average observed value of this constant was 31.5 ± 4.6, which agrees well with the values 33.5 and 31.7 derived from the data of Lingane and Loveridge for the tetramminozinc ion and lead ion, respectively.

Meites and Meites reported that the linear relation between $i_d/Cm^{2/3}t^{1/6}$ and $t^{1/6}/m^{1/3}$ begins to fail when the drop time exceeds about 6 sec. At values of $t^{1/6}/m^{1/3}$ larger than about 1.2 (drop time greater than about 6 or 7 sec.) the apparent values of $i_d/Cm^{2/3}t^{1/6}$ decreased with increasing $t^{1/6}/m^{1/3}$, so that the curves show a maximum. These results do not conclusively demonstrate a failure of eq. 1b. The decrease of $i_d/Cm^{2/3}t^{1/6}$ may only be apparent, rather than real, and a reflection of an error in the galvanometric measuring technique. The average of the oscillations of the

23 H. Strehlow and M. von Stackelberg, Z. Elektrochem., 54, 51 (1950).
24 L. Meites and T. Meites, J. Am. Chem. Soc., 73, 395 (1951).

measuring galvanometer is known to correspond closely to the true integrated average current provided the galvanometer period is equal to or greater than the drop time.[19-21, 25]   However, when the drop time exceeds the galvanometer period, as it does in the experiments of Meites and Meites, there is reason to believe that the average of the very large galvanometer oscillations will be smaller than the true average current.

According to Meites the $i_d/Cm^{2/3}t^{1/6}$ vs. $t^{1/6}/m^{1/3}$ curve in many cases is perfectly horizontal at drop times between about 2 and 7 sec. *provided no gelatin or other maximum suppressor is present.*   Meites concluded that in the absence of a maximum suppressor the original Ilkovic equation (eq. 1a) represents his data better than eq. 1b.   In most of Meites' experiments the ratio of supporting electrolyte concentration to reducible ion concentration was rather small (0.1 M supporting electrolyte and 5 millimolar reducible ion), and it would be very desirable to have similar data with a more normal large concentration of supporting electrolyte.   The data leave no doubt, however, that gelatin exerts a profound influence on the diffusion conditions around the mercury drop, and that over a drop time range between about 2 and 7 sec. it increases the apparent diffusion current.

Strehlow and von Stackelberg derived the following equation for the *anodic* diffusion current of a dropping amalgam electrode

$$i_d = 607nD^{1/2}Cm^{2/3}t^{1/6}\left(1 - \frac{BD^{1/2}t^{1/6}}{m^{1/3}}\right)$$

which differs in form from eq. 1b only by the minus sign before the second term in parenthesis, which results from the *outward* diffusion of the metal in the amalgam.   Strehlow and von Stackelberg concluded that B is about 30.   They tested this equation, using data obtained at various m and t values, with 0.0139 M cadmium amalgam in 0.1 M potassium chloride containing 0.01 per cent gelatin.   Their plots of $i_d/Cm^{2/3}t^{1/6}$ vs. $t^{1/6}/m^{1/3}$ show much more curvature of the left branches than the corresponding curves for metal ion reduction; the values of $t^{1/6}/m^{1/3}$ at which the rapid increase due to stirring begins appear to be much larger, and also more dependent on the dropping electrode capillary used.   However, the data do seem to approach asymptotically a straight line of negative slope at large values of $t^{1/6}/m^{1/3}$, in at least qualitative agreement with the foregoing equation.   It will be noted that the concentration of the amalgam was very large in proportion to the relatively small concentration of sup-

---

[25] J. K. Taylor, R. E. Smith, and I. L. Cooter, *J. Research Natl. Bur. Standards*, **42**, 387 (1949)

porting electrolyte used (ratio only 0.1/0.0139 or about 7), from which it seems doubtful that the observed currents were controlled only by the outward rate of diffusion of the cadmium in the amalgam, and highly probable that the inward diffusion of chloride ion in the solution was also a determining factor.   More conclusive results probably could be obtained by employing a more dilute amalgam, and a much larger concentration of supporting electrolyte, to eliminate completely the influence of diffusion *in the solution.*

At the time of this writing new information on the diffusion current is appearing very rapidly and some time will be required for its correlation and conclusive assessment.   It is evident, however, that the applicability of standardized diffusion current constants in practical analysis is not seriously influenced by the foregoing new information.   Under normal analytical conditions with dropping electrodes of drop time between about 2 and 5 sec., with a small amount (0.005 to 0.01 per cent) of gelatin or an equivalent maximum suppressor present, and with an adequately large concentration of supporting electrolyte (preferably at least 0.5 M), the diffusion current "constant" $i_d/Cm^{2/3}t^{1/6}$ defined on the basis of the original Ilkovic equation actually is valid to within about ±2 per cent.   When an accuracy of better than about ±2 per cent is required it appears that the diffusion current constant based on eq. 1b should be used:

$$I^0 = \frac{i_d}{Cm^{2/3}t^{1/6}\left(1 + \dfrac{39D^{1/2}t^{1/6}}{m^{1/3}}\right)}$$

Current–Time Curves during Drop Life.   Steghart,[26] McKenzie,[27] and Taylor, Smith, and Cooter[28] studied the current–time relation during the growth of individual drops and concluded that the current–time curves deviate considerably from the sixth-order parabola predicted by the Ilkovic equation.   Taylor, Smith, and Cooter employed a recording cathode ray oscillograph, a drop time of about 3.5 sec., and a solution composed of 3 millimolar cadmium ion in 0.1 M potassium chloride containing 0.01 per cent gelatin.   When they attempted to fit their data to an equation of the form $i_t = kt^n$ (where according to the original Ilkovic equation $n = 1/6$) they concluded that no single value of n applied over the entire drop life. From 0.1, 0.5, 1, and 2 sec. to the end of the drop life (*ca.* 3.5 sec.) the

[26] F. L. Steghart, *Chemistry & Industry*, p. 157, March 6, 1948.

[27] H. A. McKenzie, *J. Am. Chem. Soc.*, **70**, 3147 (1948).

[28] J. K. Taylor, R. E. Smith, and I. L. Cooter, *J. Research Natl. Bur. Standards*, **42**, 387 (1949).

observed values of n were *seriatim* 0.31, 0.249, 0.227, and 0.186. During the latter half of the drop life the current–time curve does approach closely to a sixth-order parabola, but when the drop is very young the current is abnormally small and increases more nearly with the one-third power of the time.

Airey and Smales[29] reported that the relation $i_t = kt^{1/6}$ was obeyed with an accuracy of about ± 2.5 per cent from 0.75 sec. to the end of the life of a 3.9 sec. drop. In agreement with the investigators quoted above they observed that the current during the initial stages of drop growth was smaller than corresponds to a sixth-order parabola. The dropping electrode they used was of a type with an enlarged orifice of 0.1 mm. which produced a freely falling drop time of 15 sec., but which was vibrated by an electromagnetic pulsator to cause reproducible disengagement of the drops after 3.9 sec. Evidently this type of dropping electrode provides conditions which correspond more closely to those assumed in the Ilkovic equation than does a conventional dropping electrode.

The divergence of the current–time curve from a pure sixth-order parabola is in qualitative accord with the equation for the instantaneous current given by Strehlow and von Stackelberg and Lingane and Loveridge:

$$i_t = 709nD^{1/2}Cm^{2/3}t^{1/6} + 31,560nDCm^{1/3}t^{1/3}$$

which has the form:

$$i_t = \alpha t^{1/6} + \beta t^{1/3}$$

whose curve is intermediate between a sixth-order and third-order parabola. Meites and Meites[30] demonstrated that the current–time curve obtained by Taylor, Smith, and Cooter does approach that predicted by the above equation after about the first 1 sec. of the 3.5 sec. drop, but this equation does not account for the abnormally small current during the early life of the drop.

The abnormally small early current is partially caused by the fact that the rate of mercury flow is not constant during the drop life, but is smaller at the beginning because the back pressure created by the interfacial tension is much larger when the drop is very small. However, the observed discrepancy is too large to be accounted for entirely by this effect. Airey and Smales (*loc. cit.*) suggested that the abnormally small early current

[29] L. Airey and A. A. Smales, *Analyst*, **75**, 287 (1950).

[30] L. Meites and T. Meites, *J. Am. Chem. Soc.*, **72**, 4843 (1950).

is caused by the young drop emerging in that part of the solution whose concentration has been depleted by the reaction at the preceding drop.

The average current during the drop life to which both the original Ilkovic equation and eq. 1b refer corresponds to the quantity of electricity associated with each drop divided by the drop time. Because only a small part of the total quantity of electricity accumulates during the earlier stages of drop formation, the total quantity is relatively uninfluenced by the abnormally small current during the very early life of the drop. Consequently, the exponent of t for the *average* current remains close to 1/6.

Taylor, Smith, and Cooter[28] found that the ratio of the graphically integrated average current during the drop life to the maximum current was 0.81, which is significantly smaller than the value 6/7 or 0.857 predicted by the Ilkovic equation. Shulman. Battey, and Jelatis[31] also observed a ratio of average to maximum current that was several per cent smaller than 6/7. Equation 1b predicts that the ratio of the average to maximum current should follow a relation of the form

$$\frac{i_d}{i_{max.}} = \frac{607\ a + 23,670\ b}{709\ a + 31,560\ b}$$

and, because the second term in the denominator is larger than that in the numerator, the ratio should be slightly smaller than 6/7. However, the observed ratio is considerably smaller than expected from this relation.

Taylor, Smith, and Cooter also confirmed the earlier observation of Lingane and Loveridge (*loc. cit.*) that the apparent average current (average of the oscillations) observed with ordinary galvanometers is constant and independent of the ratio of galvanometer period to drop time provided that this ratio is greater than about 1. These investigators also obtained evidence that the average of the oscillations of a long-period galvanometer corresponds very closely to the true integrated average current derived from the oscillographic measurements. This may or may not be true with other recording devices whose "equation of motion" differs from that of a moving coil galvanometer.

Smith[32] reported experiments with a dropping electrode of extraordinarily long drop time (16 sec. to 8 min.), obtained by using a restricted capillary with a very large orifice (0.216 mm.). With such very slowly forming drops current–time relationships at constant potential, as well as

[31] J. H. Schulman, H. B. Battey, and D. G. Jelatis, *Rev. Sci. Instruments*, **18**, 226 (1947).

[32] G. S. Smith, *Nature*, **163**, 290 (1949).

current–voltage curves over the life of a single drop, can be studied with ordinary polarographic equipment. According to Smith the current–time curve with these very large, slowly forming drops follows a second-order parabola $i_t = kt^{1/2}$, indicating that the diffusion conditions are quite different with such very slowly forming drops than with the drops normally used.

5. INFLUENCE OF VARIOUS FACTORS ON m AND t

Since i_d is very nearly directly proportional to $m^{2/3}t^{1/6}$ a knowledge of the variables which govern m and t is of fundamental importance in practical polarography. It is evident that m and t will depend on the dimensions of the dropping electrode capillary and on the pressure on the dropping mercury due to the difference in levels between the mercury in the reservoir and the electrode tip. Since the drop time depends on the interfacial tension at the mercury–solution interface, it is influenced by the nature of the solution, and also by the potential applied to the dropping electrode. The rate of flow of mercury also depends on temperature and to a minor extent on the interfacial tension.

The factors that govern the value of m can be predicted by the Poiseuille equation

$$V = \frac{\pi r_c^4 P t}{8 l \eta} \tag{4}$$

where V is the volume of a liquid that flows in t seconds from a capillary tube of radius r_c and length l, η is the viscosity coefficient of the liquid, and P is the difference in hydrostatic pressure between the two ends of the tube. This equation will only be strictly correct when the liquid wets the capillary tube—so that the layer of liquid in immediate contact with the wall is at rest and there is no slippage at the wall—and when the rate of flow is so small that the kinetic energy of the issuing liquid is negligible. Although this first condition is not fulfilled in the case of the dropping electrode, because mercury does not wet the glass capillary, the data to be presented later show that the error due to this fact is small enough to be neglected. Furthermore, the rate of flow of mercury is so small that its kinetic energy is negligible.

In order to apply the Poiseuille relation to the dropping electrode we employ the fact that $m = Vd/t$, where d is the density of mercury, and by combining this relation with eq. 4 we have

$$m = \frac{Vd}{t} = \frac{\pi r_c^4 d P}{8 l \eta} \tag{5}$$

If t is taken as the drop time, then V will be the volume, and Vd the weight, of a single drop.

It should be emphasized that P is the *effective* pressure on the dropping mercury, expressed in c.g.s. units (dyne cm.$^{-2}$). In the case of a liquid flowing very slowly and dropwise from a vertical capillary tube the value of P is somewhat smaller than the total hydrostatic pressure of the liquid column, because the interfacial tension at the surface of the growing drops exerts a back pressure which opposes the applied pressure. According to Kucera[33] this back pressure is expressible by

$$P_{back} = \frac{2\sigma}{r_d} \tag{6}$$

where σ is the interfacial tension in c.g.s. units (dyne cm.$^{-1}$), and r_d is the radius of the spherical drop at any instant during its life. In the case of most common liquids σ is relatively small (e. g., $\sigma = 72$ dyne cm.$^{-1}$ at 25° C. at a water–air interface, and is considerably smaller for most other liquids), but in the case of mercury σ is quite large (465 dyne cm.$^{-1}$ against air at 20° C.). Hence the back pressure is appreciable in the case of the dropping electrode and it must be taken into account.

It is convenient to employ the average value of P_{back} during the life of a drop. The volume of a drop at any instant t^* during its life is given by

$$V = \frac{mt^*}{d} = \tfrac{4}{3}\pi r_d^3 \tag{7}$$

and hence its radius at any instant is

$$r_d = \left(\frac{3\,mt^*}{4\,\pi d}\right)^{1/3} \tag{8}$$

on the justifiable assumption that the drop is spherical. The *average* radius of the mercury drop, which we designate by $\bar{r}_d$, is expressible by

$$\bar{r}_d = \frac{1}{t}\int_0^t r_d\,dt \tag{9}$$

where t is the drop time. By combining eqs. 8 and 9, performing the indicated integration, and keeping in mind that $r_d = 0$ when $t = 0$, we have

$$\bar{r}_d = \frac{3}{4}\left(\frac{3\,mt}{4\,\pi d}\right)^{1/3} \tag{10}$$

[33] G. Kucera, *Ann. Physik.*, **11**, 529 (1903).

The quantity in parenthesis raised to the one-third power is evidently the *maximum* radius attained by the drop, and hence we see that the average radius is equal to three-fourths of its maximum radius. By combining eqs. 6 and 10 and collecting the numerical constants into a single term, we find that the *average* value of the back pressure is given by

$$\overline{P}_{\text{back}} = \frac{2\,\sigma}{r_d} = 4.31\,\frac{\sigma d^{1/3}}{m^{1/3}t^{1/3}} \tag{11}$$

The effective pressure is also decreased slightly by the immersion of the capillary in the solution. For aqueous solutions every 13.5 mm. of immersion reduces the effective pressure by 1 mm. of mercury. This effect is small enough to be neglected in all but the most precise measurements.

The total pressure applied to the dropping mercury is usually expressed in terms of the height of the mercury column between the level of mercury in the reservoir and the tip of the dropping electrode. If we designate this height by h, and express it in cm., then

$$P_{\text{applied}} = hgd \text{ (dyne cm.}^{-2}) \tag{12}$$

where g is the gravitational constant. Hence the effective pressure P on the dropping mercury is given by

$$P = P_{\text{applied}} - P_{\text{back}} = hdg - 4.31\,\frac{\sigma d^{1/3}}{m^{1/3}t^{1/3}} \tag{13}$$

The expression for m then becomes

$$m = \frac{\pi r_c^4 d}{8l\eta}\left(hdg - 4.31\,\frac{\sigma d^{1/3}}{m^{1/3}t^{1/3}}\right) \tag{14}$$

In the case of mercury at 25° C. we have the numerical values

$$d = 13.53 \text{ g. cm.}^{-3}$$

$$\eta = 0.0152 \text{ dyne sec. cm.}^{-2} \text{ (poise)}$$

and

$$g = 980.6 \text{ cm. sec.}^{-2} \text{ (45° North latitude and sea level)}$$

Hence if we express m in the units mg. sec.$^{-1}$ and the radius of the capillary r_c and its length l in cm., at 25° C. eq. 14 simplifies to

$$m = 4.64 \times 10^9\,\frac{r_c^4}{l}\left(h - \frac{7.73 \times 10^{-3}\,\sigma}{m^{1/3}t^{1/3}}\right) \tag{15}$$

in which the second term in parenthesis is the correction term for the back pressure expressed in centimeters of mercury.

It should be noted that, since m is directly proportional, and t is inversely proportional, to the effective pressure P (compare eq. 5), the product $m^{1/3}t^{1/3}$ is virtually constant for a given capillary and independent of the value of h. Hence the pressure correction term, for any given capillary, is independent of h.

The interfacial tension σ at a mercury–water interface in the *absence of air*, and when the mercury is not electrically polarized, is equal to 427 dyne cm.$^{-1}$ at 20° C.[34]   In solutions of electrolytes, and in the presence of air, the interfacial tension will be somewhat smaller than this, depending on the capillary activity of the electrolyte or other capillary-active substances that may be present.   However, for the purpose of calculating the pressure correction term it will be sufficiently accurate to assume that $\sigma = 400$ dyne cm.$^{-1}$ in all electrolyte solutions.   On this basis the expression for the pressure correction term in eq. 15, for any capillary, becomes

$$h_{\text{back}} = \frac{3.1}{m^{1/3}t^{1/3}} \; cm. \tag{16}$$

With a capillary for which the quantity $m^{1/3}t^{1/3}$ has a value of 1 mg.$^{1/3}$, which is of the usual order of magnitude, we see that the back pressure amounts to 3.1 cm. of mercury, and hence it is by no means negligible.

In order to test the validity of eq. 15 in the case of the dropping electrode we may employ some typical data obtained by Maas (*loc. cit.*) which are reproduced in the first three columns of Table IV-2.   The capillary used by Maas to obtain these data consisted of a piece of very fine bore thermometer tubing 2.043 cm. in length and with a uniform internal diameter of 0.00378 cm.   The capillary was connected to the mercury reservoir by means of rubber pressure tubing and the pressure on the dropping mercury was varied by raising or lowering the reservoir.   The rate of mercury flow m and the drop time t, at various values of the total applied pressure h, were determined when the mercury was dropping into a 0.1 N solution of potassium chloride at 25° C.   The observed values of t and m are given in the second and third columns of Table IV-2, and the value of the product mt is given in the fourth column.   With the particular capillary used to obtain these data r_c^4 was equal to $(0.00189)^4 = 1.264 \times 10^{-11}$ cm.^{4}, and l was 2.043 cm.   Hence eq. 15 for this particular capillary becomes

$$m = 0.0287 \left(h - \frac{3.1}{m^{1/3}t^{1/3}} \right) \tag{17}$$

---

[34] D. C. Henry and J. Jackson, *Nature*, **142**, 616 (1938).

An approximate value of m was first calculated by neglecting the second term in parenthesis, and this approximate value of m was used to calculate the pressure term h_{back}, which was then substituted back into eq. 17 to calculate a more accurate value of m. This method of successive approximations was repeated until a constant value of m resulted. Alternatively, of course, the pressure correction term could have been computed directly from the observed values of m and t, but this would not be possible in an "unknown" case. The calculated values of the pressure correction term are given in the fifth column of the table under h_{back}, and the *effective* pressure on the dropping mercury, $h - h_{back}$, is listed in the sixth column under $h_{corr.}$. The values of m calculated by means of eq. 17 are given in the seventh column, and the percentage deviation between the observed and calculated values of m are given in the last column.

TABLE IV-2

COMPARISON OF OBSERVED AND CALCULATED RATES OF FLOW OF MERCURY FROM A CAPILLARY TUBE UNDER VARIOUS PRESSURES

Mercury dropping into 0.1 N potassium chloride solution at 25° C. $r_c = 0.00189$ cm., $l = 2.043$ cm. Experimental data obtained by Maas.

h, cm.	t, sec.	m (obs.), mg. sec.$^{-1}$	mt (obs.), mg.	h_{back} (calcd.), cm.	$h_{corr.}$, cm.	m (calcd.), mg. sec.$^{-1}$	Δm, per cent
40	4.13	1.084	4.47	1.9	38.1	1.092	+0.7
60	2.69	1.653	4.45	1.9	58.1	1.668	+0.9
80	1.99	2.221	4.42	1.9	78.1	2.240	+0.9
100	1.59	2.789	4.44	1.9	98.1	2.816	+1.0

The good agreement between the observed and calculated values of m demonstrates that the Poiseuille equation can be used to calculate m with an accuracy of at least 1 per cent, provided that proper correction is made for the back pressure due to the interfacial tension. Neglect of the back pressure would have introduced an error of over 5 per cent in the calculated value of m at a pressure of 40 cm. of mercury. It should also be noted that m is a function of r_c to the fourth power, and since the value of r_c given in Table IV-2 is probably only correct to ±0.5 per cent the probable uncertainty in the calculated values of m due to this small uncertainty in the value of r_c should be about ±2 per cent. Hence the observed deviation of 1 per cent between the observed and calculated values of m is well within the limits of the experimental error in the data.

Loveridge[35] tested eq. 15 with eighteen different capillaries over a range of pressures from 20 to 80 cm. In every case he found—in agreement with

---

[35] B. A. Loveridge, *Ph.D. Thesis*, Harvard University, 1947.

eq. 15—that the relation between m and h was expressible by

$$m = \alpha(h - \beta) \tag{18}$$

with a precision of ± 0.15 per cent. The observed back pressure term β agreed very well with the theoretical value (eq. 11).

Equation 15 predicts that m should vary slightly with the medium, because of the interfacial tension in the back pressure term. This effect is very small in different aqueous solutions because of the small differences in σ, but a significant difference is observed between m in air and in solutions. From eq. 5 the percentage change in m in air and a solution is given by

$$\Delta m\ \% = \frac{0.77 \left[\dfrac{\sigma_s}{(m_s t_s)^{1/3}} - \dfrac{\sigma_a}{(m_a t_a)^{1/3}} \right]}{h - \left[\dfrac{7.73 \times 10^{-3}\, \sigma_s}{(m_s t_s)^{1/3}} \right]} \tag{19}$$

where the subscripts s and a refer to the solution and air, respectively. Since the second term in the denominator (the back pressure) is small compared to h, it may be neglected without significant error, and eq. 19 then becomes

$$\Delta m\ \% = \frac{0.77}{h} \left[\frac{\sigma_s}{(m_s t_s)^{1/3}} - \frac{\sigma_a}{(m_a t_a)^{1/3}} \right] \tag{20}$$

Lingane and Loveridge (loc. cit.) tested this equation with four different capillaries with the results shown in Table IV-3.

Comparison of the last two columns of this table shows fairly good agreement between the observed and calculated values of $\Delta m\ \%$. The calculated values of $\Delta m\ \%$ are based on $\sigma_a = 470$ and $\sigma_s = 400$ dyne cm.$^{-1}$. The chief uncertainty in the calculated values of $\Delta m\ \%$ is due to the fact that when the mercury drops form in air they adhere to the glass around the capillary orifice and hence become much larger than if they were freely suspended. This is reflected in the observed ratios of t_{air}/t_{soln}. given in the fifth column of Table IV-3. For freely suspended drops this ratio should depend only on the values of σ_a and σ_s, and hence should be the same for all the capillaries and for all pressures on the dropping mercury. Actually this ratio varies from about 7.5 to 15 with the different capillaries at the different pressures. Adhesion of the mercury to the glass surrounding the capillary orifice has been studied by Kolthoff and Kahan,[36] who found that drop times in pure water were not reproducible and were very sensi-

---

[36] I. M. Kolthoff and G. J. Kahan, J. Am. Chem. Soc., 64, 2553 (1942).

tive to slight inclination of the capillary from the vertical. The adhesion is even more pronounced when the drops form in air. Müller[37] has also discussed this effect.

As shown in Table IV-3 the value of m in air is 0.5 to 3.6 per cent greater than in an aqueous solution, the difference being inversely dependent on h. Consequently in precise work m should be measured in the solution in question rather than in air.

When a mercury drop forms at the dropping electrode it is subjected to a gravitational force mtg and a restraining force $2 \pi r_c \sigma$, where r_c is the

TABLE IV-3

COMPARISON OF DROP TIMES AND m-VALUES IN AIR AND IN 1 N POTASSIUM CHLORIDE AT 25° C.

| Capillary | h, cm. | t, sec. | | $\dfrac{t_{air}}{t_{soln.}}$ | m, mg. sec.$^{-1}$ | | Δm, per cent | |
		Air	Soln.		Air	Soln.	Obs.	Calcd.
A	41.7	95.1	6.52	14.6	0.982	0.959	2.3	2.1
	51.7	66.5	5.16	12.9	1.214	1.203	0.9	1.6
	61.5	59.0	4.36	13.5	1.454	1.439	1.0	1.4
B	23.3	49.8	6.00	8.3	1.285	1.239	3.6	2.9
	33.3	35.3	4.09	8.6	1.875	1.824	2.7	2.0
	43.1	27.4	3.19	8.6	2.454	2.409	1.8	1.6
	53.1	23.0	2.56	9.0	3.040	2.983	1.9	1.3
C	24.7	42.7	4.52	9.5	2.062	2.004	2.8	2.7
	34.7	29.5	3.04	9.7	3.033	2.983	1.7	1.9
	44.7	17.8	2.36	7.5	3.964	3.927	0.9	1.3
	54.5	14.0	1.92	7.3	4.868	4.842	0.5	1.0
D	29.6	10.4	1.37	7.6	7.095	6.960	1.9	2.0
	39.6	7.76	1.01	7.7	9.454	9.372	0.9	1.5
	49.6	6.24	0.79	7.9	11.90	11.84	0.5	1.2

radius of the capillary and σ the interfacial tension between the mercury and the solution. The drop continues to grow until mtg becomes equal to $2 \pi r_c \sigma$, at which point it falls. Hence the drop weight mt is directly proportional to σ:

$$mt = \frac{2 \pi r_c \sigma}{g} \qquad (21)$$

For a given capillary (constant r_c) in a given supporting electrolyte (constant σ) the drop weight should be constant and independent of the rate of flow, i. e., independent of the pressure on the dropping mercury. The data in Table IV-2 show that this is true to within about ±1 per cent.

---

[37] O. H. Müller, J. Am. Chem. Soc., **66,** 1019 (1944).

By combining eq. 15 and 21 it is found that the drop time for a given capillary in a given electrolyte should be inversely proportional to the applied pressure corrected for the back pressure due to interfacial tension. Loveridge (*loc. cit.*) tested this relation with a large number of different capillaries and found that it was obeyed to within about 2 per cent.

6. RELATION BETWEEN DIFFUSION CURRENT AND PRESSURE ON THE DROPPING MERCURY

As shown in the preceding section the relations between the rate of flow of mercury, the drop time, and the pressure on the dropping mercury are

$$m = k' h_{\text{corr.}} \tag{22}$$

$$t = \frac{k''}{h_{\text{corr.}}} \tag{23}$$

where $h_{\text{corr.}}$ is the net pressure in centimeters of mercury after correction for the back pressure due to the interfacial tension, and k' and k'' are constants which depend on the geometrical characteristics of the capillary. Hence we have

$$m^{2/3}t^{1/6} = (k' h_{\text{corr.}})^{2/3} \left(\frac{k''}{h_{\text{corr.}}} \right)^{1/6} = k''' h_{\text{corr.}}^{1/6} \tag{24}$$

and from this relation and eq. 1a:

$$i_d = km^{2/3}t^{1/6} = \text{const.} \times h_{\text{corr.}}^{1/2} \tag{25}$$

Because the linear relation between i_d and $m^{2/3}t^{1/6}$ is only a good approximation (± 2 per cent with drop times greater than 1.5 sec.), it is evident that eq. 25 cannot be highly exact. From eq. 1b a more correct relation between i_d and h should be

$$i_d = km^{2/3}t^{1/6} \left(1 + \frac{at^{1/2}}{m^{1/3}} \right) = = \alpha h^{1/2} \left(1 + \frac{\beta}{h^{1/2}} \right) \tag{25a}$$

or

$$\frac{i_d}{h^{1/2}} = \alpha + \frac{\gamma}{h^{1/2}} \tag{25b}$$

where k, a, α, β, and γ are constants for a given capillary in a given solution. Equation 25b predicts that $i_d/h^{1/2}$ should not be strictly constant but should decrease slightly with increasing values of h.

Equation 25 was first derived and tested by Ilkovic,[38] and later by Maas (*loc. cit.*), but these authors did not apply the correction for the back pressure. Loveridge[39] tested eq. 25 and eq. 25b with four different capillaries with the results shown in Table IV-4. The data with capillaries F and G were obtained with lead ion in 1 N potassium chloride, and the data with capillaries 3 and 4 were obtained with zinc in 1 M ammonia–1 M ammonium

TABLE IV-4

THE DIFFUSION CURRENT AS A FUNCTION OF THE EFFECTIVE HEAD OF MERCURY

Capillary	h, cm.	t, sec.	mt, mg.	P_{back}	$h_{corr.}$	i_d, microamp.	$\frac{i_d}{h^{1/2}}$
F	40.0	4.49	4.81	1.8	38.2	10.88	1.76
	50.0	3.60	4.87		48.2	12.09	1.74
	60.0	2.92	4.79		58.2	13.04	1.71
	70.0	2.36	4.92		68.2	14.00	1.70
G	30.0	2.50	7.48	1.6	28.4	18.68	3.53
	40.0	1.82	7.47		38.4	21.46	3.47
	50.0	1.41	7.21		48.4	23.93	3.44
	60.0	1.18	7.28		58.4	26.44	3.46
	70.0	1.02	7.39		68.4	29.36	3.54
3	20.0	3.08	4.43	1.9	18.1	12.96	3.05
	30.0	2.04	4.54		28.1	15.87	2.99
	40.0	1.56	4.62		38.1	18.38	2.98
	50.0	1.22	4.57		48.1	20.86	3.01
	60.0	0.99	4.57		58.1	23.76	3.11
	70.0	0.80	4.24		68.1	27.37	3.31
	80.0	0.69	4.18		78.1	31.29	3.54
4	30.0	3.06	4.12	1.9	28.1	12.60	2.38
	40.0	2.32	4.19		38.1	14.49	2.38
	50.0	1.94	4.40		48.1	16.08	2.32
	60.0	1.56	4.29		58.1	17.54	2.30
	70.0	1.35	4.34		68.1	18.99	2.30

chloride. Gelatin (0.01 per cent) was present as a maximum suppressor. The diffusion currents were corrected for the residual current observed with the supporting electrolyte alone with each capillary at each value of h. The temperature was 25.00° C. The back pressure correction was calculated from the relation $P_{back} = 3.1/(mt)^{1/3}$ (see eq. 16).

As predicted by eq. 25b the ratio $i_d/h^{1/2}$ shows a significant decrease with increasing values of h until the drop time becomes smaller than about 1.5 sec. With smaller drop times it increases because of the same stirring effect which causes $i_d/(Cm^{2/3}t^{1/6})$ to increase at rapid dropping rates.

[38] D. Ilkovic, *Collection Czechoslov. Chem. Communs.*, **6**, 498 (1934).
[39] B. A. Loveridge, *Ph.D. Thesis*, Harvard University, 1947.

7. INFLUENCE OF POTENTIAL OF THE DROPPING ELECTRODE ON DIFFUSION CURRENT

The interfacial tension at a mercury–electrolyte solution interface varies with the potential impressed on the mercury. Starting at relatively positive potentials σ first increases as the potential is made more negative, passes through a maximum (the "electrocapillary zero"), and then decreases at relatively negative potentials. The resulting curve is known as the electrocapillary curve (see Chap. VIII). Since from eq. 21 the drop time is directly proportional to σ, the curve obtained by plotting t vs. the potential of the dropping electrode parallels the electrocapillary curve. The rate of flow of mercury also depends on σ through the back pressure term in eq. 14, but since the back pressure correction is relatively small it is to be expected that m will change only very slightly with changing potential. Because i_d depends on $t^{1/6}$ it is evident that it will change significantly with the potential of the dropping electrode.

The influence of the potential of the dropping electrode on the quantities m, t, and the product $m^{2/3}t^{1/6}$ is demonstrated by some typical data obtained by Lingane and Kolthoff[40] given in Table IV-5.

It will be noted that m was practically constant and independent of the potential of the dropping electrode. On the other hand, the drop time t first increased, passed through a maximum at about -0.5 v., and then decreased rapidly with increasing negative potential, according to the electrocapillary curve. Corresponding to the variation of t, the product $m^{2/3}t^{1/6}$ first increased slightly, passed through a very flat maximum, and then decreased with increasing negative potential. This is shown more clearly by the curves of these data in Fig. IV-6. The variation of the product $m^{2/3}t^{1/6}$ with changing potential of the dropping electrode is much less than that of t since it depends on only the sixth root of t, and for practical purposes $m^{2/3}t^{1/6}$ may be assumed to be constant (± 1 per cent) over the potential range from zero to about -1.0 v., but at more negative potentials its decrease must be taken into account. These results agree with similar data obtained by Ilkovic and by Maas.

The other data in Table IV-5 show that the product $m^{2/3}t^{1/6}$ did not change appreciably during the discharge of cadmium ions, thallous ions, or oxygen, but remained the same as in the pure 0.1 N potassium chloride solution. The data also demonstrate that the product $m^{2/3}t^{1/6}$ is independent of the chloride ion concentration between 0.001 and 1 N.

Since, according to the Ilkovic equation and the experimental data already discussed, the diffusion current is proportional to $t^{1/6}$, it is to be

[40] J. J. Lingane and I. M. Kolthoff, *J. Am. Chem. Soc.*, **61**, 825 (1939).

TABLE IV-5

THE PRODUCT $m^{2/3}t^{1/6}$ AS FUNCTION OF THE POTENTIAL OF THE DROPPING ELECTRODE AND COMPOSITION OF THE SOLUTION AT 25° C.

$P = 21.8 \pm 0.2$ cm. 0.2 ml. of 0.1 per cent sodium methyl red added per 50 ml. of solution.

$E_{d.e.}$ vs. S.C.E., volts	i, microamp.	m, mg. sec.$^{-1}$	t, sec.	$m^{2/3}t^{1/6}$, mg.$^{2/3}$ sec.$^{-1/2}$
(a) 0.1 N KCl				
0.0	−0.18	2.651	2.75	2.27
−0.5	+0.10	2.621	3.08	2.29
−0.8	0.21	2.626	2.88	2.28
−1.1	0.29	2.625	2.66	2.24
−1.5	0.38	2.672	2.18	2.18
−1.9	0.70	2.681	1.56	2.08
(b) 0.0011 M CdSO₄ in 0.1 N KCl				
−0.8	8.90	2.605	2.86	2.26
(c) 0.0011 M CdSO₄ in 1 N KCl				
−0.8	8.92	2.603	2.85	2.26
(d) 0.001 M TlCl, no other salt present				
−0.8	10.9	2.621	2.97	2.28
(e) (d) repeated after saturating solution with air				
−0.8	14.8	2.646	2.99	2.29

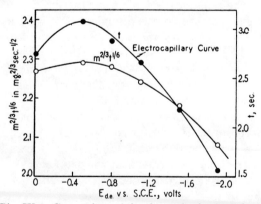

Fig. IV-6. Comparison of the change in the drop time and in the quantity $m^{2/3}t^{1/6}$ with increasing negative potential.

expected that it will decrease appreciably at potentials more negative than about -1.0 v. This effect is often observed, especially with fairly large concentrations of reducible substances that are reduced at potentials more negative than about -1.0 v. A good illustration of this effect is furnished by the data given in Table IV-6, obtained by Ilkovic (*loc. cit.*) in the electrolysis of 0.001 M mercuric chloride in 0.01 N sodium chloride as supporting electrolyte. It is evident that the decrease of i_d with increasing negative potential must be taken into account when comparing the diffusion currents of the same concentration of two substances whose reduction potentials are far apart.

The influence of the potential of the dropping electrode on i_d has also been investigated by Kolthoff and Orlemann,[41, 42] who verified the linear

TABLE IV-6

DECREASE OF THE DIFFUSION CURRENT AT NEGATIVE POTENTIALS

Data obtained by Ilkovic in the electrolysis of 0.001 M mercuric chloride in 0.01 N sodium chloride as supporting electrolyte.

$E_{d.e.}$ vs. S.C.E., volts	t (ten drops), sec.	i_d, mm.	$i_d/t^{1/6}$
-0.65	20.3	31.2	18.89
-0.85	19.7	31.0	18.88
-1.05	18.55	30.8	18.93
-1.25	17.5	30.4	18.87
-1.45	15.7	30.0	18.96
-1.65	13.65	29.5	19.06

relation between i_d and $t^{1/6}$ in the reduction of cupric ion and manganous ion on 0.1 M potassium chloride. These authors pointed out that the relative values of the drop times at two different potentials are independent of the characteristics of the dropping electrode capillary *for a given supporting electrolyte*. Hence, once the relative values have been determined with one capillary, they may be used to correct diffusion currents for the effect of the potential with other capillaries in the same supporting electrolyte.

An illustration of the magnitude of this correction has been given by Kolthoff and Orlemann (*loc. cit.*) in the case of a mixture of cupric and manganous ions in 0.1 N potassium chloride. Polarograms of this mixture show a diffusion current for the reduction of cupric ion at potentials more negative than -0.2 v. *vs.* S.C.E. The manganese wave occurs at -1.5 v. and at potentials more negative than this both substances contribute to

[41] I. M. Kolthoff and E. F. Orlemann, *J. Am. Chem. Soc.*, **63,** 2085 (1941).
[42] I. M. Kolthoff, *Ind. Eng. Chem., Anal. Ed.*, **14,** 195 (1942).

the total diffusion current. With 1.01 millimolar copper and 1 millimolar manganese the diffusion current at -0.5 v. was 6.19 microamp. (corrected for residual current), and the total diffusion current at -1.7 v. was 11.85 microamp. The ratio of the drop times at the two potentials was $t_{1.7}/t_{0.5} = 0.93$. Hence the contribution of the copper to the total diffusion current at -1.7 v. was not 6.19 microamp. but $0.93 \times 6.19 = 5.75$ microamp., and the diffusion current of the manganese at -1.7 v. was therefore $11.85 - 5.75 = 6.10$ microamp. Failure to correct for the effect of the potential on the diffusion current of the copper would have led to an error of -7 per cent in the calculation of the contribution of manganese to the total diffusion current at -1.7 v.

8. INFLUENCE OF TEMPERATURE ON THE DIFFUSION CURRENT

The influence of temperature on the diffusion current can be predicted by means of the Ilkovic equation.[43] In order to compute the temperature coefficient of i_d it is convenient to write the Ilkovic equation as

$$i_d = knD^{1/2}Cm^{2/3}t^{1/6} \tag{26}$$

where the constant k is substituted for the constant 607 in eq. 1, because it is a function of temperature. Every term in this equation, except n, is a function of temperature, and by differentiating with respect to temperature we find that the temperature coefficient of i_d should be given by

$$\frac{1}{i_d}\frac{di_d}{dT} = \frac{1}{k}\frac{dk}{dT} + \frac{1}{2D}\frac{dD}{dt} + \frac{1}{C}\frac{dC}{dT} + \frac{2}{3m}\frac{dm}{dT} + \frac{1}{6t}\frac{dt}{dT} \tag{27}$$

The theoretical significance of the constant k has been discussed in Chapter II, where it was shown that

$$k = \frac{3455}{d^{2/3}} \tag{28}$$

where d is the density of mercury, and the constant 3455 is a combination of numerical and geometrical constants which do not depend on temperature. Hence the temperature coefficient of k is governed solely by the temperature coefficient of the density of mercury, and by differentiating eq. 28 we have

$$\frac{1}{k}\frac{dk}{dT} = -\frac{2}{3d}\frac{dd}{dT} \tag{29}$$

The temperature coefficient of d is -0.000181 deg.$^{-1}$ at temperatures in the neighborhood of $25°$, and hence the temperature coefficient of k is $- 2/3$

---

[43] D. Ilkovic, *Collection Czechoslov. Chem. Communs.*, **10**, 249 (1938).

$(-0.000181) = +0.00012$ deg.$^{-1}$, or k increases by 0.012 per cent per degree increase in temperature.

The temperature coefficient of the diffusion coefficient has been discussed in Chapter III, and it was shown that for ideal ions, or actual ions at infinite dilution:

$$\frac{1}{D}\frac{dD}{dT} = \frac{1}{\lambda^0}\frac{d\lambda^0}{dT} + \frac{1}{T} \tag{30}$$

where λ^0 is the equivalent ionic conductance at infinite dilution at the absolute temperature T.

The temperature coefficient of C is equal to the temperature coefficient of the density of the solution, and it is so small (ca. -0.025 per cent deg.$^{-1}$ for dilute aqueous solutions) that it can be neglected.

The temperature coefficient of m can be derived from eq. 5 or eq. 14. In order to calculate the temperature coefficient of m from eq. 14 we may neglect the small back pressure term, and eq. 14 then becomes

$$m = \frac{\pi r_c^4 d}{8\ l\eta}\ (hgd) \tag{31}$$

The coefficient of expansion of the glass capillary is so small that we may assume without appreciable error that r_c and l are independent of temperature. The temperature coefficient of m is determined practically entirely by the temperature coefficients of the density d and the viscosity η of mercury. If the experimental arrangement is such that only the temperature of the cell and capillary is varied, while that of the mercury column above the capillary remains constant, then the effective pressure hgd will be a constant in eq. 31 and the temperature coefficient of m will be given by

$$\frac{1}{m}\frac{dm}{dT} = \frac{1}{d}\frac{dd}{dT} - \frac{1}{\eta}\frac{d\eta}{dT} \tag{32}$$

On the other hand, if the temperatures of both the cell and the mercury column are varied then hgd becomes a function of temperature, and we have

$$\frac{1}{m}\frac{dm}{dT} = \frac{2}{d}\frac{dd}{dT} - \frac{1}{\eta}\frac{d\eta}{dT} \tag{33}$$

The temperature coefficient of the density of mercury is -0.000181 deg.$^{-1}$, while that of the viscosity of mercury is[44] -0.0038 deg.$^{-1}$. Hence, under the experimental conditions for which eq. 32 is valid, we find that the temperature coefficient of m is $-0.00018 + 0.0038 = +0.0036$ deg.$^{-1}$, whereas

[44] *International Critical Tables*, **5**, 7 (1929).

under the conditions for which eq. 33 holds the temperature coefficient of m is $-0.0004 + 0.0038 = +0.0034$ deg.$^{-1}$, and the slight difference is negligible.

Lingane[45] determined the temperature coefficient of m experimentally and found a value of $+0.0031$ deg.$^{-1}$ ($+0.31$ per cent deg.$^{-1}$) between 0° and 25°, which agrees very well with the predicted value.

The drop time t is proportional to the interfacial tension at the mercury-solution interface, and its variation with temperature is so small that the last term in eq. 27 can be neglected.

By combining the foregoing temperature coefficients we obtain the fol-

TABLE IV-7

DIFFUSION CURRENTS OF SEVERAL METAL IONS AS A FUNCTION OF TEMPERATURE
(DATA OF NEJEDLY)

Diffusion currents measured with excess potassium chloride as supporting electrolyte; the values given are the ratios of i_d at the indicated temperatures to i_d at 20° C.

Ion	Temperature, ° C.				Temp. coeff. 20–50°, per cent
	20	50	80	95	
Tl$^+$	1.0	1.4	2.0	2.6	1.3
Pb^{++}	1.0	1.6	4.7	7.5	2.0
Cd^{++}	1.0	1.5	2.1	2.6	1.7
Zn^{++}	1.0	1.6	2.2	3.0	2.0
Mn^{++}	1.0	1.7	2.6	—	2.3
In^{+++}	1.0	1.6	2.2	—	2.0

lowing expression for the temperature coefficient of the diffusion current of reducible ions in the neighborhood of 25° C.

$$\frac{1}{i_d} \frac{di_d}{dT} = 0.0037 + \frac{1}{2 \lambda^0} \frac{d\lambda^0}{dT} \tag{34}$$

Since the first term in this equation is much smaller than the second, the temperature coefficient of i_d is governed chiefly by the temperature coefficient of the equivalent conductance of the reducible ion. The temperature coefficients of the equivalent conductances of most ions are between 0.02 and 0.027 deg.$^{-1}$, with the exception of H^+ and OH^- ions for which the values are, respectively, 0.0157 and 0.018 deg.$^{-1}$. Hence the temperature coefficient of i_d should be between about 1.3 and 1.6 per cent deg.$^{-1}$ for most common ions, and should be close to 1.05 per cent deg.$^{-1}$ in the discharge of hydrogen ions.

Nejedly[46] measured the diffusion currents of various metal ions in excess

[45] J. J. Lingane, *Ind. Eng. Chem., Anal. Ed.*, **14**, 655 (1942).
[46] V. Nejedly, *Collection Czechoslov. Chem. Communs.*, **1**, 319 (1929).

potassium chloride as supporting electrolyte at various temperatures between 20° and 95° C. The data he obtained are summarized in Table IV-7, in which the last column contains the average observed temperature coefficient over the temperature range from 20° to 50° C. Similar data have been reported by von Stackelberg, Klinger, Koch, e Krath.[47]

The observed average temperature coefficients from 20° to 50° range from 1.3 to 2.3 per cent deg.$^{-1}$, and are in good agreement with the values to be expected from eq. 34. The data are not sufficiently precise to warrant a more detailed comparison with the calculated values. It will be noted that the temperature coefficient increased markedly with increasing temperature, especially in the case of lead ions. Nejedly also found that at the higher temperatures the diffusion currents of these metal ions decreased with time. This effect was particularly marked in the case of lead ions, and

TABLE IV-8

INFLUENCE OF CAPILLARY TILT

Vertical angle	i_d		i_d (av.)
	Series 1	Series 2	
0.0°	22.66	22.62	22.64 ± 2
3.5°	22.59	22.56	22.58 ± 2
5.5°	22.54	22.51	22.52 ± 2
8.0°	22.42	22.34	22.38 ± 4
10.5°	22.50	22.25	22.37 ± 13

it persisted even when the solutions were acidified. Nejedly attributed it to an adsorption of the metal ions on the glass wall of the cell.

No data are available for the diffusion currents of uncharged substances as a function of temperature, but it is to be expected that the temperature coefficient will be about the same as in the case of reducible ions.

From the practical viewpoint it is evident that the temperature should be controlled to at least ±0.5°, in order to keep variations due to the effect of temperature within ±1 per cent.

9. INFLUENCE OF TILTING THE DROPPING ELECTRODE

In setting up a dropping electrode care should be observed that the capillary is not tilted appreciably from the vertical, as irregular dropping and a variable diffusion current may result. The influence on the diffusion current of tilting the capillary is illustrated by the data in Table IV-8, obtained by Loveridge (loc. cit.) with lead ion in 1 M potassium chloride.

[47] M. von Stackelberg, P. Klinger, W. Koch, and E. Krath, Forschungsber. Tech. Mitt. Krupp, 2, 59 (1939).

The inclination of the capillary was measured with a plumb line and a protractor scale attached to the stand tube. The applied mercury pressure was kept constant by the fixed position of the mercury reservoir. The first series was run with increasing inclination and was followed by the second series of readings as the capillary was returned to a vertical position.

It is seen that an inclination of up to about 5° has little if any influence. Larger inclinations cause not only a decrease in the current but also a poorer degree of reproducibility, due to irregular drop formation.

Müller[48] called attention to the fact that the formation of the mercury drops will be irregular when the capillary tip is cut off at an angle or when the capillary is tilted. In order to obtain normal drop formation, without adhesion of the mercury to the glass around the orifice, the angle between the cut surface and the horizontal must not be greater than about 5°.

10. COMPARISON OF OBSERVED AND THEORETICAL DIFFUSION CURRENTS

The evidence presented in preceding pages engenders confidence that the original Ilkovic equation (within its recognized limitations) and the modified equation (1b) are capable of accounting quite satisfactorily for the influence of each of the many factors that govern the diffusion current. In this section we are concerned with the degree of correctness of the numerical constants in these equations, i. e., a direct comparison of observed diffusion currents with those computed from the theoretical equations. For such a comparison to be conclusive, that is, to calculate the theoretical diffusion currents, it is necessary to know the actual diffusion coefficient of the substance in question. Unfortunately, actual experimental diffusion coefficient data under the particular conditions extant in a polarographic supporting electrolyte are not available in even a single instance, and until such data have been obtained a really conclusive test of the correctness of the numerical constants in the theoretical equations will not be possible.

It is possible, however, to test the constants approximately by employing diffusion coefficients of ions computed from the corresponding equivalent ionic conductances at infinite dilution by means of the relation

$$D^0 = \frac{RT}{zF^2} \lambda^0 = 2.67 \times 10^{-7} \frac{\lambda^0}{z} \text{ (cm.}^2 \text{ sec.}^{-1} \text{ at } 25° \tag{36}$$

In this relation, which was derived in Chapter III, R is the molar gas constant, T is the absolute temperature, z is the charge on the ion without regard to sign, F is the faraday, and λ^0 is the equivalent conductance of the ion at infinite dilution. This relation is valid only at infinite dilution.

---

[48] O. H. Müller, J. Am. Chem. Soc., **66**, 1022 (1944).

A comparison of observed diffusion currents of various ions with the theoretical values computed by eq. 1a and 1b, using infinite dilution values of diffusion coefficients from eq. 36, is presented in Table IV-9. The experimental data for lead, thallous, cadmium, zinc, iodate, and ferricyanide ions were obtained by Lingane and Kolthoff[49] and the data for cupric ion were reported by Kolthoff and Orlemann.[50] The diffusion current of iodate ion corresponds to the 6-electron reduction to iodide ion, that of ferricyanide ion results from the 1-electron reduction to ferrocyanide ion, and that of chromate ion pertains to the 3-electron reduction to the chromic state.

The observed diffusion currents of lead, thallous, cupric, iodate, and

TABLE IV 9

OBSERVED AND THEORETICAL DIFFUSION CURRENTS AT 25° C.

Except as otherwise noted the supporting electrolyte was 0.1 M KCl containing either 0.0002 to 0.0004 per cent sodium methyl red or 0.01 per cent gelatin as maximum suppressor. The diffusion currents are for $C = 1$ millimolar.

Ion	$D^0 \times 10^5$, cm.^{2} sec.$^{-1}$	m, mg. sec.$^{-1}$	t, sec.	i_d , microamp.		
				Obs.	eq. 1a	eq. 1b
Pb^{++}	0.98	2.63	2.88	8.78	8.69	9.62
Tl$^+$	2.00	2.63	2.88	6.13	6.18	7.10
Cd^{++}	0.72	2.60	2.85	8.00	7.42	8.00
Zn^{++}	0.72	2.63	2.66	7.65	7.29	7.94
Cu^{++}	0.72	1.92	3.64	6.20	6.28	6.94
IO$_3^-$	1.09	2.67	2.18	26.3	26.2	29.0
Fe(CN)$_6^{---}$	0.89	2.63	2.88	3.78	4.13	4.55
CrO$_4^{--}$	1.07	1.54	3.36	9.33^a	9.68	11.00

^{a} In 1 M NaOH.

chromate ions agree better with the Ilkovic equation (eq. 1a) than with eq. 1b, but this merely reflects a compensation of errors. The fact that the actual diffusion coefficients are smaller than the ideal infinite dilution values compensates for the neglect of the curvature of the electrode in the original Ilkovic equation. Without exception the observed diffusion currents are somewhat smaller than the values predicted by eq. 1b, because the actual diffusion coefficients are smaller than the infinite dilution values on which the calculated currents are based. The observed diffusion currents of cadmium and zinc ions are considerably larger than the values predicted by eq. 1a and are in quite good agreement with the predictions of eq. 1b, probably because the predominant ionic species in the presence of excess

[49] J. J. Lingane and I. M. Kolthoff, *J. Am. Chem. Soc.*, **61**, 825 (1939); **62**, 852 (1940).

[50] I. M. Kolthoff and E. F. Orlemann, *J. Am. Chem. Soc.*, **63**, 2085 (1941).

chloride ion are $CdCl^+$ and $ZnCl^+$ which, being only unipositive, have larger diffusion coefficients than the dipositive Cd^{++} and Zn^{++}.

A conclusive test of the numerical constant in the Ilkovic equation must wait until accurate experimental values of the various diffusion coefficients in the actual supporting electrolytes, rather than at infinite dilution, are available. A program designed to obtain such data is now in progress in the laboratory of one of the authors (J. J. L.).

TABLE IV-10

DIFFUSION CURRENT CONSTANTS OF METALS IN VARIOUS SUPPORTING ELECTROLYTES
AT 25° C.

N.R. signifies that the metal complex is not reducible, and i denotes insolubility.
Values in italics are uncertain because of poorly developed diffusion current.

Supporting electrolyte	As(III)	Bi(III)	Sb(III)	Sn(II)	Sn(IV)	Pb	Cd	Zn	Cu
0.1 N KCl		i	i	i	i	3.80	3.51	3.42	3.23
1 N HCl	*8.6*	5.23	5.54	4.07	*4.8*	3.86	3.58	*a*	3.39
0.5 M H₂SO₄	*8.4*	4.31	4.94	3.54	i	i	*2.6*	*a*	*2.12*
1 N HNO₃	*8.8*	4.64	5.10	4.02	i	3.67	3.06	*a*	3.24
1 N NaOH	N.R.	i	4.54	3.45	N.R.	3.39	i	3.14	2.91
Acidic tartrate	C	3.12	*3.4*	2.41	N.R.	2.37	2.34	*a*	2.37
0.5 M sodium tartrate	N.R.	*3.0*	*3.9*	2.48	N.R.	2.30	2.34	2.30	2.24
Alkaline tartrate	N.R.	*c*	3.54	2.86	N.R.	2.39	*b*	2.65	*a*
1 N NH₄Cl + 1 M NH₃		i	i	i	i	i	3.68	3.99	3.75

[a] Wave masked by final current increase (discharge of hydrogen or sodium ion).
[b] Diffusion current not well defined, and not proportional to concentration of cadmium.
[c] No definite limiting current.

11. EFFECT OF COMPLEX FORMATION ON DIFFUSION CURRENTS OF METALS

The diffusion coefficient of a substance depends on its molecular state (size), and hence complex metal ions have different diffusion current constants than "simple" metal ions (aquo complexes). This effect of complex formation is shown by the data in Table IV-10 obtained by Lingane.[51] The values listed are the diffusion current constants $i_d/(Cm^{2/3}t^{1/6})$ at 25°. Values in italics are uncertain because the diffusion currents were not well developed. In all cases 0.01 per cent gelatin was present as a maximum suppressor.

It should be noted that the diffusion current constants are in all cases larger in hydrochloric acid than in sulfuric or nitric acid solutions. In hy-

[51] J. J. Lingane, *Ind. Eng. Chem., Anal. Ed.*, **15**, 589 (1943).

drochloric acid the metals are present as chloro complex ions which are smaller—and thus possess larger diffusion coefficients—than the aquo complexes present in sulfuric and nitric acid solutions. The fact that the values for cadmium, zinc, and copper in ammoniacal medium are larger than in the other supporting electrolytes suggests that the ammonia complexes of these metals are smaller than the complexes present in the other solutions.

The values in the tartrate media are smaller than in any of the other solutions, which is not surprising in view of the relatively large size of a tartrate complex ion. Furthermore, the diffusion current constants correspond to nearly identical values of the diffusion coefficients of the tartrate complexes of the various metals. This leveling effect is due to the fact that the coordinating tartrate ions are so large compared to the size of the central metal ion that differences in the size of the metal ion, and even in the type and orientation of the bonds, have only a very minor influence on the effective sizes of the different complexes.

12. INFLUENCE OF SOLVENT VISCOSITY ON THE DIFFUSION CURRENT

In general the diffusion currents of most substances are relatively smaller in nonaqueous solvents than in aqueous medium, because diffusion coefficients are usually smaller in nonaqueous media. Decreased diffusion coefficients may result either from increased viscosity or change in the size of the solvated species, and since in different cases these two effects may tend either to reinforce or to compensate each other, a quantitative interpretation of the separate influence of each is not a simple matter.

For diffusing particles that are large compared to the solvent molecules the Stokes-Einstein relation predicts that the diffusion coefficient D should be inversely proportional to the viscosity coefficient η of the medium. Because as a good approximation the diffusion current is directly proportional to $D^{1/2}$ the relation $i_d\eta^{1/2}$ = const. should be obeyed in those cases where the change of D is due solely to changes in viscosity. However, if the change of D is also partly due to a change in the nature (size) of the solvated species it is evident that the product $i_d\eta^{1/2}$ will not be constant.

Brasher and Jones[52] found that the diffusion currents of various metal ions in supporting electrolytes composed of 0.01 to 9 M sulfuric acid, 0.1 to 7 M sodium hydroxide, and 0.05 to 1 M sodium sulfate were inversely proportional to $\eta^{1/2}$ in agreement with the foregoing relation. Lingane and Carritt[53] also observed that $i_d\eta^{1/2}$ was very nearly constant in the reduction

[52] D. M. Brasher and F. R. Jones, *Trans. Faraday Soc.*, **42**, 775 (1946).
[53] J. J. Lingane and D. E. Carritt, unpublished investigation.

of $+6$ molybdenum from various concentrations of sulfuric acid between 0.2 and 12 M. In these instances it appears that the nature of the metal ions is not significantly altered by very large changes in the concentration of supporting electrolyte and that the observed changes in the diffusion currents are due almost entirely to changes in viscosity.

Vavruch[54] claimed that $i_d\eta^{1/2}$ increased significantly when the viscosities of 0.1 M solutions of sodium chloride, sodium nitrate, and potassium sulfate, containing various metal ions, was increased by addition of up to 50 per cent sucrose, i. e., that the decreased diffusion currents could not be attributed solely to the increased viscosity. McKenzie[55] was unable to confirm Vavruch's conclusion, and reported that the product $i_d\eta^{1/2}$ was constant in the reduction of lead ion, cadmium ion, zinc ion, maleic acid, and Orange II, and in the oxidation of ascorbic acid, in various concentrations of sucrose up to 43 per cent (relative viscosity 4.86). McKenzie also concluded that changes in viscosity produced by lyophilic colloids (gelatin, pectin, and methyl cellulose) have a much smaller influence on the diffusion current than that predicted by the relation $i_d\eta^{1/2} =$ const.

Recently Matsuyama[56] has thoroughly and systematically investigated the diffusion currents of many metal ions in ethanol–water mixtures from zero to 90 per cent ethanol by volume. With increasing proportions of ethanol the diffusion currents decreased markedly and in most instances passed through a flat minimum in the range from 60 to 80 per cent ethanol. The minimum currents were one-half to two-thirds of the values in pure aqueous medium. The decrease in the diffusion current of hydrogen ion is exceptionally great; in 90 per cent ethanol it is only 30 per cent of its value in pure aqueous medium. In all of the twelve cases studied Matsuyama's data show a marked variation of $i_d\eta^{1/2}$ with increasing ethanol content— clearly demonstrating that the change in viscosity is not the only factor responsible for the change in diffusion current in this mixed solvent. In all cases the product $i_d\eta^{1/2}$ first increases, then passes through a maximum in the vicinity of 20 to 25 per cent ethanol, and finally decreases markedly with further increase in the proportion of ethanol. Matsuyama attributed the inconstancy of the $i_d\eta^{1/2}$ values to changes in the effective size of the diffusing ions caused by changes in degree of solvation, and to partial association of the reducible cations with anions which appears to be favored by increasing ethanol content.

[54] I. Vavruch, *Collection Czechoslov. Chem. Communs.*, **12**, 429 (1947).

[55] H. A. McKenzie, *J. Council Sci. Ind. Research, Australia*, **21**, 210 (1948).

[56] G. Matsuyama, *Ph.D. Thesis*, University of Minnesota, 1948.

CHAPTER V

Polarography in Nonaqueous Media

Polarography is not limited to aqueous solutions but can be applied in other solvents that are sufficiently polar to provide solutions that conduct well. This is fortunate because a great many organic substances are too insoluble in water to permit their polarographic determination in purely aqueous supporting electrolytes. A very common expedient in such cases is the use of ethanol or ethanol–water solvent mixtures. The properties of ethanol and methanol are similar enough to those of water so that polarographic characteristics in them, or in their mixtures with water, usually are pretty much the same as in aqueous media.

One of the distinguishing characteristics of polarograms in nonaqueous media is that diffusion currents are generally considerably smaller than in aqueous supporting electrolytes. This results in part from the greater viscosity of most nonaqueous solvents, which decreases diffusion coefficients, and also in part from more specific influences, such as change in the nature —and hence size—of the solvated reducible species. In strongly acid (glacial acetic acid) or strongly basic (liquid ammonia) solvents unique protolytic effects are encountered, and these can produce profound mutations of the polarographic characteristics of certain substances.

Choice of supporting electrolyte usually presents much more of a problem with nonaqueous solvents than with water, chiefly because of the limited solubilities of otherwise suitable inorganic salts in most nonaqueous solvents. This problem can be minimized by employing mixtures of other solvents with water rather than the anhydrous solvents themselves. Tetraalkylammonium salts and lithium salts are among the most useful supporting electrolytes for measurements in nonaqueous media.

1. ETHANOL AND METHANOL

Ethanol and methanol, either anhydrous or mixed with water, are among the most commonly used nonaqueous solvents, and numerous examples of their use in specific cases will be found in various other sections, especially those dealing with the polarography of organic substances.

In general, diffusion currents in ethanol or ethanol–water mixtures are somewhat smaller than in water. A typical example is found in the study of Peracchio and Meloche[1] of the polarography of the alkali metal ions in ethanol–water mixtures, and in a further study by Zlotowski and Kolthoff.[2] The latter authors emphasized the advantages of 50 to 80 per cent ethanol–water mixtures over pure aqueous medium for the determination of the alkali metals.

Most recently Matsuyama[3] has very thoroughly investigated the change in diffusion current of a dozen metal ions in ethanol–water mixtures containing up to 90 per cent ethanol. His results, which have been discussed Chapter IV, definitely prove that the decreased diffusion current with increasing ethanol concentration is not due entirely to the effect of viscosity but that other factors are also operative.

Shreve and Markham[4] have systematically investigated the polarography of p-nitroaniline in ethanol–water mixtures, and their results are probably typical of those to be expected with other organic compounds in this solvent pair. With increasing proportions of ethanol up to 14 M (about 80 per cent by volume) the usual decrease in diffusion current was observed, but the general characteristics of the single 6-electron reduction wave were not very greatly altered. In various buffers of pH 1 to 9, the half-wave potential shifted in the negative direction by 100 to 200 mv., and the wave slope increased slightly as the ethanol concentration was increased from zero up to 12 M. Since the half-wave potentials were measured against an aqueous saturated calomel electrode, this shift includes any change in the liquid-junction potential as well as the change in the true reduction potential.

2. ETHYLENE GLYCOL

Gentry[5] has reported very briefly on the polarographic behavior of oxygen and several metal ions in anhydrous ethylene glycol media containing 0.07 M potassium chloride as supporting electrolyte. Oxygen undergoes the same stepwise reduction as in aqueous media. Cadmium, zinc, cupric, cuprous, ferrous, and thallous ions all produce well-developed normal waves

[1] E. S. Peracchio and V. W. Meloche, *J. Am. Chem. Soc.*, **60**, 1770 (1938).

[2] I. Zlotowski and I. M. Kolthoff, *J. Am. Chem. Soc.*, **64**, 1297 (1942); *Ind. Eng. Chem., Anal. Ed.*, **14**, 473 (1942).

[3] G. Matsuyama, *Ph.D. Thesis*, University of Minnesota, 1948.

[4] O. D. Shreve and E. C. Markham, *J. Am. Chem. Soc.*, **71**, 2993 (1949).

[5] C. H. R. Gentry, *Nature*, **157**, 479 (1946).

whose half-wave potentials closely parallel the values in aqueous medium. The diffusion current of thallous ion (and presumably those of the other metal ions) is directly proportional to concentration. Because of the relatively great viscosity of ethylene glycol the diffusion current constants are only about one-fourth as large as in aqueous medium. Aside from this decreased sensitivity, the properties of ethylene glycol as a polarographic solvent appear to be very satisfactory.

In mixed water–ethylene glycol media the diffusion current of thallous ion is inversely proportional to the square root of the viscosity coefficient.

3. GLACIAL ACETIC ACID

A preliminary study by MacGillavry[6] of anhydrous acetic acid as a polarographic solvent did not yield conclusive results. A more systematic investigation by Bachman and Astle[7] emphasizes some of the difficulties attending the use of this solvent.

The solubility of oxygen in acetic acid is greater than in water and thorough removal of dissolved air is even more essential than with aqueous media. The relatively large resistance of solutions in acetic acid tends to distort the wave forms, and correction for iR drop through the cell is important. Third, the reduction of the solvated hydrogen ion occurs relatively easily in acetic acid and limits this solvent to substances whose half-wave potentials are more positive than about -1.4 v. vs. S.C.E.

Using 0.25 M ammonium acetate as supporting electrolyte Bachman and Astle found that metal ions whose half-wave potentials are more negative than -0.3 v. vs. S.C.E. (Cd^{++}, Zn^{++}, Co^{++}, Cr^{+++}, Sb^{+++}, and Pb^{++}) yield normal waves whose diffusion currents are directly proportional to concentration. The half-wave potentials (referred to the aqueous saturated calomel electrode) of these metal ions are 0.1 to 0.25 v. more negative than in aqueous medium. The diffusion current constants in acetic acid are about two-thirds as large as in aqueous solutions, due to the greater viscosity of glacial acetic acid. Benzil and benzoin produce normal reduction waves in 0.25 M ammonium acetate with half-wave potentials of -0.6 and -1.2 v. vs. S.C.E., respectively.

Cupric ion, ferric ion, mercuric ion, $+4$ lead, and quinone (all of which are reduced at a potential more positive than -0.3 v.) produce waves which are distorted by very large maxima and abrupt discontinuities which render the curves unsuitable for practical purposes.

---

[6] D. MacGillavry, Trans. Faraday Soc., **32**, 1447 (1936).
[7] G. B. Bachman and M. J. Astle, J. Am. Chem. Soc., **64**, 1303 (1942).

4. LIQUID AMMONIA

Systematic investigations of liquid ammonia as a polarographic solvent have been carried out by Laitinen in collaboration with Nyman,[8] by Laitinen and Shoemaker,[9] and by Nyman,[10] with most interesting results.

More or less conventional cells were employed and solutions were prepared by condensing purified ammonia into the cell at $-36°$ C. All measurements were made in a thermostat at $-36.0 \pm 0.2°$ C. At this temperature the vapor pressure of ammonia (665 mm.) is far enough below atmospheric pressure so that the handling of the solutions presents no great difficulties. The choice of supporting electrolyte is somewhat of a problem due to the limited solubilities in liquid ammonia of salts comprising sufficiently difficultly reducible cations. Tetraalkylammonium salts were found to be fairly satisfactory.

Using a saturated solution of tetrabutylammonium iodide (0.0057 M) as supporting electrolyte Laitinen and Nyman observed that the alkali metal ions undergo reversible reduction to the metallic state and produce well-developed diffusion currents which obey the Ilkovic equation. The half-wave potentials against a lead–0.1 N lead nitrate reference electrode are Li, -1.67 v.; Na, -1.31 v.; K, -1.24 v.; Rb, -1.21 v.; and Cs, -1.15 v. The observed diffusion currents of 0.001 M lithium, sodium, rubidium, and cesium ions averaged 10 to 12 per cent larger than the values predicted by the Ilkovic equation; with potassium ion the observed value was 2 per cent high. This was logically attributed to the fact that the supporting electrolyte concentration was too small (0.0057 M) to completely eliminate the migration current. The diffusion coefficients of the alkali metal ions in liquid ammonia at $-36°$ are about five times larger than in aqueous media at 25°, and correspondingly the diffusion current constants are two to three times greater.

Laitinen and Shoemaker concluded that mercuric ion in liquid ammonia is reversibly reduced to the metal, and that mercurous ion is unstable in this solvent and disproportionates to mercuric ion and mercury. The potential of a mercury pool anode is independent of the concentration of nitrate, chloride, iodide, or ammonium ions and depends only on the mercuric ion concentration, indicating that the corresponding mercuric salts are soluble, and—in the case of ammonium ion—that no appreciable solvolysis occurs to form species such as $HgNH_2^+$.

The same authors recommended thallous ion as a pilot ion to define the

[8] H. A. Laitinen and C. J. Nyman, *J. Am. Chem. Soc.*, **70**, 2241, 3002 (1948).

[9] H. A. Laitinen and C. E. Shoemaker, *J. Am. Chem. Soc.*, **72**, 663 (1950).

[10] C. J. Nyman, *J. Am. Chem. Soc.*, **71**, 3914 (1949).

polarographic potential scale in liquid ammonia. The reduction wave of thallous ion shows a rounded maximum but this can be suppressed by a trace of methyl cellulose.

Laitinen and Nyman showed that the dropping mercury electrode functions as an "electron electrode" in liquid ammonia when the cation of the supporting electrolyte is nonreducible. Under this condition the cathodic reaction is the dissolution of electrons from the electrode.

5. MOLTEN SALT MEDIA

Some very interesting results on the polarography of metal ions in molten salt media have been reported by Nachtrieb and Steinberg.[11] The melt used was a ternary eutectic composed of 66.65 mole per cent ammonium nitrate, 25.76 per cent lithium nitrate, and 7.59 per cent ammonium chloride, the melting point being 86.2° C. Experiments were performed at 125.0 ± 0.5° C., using a conventional dropping mercury electrode and a mercury pool anode.

Normal reduction waves were obtained with nickel (II), copper (II), and bismuth (III); the waves of the latter two exhibited maxima, but in the case of copper the maximum could be eliminated by addition of a trace of potassium iodide. The limiting currents were diffusion controlled and directly proportional to the metal salt concentration. In the case of nickel nitrate between 2 and 13 millimolar the observed value of $i_d/Cm^{2/3}t^{1/6}$ was 1.18 ± 0.04. This corresponds to a diffusion coefficient at 125° of 9.2 × 10^{-7} cm.^{2} sec.$^{-1}$, which is about one-eighth the value for the aquo nickel ion in aqueous media at 25°.

The use of solid microelectrodes in molten salts has been studied by Lyalikov and Karmazin.[12] A platinum point electrode surrounded by an open-end glass tube was used. An inert gas bubbled through the mantle tube causes periodic, intermittent immersion of the electrode. Molten potassium nitrate (m.p. 333°) was used in most of the experiments and fused potassium pyrosulfate in a few other cases. Cadmium, copper, and nickel salts in molten potassium nitrate produce more or less normal c.v. curves whose limiting currents were directly proportional to the metal salt concentration up to concentrations of a few tenths of a millimole per mole of potassium nitrate, but which deviated from linearity in the direction of being relatively too large with larger metal salt concentrations. It was claimed that phosphate ion (present as Na_3PO_4) produces a wave in molten potassium nitrate and that this wave is suppressed by addition of

[11] N. H. Nachtrieb and M. Steinberg, J. Am. Chem. Soc., 70, 2613 (1948).
[12] Yu. S. Lyalikov and V. I. Karmazin, Zavodskaya Lab., 14, 138, 144 (1948).

barium nitrate.   No reduction waves were observed with cupric sulfate or nickelous sulfate in molten potassium pyrosulfate.

The decomposition potentials of several metal chlorides in molten mixtures of aluminum chloride and sodium chloride have been determined polarographically by Delimars'kii, Skobets, and Berenblyum.[13]

[13] Yu. K. Delimars'kii, E. M. Skobets, and L. S. Berenblyum, *J. Phys. Chem.* (*U. S. S. R.*), **22,** 1108 (1948).

CHAPTER VI

Unusual Diffusion Current Phenomena

1. INTERFERING ELECTRODE REACTIONS

When a mixture of reducible substances is electrolyzed at a potential at which all are reduced the total diffusion current will usually be the sum of the diffusion currents that each substance would produce in the same supporting electrolyte if it were present alone at the same concentration as in the mixture. In other words, the several electrode reactions usually proceed without interfering with each other. If this were not generally true polarographic analysis would be of very little practical value.

However, this rule is not invariably true. There are instances in which the reduction product of one reaction may react with another reducible substance in a manner that prevents the reduction of the second substance more or less completely. When this occurs the total diffusion current will be smaller than expected from the additivity principle.

An interesting case of interfering electrode reactions is observed with mixtures of iodate ion and cadmium ion in a neutral, unbuffered supporting electrolyte.[1] Curve *1* in Fig. VI-1 is the polarogram of a 0.500 millimolar solution of potassium iodate in neutral 0.1 M potassium chloride, and curve *2* was obtained with the same concentration of iodate ion in the same supporting electrolyte but with 1.89 millimolar cadmium sulfate added. The cadmium wave in curve *2* at −0.6 v. is normal in all respects, but the iodate wave is scarcely visible. The total current at potentials at which the iodate ion is reduced is far smaller than the sum of the individual diffusion currents of the iodate ion and cadmium ion. On the other hand, with a mixture of thallous ion and iodate ion in neutral 0.1 M potassium chloride the additivity principle is obeyed, as shown by the polarograms in Fig. VI-2.

At first glance it might be thought that cadmium ion interferes in some way with the reduction of iodate ion, preventing its complete reduction, but this is not true. The contribution of iodate ion to the total diffusion current in the mixture is exactly the same as in the absence of cadmium ion, and it is actually the contribution of cadmium ion to the total current that is greatly decreased at potentials at which the iodate ion is reduced.

---

[1] J. J. Lingane, *Ph.D. Thesis*, University of Minnesota, 1938.

In a neutral and unbuffered supporting electrolyte the reduction of iodate ion liberates hydroxide ion at the surface of the dropping electrode

$$IO_3^- + 3H_2O + 6e \rightleftharpoons I^- + 6OH^- \tag{1}$$

As cadmium ion diffuses up to the electrode surface it meets the outwardly

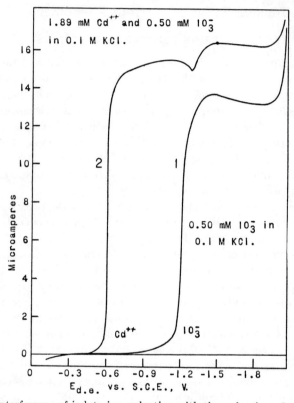

Fig. VI-I. Interference of iodate ion reduction with the reduction of cadmium ion.

diffusing hydroxide ion in the diffusion layer and cadmium hydroxide precipitates

$$Cd^{++} + 2OH^- \rightleftharpoons Cd(OH)_2 \tag{2}$$

Consequently when the potential of the d.e. is made sufficiently negative so that iodate ion is reduced, an amount of cadmium ion equivalent to the hydroxyl ion produced is removed from the solution and the contribution of cadmium ion to the total current is diminished correspondingly. When increasing amounts of cadmium ion are added to a neutral unbuffered iodate solution the current at -1.5 v. remains virtually constant until an excess of cadmium ion is present, and it then increases in direct proportion to the excess cadmium ion concentration.   This phenomenon is not observed

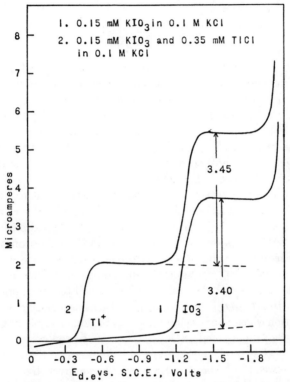

Fig. VI-2. Noninterference of iodate ion and thallous ion.

with mixtures of thallous ion and iodate ion because thallous hydroxide happens to be soluble.

From the relations pertaining to diffusion to the d.e. discussed in Chapter II, the flux of iodate ion at the electrode surface is directly proportional to the quantity $C_{IO_3} D_{IO_3}^{1/2}$, and that of cadmium ion is proportional to $C_{Cd} D_{Cd}^{1/2}$, where the C values are millimolar concentrations in the body of the solution, and the D values are the respective diffusion coefficients.   Since the reduction of each iodate ion produces 6 hydroxide ions, and 2 hydroxide ions react with each cadmium ion, it is evident that equivalent amounts of hydroxide ion and cadmium ion will exist at the electrode surface when

$$C_{Cd}D_{Cd}^{1/2} = 3C_{IO_3}D_{IO_3}^{1/2} \tag{3}$$

If the precipitation of cadmium hydroxide were complete, then the total current at -1.5 v. would remain constant until

$$\frac{C_{Cd}}{C_{IO_3}} = 3\left(\frac{D_{IO_3}}{D_{Cd}}\right)^{1/2} \tag{4}$$

and would only increase when the ratio C_{Cd}/C_{IO_3} exceeded $3(D_{IO_3}/D_{Cd})^{1/2}$. At infinite dilution at 25° the diffusion coefficient of iodate ion is 1.09×10^{-5} and that of cadmium ion is 0.72×10^{-5} cm.² sec.⁻¹, from which the theoretical critical value of the concentration ratio is 3.44. The observed critical concentration ratio agrees reasonably well with this predicted value. For example, the ratio C_{Cd}/C_{IO_3} for curve *2* in Fig. VI-1 is $1.89/0.50 = 3.78$, and, as expected, the total current at -1.5 v. is somewhat greater than the diffusion current of the iodate alone.

Actually the precipitation of cadmium hydroxide will not be perfectly complete (the solubility of cadmium hydroxide in pure water at 25° is 1.8×10^{-5} M). Consequently the current at -1.5 v. should begin to increase when the ratio C_{Cd}/C_{IO_3} is slightly smaller than the value computed above.

Since the *net* flux of cadmium ion at the electrode surface is proportional to $C_{Cd}D_{Cd}^{1/2} - 3C_{IO_3}D_{IO_3}^{1/2}$, and the reduction of cadmium ion requires 2 electrons, the net contribution of cadmium ion to the total current will be proportional to $2(C_{Cd}D_{Cd}^{1/2} - 3C_{IO_3}D_{IO_3}^{1/2})$. Because 6 electrons are involved in the reduction of each iodate ion the contribution of iodate ion to the total current will be proportional to $6C_{IO_3}D_{IO_3}^{1/2}$. The proportionality constants are defined by the Ilkovic equation, and it follows that the total current at potentials between -1.5 and -1.8 v. should be given by

$$i = 607m^{2/3}t^{1/6}[2(C_{Cd}D_{Cd}^{1/2} - 3C_{IO_3}D_{IO_3}^{1/2}) + 6C_{IO_3}D_{IO_3}^{1/2}] \tag{5}$$

with the proviso, of course, that the term $(C_{Cd}D_{Cd}^{1/2} - 3C_{IO_3}D_{IO_3}^{1/2})$ cannot have a negative value and hence is taken as zero when $3C_{IO_3}D_{IO_3}^{1/2}$ is greater than $C_{Cd}D_{Cd}^{1/2}$. When $C_{Cd}D_{Cd}^{1/2}$ is greater than $C_{IO_3}D_{IO_3}^{1/2}$ the total current should be the same as in a solution containing cadmium ion alone at the same concentration. Conversely, when $C_{IO_3}D_{IO_3}^{1/2}$ is greater than $C_{Cd}D_{Cd}^{1/2}$ the total current will be the same as in a solution containing iodate ion alone at the same concentration.

Another example of mutually interfering electrode reactions was discovered by Kolthoff and Miller[2] in the simultaneous reduction of oxygen

---

[2] I. M. Kolthoff and C. S. Miller, *J. Am. Chem. Soc.*, **63**, 1013 (1941).

and hydrogen ions, as illustrated in Fig. VI-3.   Curve II is the polarogram of an air-free 1 millimolar solution of hydrochloric acid in 0.1 N potassium chloride, and curve I was obtained after saturating the solution with air. At potentials between -1.7 and -1.8 v. the total current is seen to be virtually the same in the presence as in the absence of oxygen.   At -1.7 v. the reduction of oxygen proceeds according to

$$O_2 + 2H_2O + 4e \rightleftharpoons 4OH^- \tag{6}$$

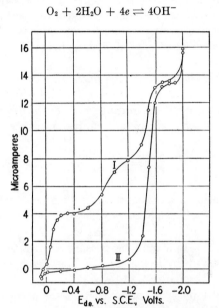

Fig. VI-3. Influence of the preceding discharge of oxygen on the diffusion current of hydrogen ion: (II) air-free 0.001 N HCl, containing a trace of methyl red; (I) after saturating the solution with air.

when the solution is neutral and unbuffered, or according to

$$O_2 + 4H^+ + 4e \rightleftharpoons 2H_2O \tag{7}$$

when excess hydrogen ion is present (as in Fig. VI-3).   Thus the hydroxide ion produced by the reduction of oxygen combines with an equivalent amount of hydrogen ion in the diffusion layer at the electrode, and the contribution of hydrogen ion to the total current is diminished correspondingly.

When either increasing amounts of hydrogen ion are added to an oxygen-containing solution, or increasing amounts of oxygen are dissolved in a solution of a strong acid, the total current at -1.7 v. remains virtually constant until the flux of hydrogen ion at the electrode surface is 4 times the flux of oxygen, that is, until $4C_{O_2}D_{O_2}^{1/2} = C_H D_H^{1/2}$.   With an excess of either hydrogen ion or oxygen the total current at -1.7 v. is the same as if the other were absent.

The total current at -1.7 v. should obey the relation

$$i = 607m^{2/3}t^{1/6}[(C_H D_H^{1/2} - 4C_{O_2}D_{O_2}^{1/2}) + 4C_{O_2}D_{O_2}^{1/2}] \qquad (8)$$

with the proviso that the quantity $C_H D_H^{1/2} - 4C_{O_2}D_{O_2}$ cannot be negative, and hence is set equal to zero when an excess of oxygen is present. When an excess of oxygen is present the entire term in square brackets reduces to $4C_{O_2}D_{O_2}^{1/2}$, and when an excess of hydrogen ion is present it becomes simply $C_H D_H^{1/2}$.

Lingane and Davis[3] found that this phenomenon could be used as the basis of an amperometric titration of oxygen with hydrogen ion. The current at -1.7 v. remains constant until the ratio of the oxygen and hydrogen ion concentrations in the body of the solution becomes

$$\frac{C_H}{C_{O_2}} = 4\left(\frac{D_{O_2}}{D_H}\right)^{1/2} \qquad (9)$$

and it then increases in direct proportion to the excess hydrogen ion added. Since the diffusion coefficients of oxygen and hydrogen ion are,[4, 5] respectively, 2.6×10^{-5} and 8.7×10^{-5} cm.^{2} sec.$^{-1}$, the end point is observed when $C_H = 2.17C_{O_2}$. It should be possible to titrate other substances whose reduction uses up hydrogen ion, or liberates hydroxide ion at the electrode surface, in this manner.

Kolthoff and Miller (loc. cit.) observed that the hydroxide ion liberated at the electrode surface during the reduction of oxygen from a neutral unbuffered solution decreases the apparent diffusion current of cadmium ion due to the partial precipitation of cadmium hydroxide. The same effect would doubtless be obtained with any metal ion whose hydroxide is insoluble.

Lingane and Niedrach[6] observed other examples of interfering electrode reactions with mixtures of $+4$ selenium or $+4$ tellurium and metal ions. Curve a in Fig. VI-4 was obtained with 1 millimolar $+4$ selenium (selenite ion) alone in 1 M ammonium chloride–ammonia at pH $= 8.4$ in the presence of 0.003 per cent gelatin as a maximum suppressor. The well-developed

[3] J. J. Lingane and O. L. Davis, unpublished experiments, University of California, 1941.

[4] I. M. Kolthoff and C. S. Miller, J. Am. Chem. Soc., **63**, 1013 (1941).

[5] J. J. Lingane and R. L. Pecsok, J. Am. Chem. Soc., **71**, 425 (1949).

[6] J. J. Lingane and L. W. Niedrach, J. Am. Chem. Soc., **71**, 196 (1949).

wave at -1.4 v. results from the reduction

$$SeO_3^{--} + 6H^+ + 6e = Se^{--} + 3H_2O \tag{10}$$

the hydrogen ion being furnished by the dissociation of ammonium ion, $NH_4^+ = NH_3 + H^+$. Curves b, c, and d were obtained in the presence of 0.302, 1.00, and 2.00 millimolar $+2$ copper, and they show the familiar doublet wave of the tetramminocupric ion preceding the selenium wave.

With increasing amounts of copper the *apparent* height of the selenium wave decreases because at potentials more negative than -1.4 v. the

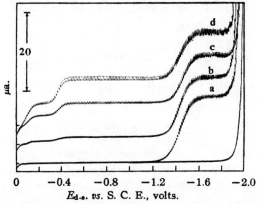

Fig. VI-4. Polarograms of 1 millimolar selenium (IV) in 1 M ammonium chloride–ammonia at pH 8.4 with (*a*) 0, (*b*) 0.302, (*c*) 1.00, and (*d*) 2.00 millimolar copper (II). Gelatin (0.003 per cent) was used as maximum suppressor. The galvanometer zero for each curve is indicated by the short marks on the left-hand ordinate.[6]

selenide ion produced at the electrode surface by the reduction of the selenite ion reacts with the incoming tetramminocupric ion in the diffusion layer, precipitating cupric selenide

$$Cu(NH_3)_4^{++} + Se^{--} = CuSe + 4NH_3 \tag{11}$$

Thus, there is no actual diminution of the diffusion current of the selenite ion, but rather a decreased contribution of copper to the total diffusion current at potentials at which the selenite ion is reduced. With increasing amounts of copper the total current at -1.6 to -1.8 v. remains nearly constant until the quantity $CD^{1/2}$ for the tetramminocupric ion becomes equal to the corresponding quantity for the selenite ion, and the total current then increases in direct proportion to the copper added in excess.

In the preceding examples one interfering ion (hydroxide ion) was pro-

duced for each electron absorbed, and hence an excess of the more easily
reduced substance (cadmium ion in the cadmium–iodate case, and oxygen
in the oxygen–hydrogen ion case) completely masked the wave of the more
difficultly reduced substance (iodate or hydrogen ion). The selenite–copper
case is different in that only one selenide ion is produced per 6 electrons
consumed (reaction 10), and this is the reason why the selenite wave does
not disappear when an excess of copper is present.

The total current at -1.6 to -1.8 v. with mixtures of selenite ion and
tetramminocupric ion is given by

$$i = 607m^{2/3}t^{1/6}[2(C_{Cu}D_{Cu}^{1/2} - C_{Se}D_{Se}^{1/2}) + 6C_{Se}D_{Se}^{1/2}] \tag{12}$$

or

$$i = 607m^{2/3}t^{1/6}(2C_{Cu}D_{Cu}^{1/2} + 4C_{Se}D_{Se}^{1/2}) \tag{13}$$

when $C_{Cu}D_{Cu}^{1/2}$ is greater than $C_{Se}D_{Se}^{1/2}$. When $C_{Cu}D_{Cu}^{1/2}$ is less than $C_{Se}D_{Se}^{1/2}$
the total current is

$$i = 607m^{2/3}t^{1/6}(6C_{Se}D_{Se}^{1/2}) \tag{14}$$

and thus is the same as in the absence of copper.

When a selenite solution is titrated amperometrically with cupric ion in
ammoniacal medium the current at -1.6 v. should remain nearly constant
until

$$C_{Cu} = C_{Se}\left(\frac{D_{Se}}{D_{Cu}}\right)^{1/2} \tag{15}$$

In terms of the respective diffusion current constants $607nD^{1/2}$ (experimentally determinable as $i_d/Cm^{2/3}t^{1/6}$) eq. 15 becomes

$$C_{Cu} = C_{Se}\left(\frac{I_{Se}}{3I_{Cu}}\right) \tag{16}$$

According to Lingane and Niedrach (loc. cit.) $I_{Se} = 11.0$ microamp. liter
sec.$^{1/2}$ millimole^{-1} mg.$^{-1}$ in 1 M ammonium chloride–ammonia of pH = 8.4
at 25°, and $I_{Cu} = 3.75$ in the same medium.[7] Therefore the end point should
occur when $C_{Cu} = 0.98C_{Se}$ if the precipitation of cupric selenide is complete.

From eq. 13 the apparent height of the selenite wave alone in the presence
of excess copper should be proportional to $4C_{Se}D_{Se}^{1/2}$, whereas in the absence

---

[7] J. J. Lingane, Ind. Eng. Chem., Anal. Ed., **15**, 589 (1943).

of copper it is proportional to $6C_{Se}D_{Se}^{1/2}$.   Therefore, with increasing amounts of copper the apparent height of the selenite wave should decrease to two-thirds of its initial value and then remain constant after excess copper is present.   Lingane and Niedrach found that the selenite wave decreased to 72 per cent of its initial value, which indicates that the precipitation of cupric selenide is not quite complete.

Lingane and Niedrach also observed that the apparent height of the reduction wave of +4 tellurium in strongly alkaline medium was decreased in the presence of hydrogen plumbite ion, as shown in Fig. VI-5.   The wave

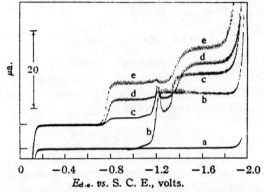

Fig. V-5. Polarograms of 1 millimolar tellurium (IV) in 1 M sodium hydroxide containing 0.003 per cent gelatin with (a) 0, (b) 0.30, (c) 1.20, and (d) 2.00 millimolar lead ion added.[6]

at −1.2 v. corresponds to

$$TeO_3^{--} + 3H_2O + 6e \rightleftharpoons Te^{--} + 6OH^- \tag{17}$$

and that at −0.8 v. to

$$HPbO_2^- + H_2O + 2e \rightleftharpoons Pb + 3OH^- \tag{18}$$

At potentials where the tellurite ion is reduced the contribution of plumbite ion to the total current decreases as a result of the precipitation of lead telluride in the diffusion layer

$$Te^{--} + HPbO_2^- + H_2O \rightleftharpoons PbTe + 3OH^- \tag{19}$$

Hence the *apparent* height of the tellurite wave decreases with increasing concentrations of plumbite ion until $C_{Pb}D_{Pb}^{1/2}$ becomes equal to $C_{Te}D_{Te}^{1/2}$, and it then remains constant.   The expressions for the total current at −1.6 v. are identical in form with eqs. 12 and 14.

It is evident that the apparent height of the tellurite wave alone in the presence of excess plumbite ion should be two-thirds of its initial value in the absence of lead, and this is exactly what is observed. With 1 millimolar tellurite ion the apparent height of the tellurite wave was 81, 69, 68, and 66 per cent of its original value when the respective concentrations of plumbite ion were 0.30, 0.70, 1.20, and 2.00 millimolar. Evidently, the precipitation of lead telluride in the diffusion layer is virtually complete, and the amperometric titration of tellurite ion with plumbite ion should yield accurate results.

Addition of copper, $Cu(OH)_4^{--}$, to a strongly alkaline tellurite solution produces the same effect as plumbite ion.

2. THE "WATER CURRENT"

Orlemann and Kolthoff[8, 9] discovered that under certain conditions an anomalous current is observed with the d.e. at potentials more negative than -0.9 v. $vs.$ S.C.E.   They attributed this current to the direct combination of electrons and water molecules in an adsorbed layer on the electrode surface

$$H_2O + e \rightarrow \tfrac{1}{2}H_2 + OH^- \tag{20}$$

That this "water current" is not due merely to stirring at the electrode surface was established by experiments which showed that hydroxide ion is produced at the electrode surface when the anomalous current is observed.

The water current is observed only when the concentration of the neutral unbuffered supporting electrolyte (alkali and alkaline earth chlorides and alkali metal nitrates) is greater than 0.5 M, and when a current due to the reduction of some other substance is flowing.   Addition of small amounts of gelatin and other substances that are strongly adsorbed on the surface of the d.e. eliminates the water current.

Orlemann and Kolthoff observed that the anomalous current does not appear when a small stationary mercury electrode is used.   They concluded that water molecules are brought into an adsorbed layer at the electrode surface only during the establishment of the electrical double layer, and therefore only when the electrode area is continually increasing.   This interpretation assumes that water molecules are rendered reducible by virtue of the polarization which they undergo when they are present in an adsorbed layer on the electrode surface.

---

[8] E. F. Orlemann and I. M. Kolthoff, *J. Am. Chem. Soc.*, **64,** 833 (1942).

[9] I. M. Kolthoff and E. F. Orlemann, *Ind. Eng. Chem., Anal. Ed.*, **14,** 321 (1942).

It was found that the water current, i_{H_2O}, is related to the total current i and to the characteristics of the d.e. by the equation

$$i_{H_2O} = \frac{ki}{m^{1/3}t^{4/3}} \tag{21}$$

3. HYDROLYSIS CURRENT OF METAL IONS

In unbuffered solutions of certain metal salts the hydrogen ion produced by "hydrolysis" of the metal ion contributes to the total diffusion current at potentials more negative than the reduction potential of hydrogen ion (ca. -1.4 v. vs. S.C.E.). For example, polarograms obtained with chromic chloride in unbuffered potassium chloride or sodium perchlorate as supporting electrolytes show two reduction waves, the first of which results from $Cr^{+++} + e \rightleftharpoons Cr^{++}$ and the second from $Cr^{++} + 2e \rightleftharpoons Cr$ (or $Cr^{+++} + 3e \rightleftharpoons Cr$). The height of the first wave is directly proportional to the concentration of chromic chloride, but the second wave is considerably larger than twice the height of the first. The height of the second wave is not directly proportional to the concentration of chromic chloride, but becomes increasingly too large with decreasing chromic chloride concentration. This is due to the fact that the aquochromic ion is a weak acid and undergoes appreciable protolytic ionization ("hydrolysis")

$$Cr(H_2O)_6{}^{+++} \rightleftharpoons Cr(OH)(H_2O)_5{}^{++} + H^+; \quad K = 1.58 \times 10^{-4} \tag{22}$$

and the hydrogen ion thus produced contributes to the total diffusion current at potentials at which the second chromic ion wave occurs,

$$2H^+ + 2e \rightleftharpoons H_2 \tag{23}$$

Because the concentrations of hydrogen ion and hydrolyzed chromic ion are equal in the body of the solution, and the hydrogen ion which diffuses up to the surface of the d.e. is neutralized by the hydroxyl ion liberated at the electrode surface by reduction of the hydrolyzed chromic ion

$$Cr(OH)(H_2O)_5{}^{++} + 3e \rightleftharpoons Cr + 5H_2O + OH^- \tag{24}$$

as well as by the reversal of the hydrolytic equilibrium (eq. 22) in the diffusion layer, there would be no net contribution at all of hydrogen ion to the total diffusion current if the diffusion coefficients of hydrogen ion and chromic ion were equal. The observed "hydrolysis current" results from the fact that the diffusion coefficient of hydrogen ion is much larger than that of chromic ion.

Lingane and Pecsok[10] demonstrated that the hydrolysis current (excess

---

[10] J. J. Lingane and R. L. Pecsok, J. Am. Chem. Soc., **71**, 425 (1949).

height of the second chromic wave) can be interpreted quantitatively by the equation

$$i_H = 605(D_H^{1/2} - D_{Cr}^{1/2})C_H m^{2/3} t^{1/6} \qquad (25)$$

or the equivalent relation

$$i_H = (I_H - I_{Cr})C_H m^{2/3} t^{1/6} \qquad (26)$$

where D_H and D_{Cr} are the diffusion coefficients of hydrogen ion and hydrolyzed chromic ion, I_H and I_{Cr} are the corresponding diffusion current constants ($605D^{1/2}$) and C_H is the equilibrium concentration of hydrogen ion in the body of the hydrolyzed solution.

Since the degree of hydrolysis increases with increasing dilution, the *relative* value of i_H increases with decreasing concentration of the chromic salt. Consequently, a nonlinear dependence of total diffusion current on concentration results with unbuffered solutions of hydrolyzable metal ions, when the current is measured at potentials more negative than the reduction potential of hydrogen ion, and hence buffered solutions should be employed in practical determinations of such metals.

4. COMPENSATING ANODIC-CATHODIC DIFFUSION CURRENTS

Consider a substance A which is reduced at the d.e. to produce a cathodic wave (positive current)

$$A + ne \rightarrow B \qquad (27)$$

and another substance C which is oxidized at the d.e. to produce an anodic wave (negative current)

$$C \rightarrow D + me \qquad (28)$$

If the reduction potential (half-wave potential) of A is more positive than the oxidation potential of C, then ordinarily if A and C were mixed in solution the direct reaction

$$mA + nC \rightarrow B + D \qquad (29)$$

would occur, and a polarogram of the mixture would show only a diminished cathodic wave of A if excess A had been added, a diminished anodic wave of C if excess C had been added, or no wave at all if A and C had been mixed in their exact stoichiometric ratio m/n.

This is the usual result when the thermodynamic condition for direct reaction is satisfied (reduction potential of A more positive than oxidation potential of C).   In some cases, however, even though this thermodynamic condition is satisfied, the *rate* of the reaction between A and C is so very slow that a polarogram of the mixture shows both the cathodic wave of A and the anodic wave of C.   In such cases the cathodic current of A and the anodic current of C compensate each other over the range of potentials between the two half-wave potentials, and the *net* current may be either cathodic, anodic, or zero depending on whether A is present in excess, C is present in excess, or they are present in equivalent concentrations.

This interesting phenomenon was first recognized by Kolthoff and Mil-

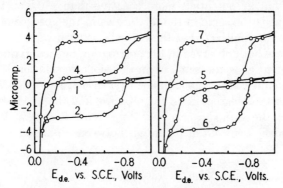

Fig. VI-6. Experimental current–voltage curves of oxygen (curves *3* and *7*) sulfide ion in absence of air (curves *2* and *6*), and composite curves (curves *4* and *8*) in alkaline sulfide solutions saturated with air.   Curves *1* and *5* are the residual current curves.   Curves *2* and *4* were obtained with 7×10^{-4} *M* sulfide ion, and curves *6* and *8* with 9.5×10^{-4} *M* sulfide ion, in 0.1 *N* sodium hydroxide.

ler[11] with alkaline solutions containing sulfide ion and dissolved oxygen, as illustrated in Fig. VI-6.   The cathodic curves *3* and *7* were obtained in *air-saturated*, 0.1 *M* sodium hydroxide and they correspond to

$$O_2 + 2e + 2H_2O \rightleftharpoons H_2O_2 + 2OH^- \tag{30}$$

The anodic curves *2* and *6* were obtained with 0.7 and 0.95 millimolar sulfide ion, respectively, in *air-free* 0.1 *M* sodium hydroxide, and the anodic current results from

$$Hg + S^{--} \rightleftharpoons HgS + 2e \tag{31}$$

Curves *4* and *8* resulted with 0.7 and 0.95 millimolar sulfide ion in *air-saturated* 0.1 *M* sodium hydroxide.   Curves *1* and *5* are the residual current

[11] I. M. Kolthoff and C. S. Miller, *J. Am. Chem. Soc.*, **62**, 2171 (1940).

curves of the 0.1 M sodium hydroxide without any oxygen or sulfide ion present.

Although the standard free energy change of the direct reaction

$$O_2 + Hg + 2H_2O + S^{--} \rightleftharpoons H_2O_2 + HgS + 2OH^- \tag{32}$$

is negative and very large, so that spontaneous reaction *should* occur, the rate is so slow that very little direct reaction takes place during the time required to measure the polarogram of the mixture. The decreased current at potentials between -0.2 and -0.6 v. is a result of a compensation of the cathodic oxygen current by the anodic sulfide current. This is proven by the fact that at potentials more negative than -0.8 v. the cathodic oxygen current is the same in the mixture as in the absence of sulfide ion, and by the additional fact that the cathodic oxygen wave and the anodic sulfide wave are both observed in the polarogram of the mixtures, and each half-wave potential is the same as in the separate solutions. Because of the current compensation the cathodic oxygen wave actually occurs in the anodic part of the polarogram of the mixture, and the anodic sulfide wave is reflected in the cathodic part.

The *net* diffusion current at potentials between -0.2 and -0.6 v. obeys the relation

$$i_{net} = 605 m^{2/3} t^{1/6} (2C_{O_2} D_{O_2}^{1/2} - 2C_S D_S^{1/2}) \tag{33}$$

or the equivalent equation

$$i_{net} = m^{2/3} t^{1/6} (C_{O_2} I_{O_2} - C_S I_S) \tag{34}$$

where I is the diffusion current constant $(605 n D^{1/2})$. The net diffusion current is zero (equal to the residual current) when

$$\frac{C_{O_2}}{C_S} = \left(\frac{D_S}{D_{O_2}}\right)^{1/2} = \frac{I_S}{I_{O_2}} \tag{35}$$

In curve *4* of Fig. VI-6 this critical ratio has been exceeded and the net current is cathodic, whereas in curve *8* the existing ratio is less than the critical ratio and the net current is anodic.

This behavior can be made the basis of an *amperometric titration* of oxygen with sulfide ion or *vice versa*. It is a unique type of amperometric titration because the substance titrated and the reagent do not react directly.

The current compensation phenomenon can also be utilized for the *potentiometric* titration of oxygen with sulfide ion, using the dropping electrode as indicator electrode and measuring its zero current potential against a reference electrode in the ordinary potentiometric manner. From Fig. VI-6 it is seen that the potential at which the current–voltage curve of the mixture passes through zero current undergoes a large abrupt change at the "end point." This zero current potential (or "mixed potential" according to Kolthoff and Miller) changes from -0.20 v. with 0.7 millimolar sulfide ion (curve 4) to -0.67 v. with 0.95 millimolar sulfide ion (curve 8).

Kolthoff and Miller also observed this current compensation phenomenon with mixtures of oxygen and cyanide ion in dilute sodium hydroxide, and with air-free mixtures of quinone and hydrogen cyanide in buffered solutions of pH = 4.7. In these instances the anodic current results from the "depolarization" of the d.e. by cyanide ion or hydrogen cyanide to form unionized mercuric cyanide

$$Hg + 2CN^- \rightleftharpoons HgCN_2 + 2e \qquad (36)$$

which occurs in the neighborhood of -0.6 v. *vs.* S.C.E. in neutral or alkaline media.

The influence of this compensation effect of cyanide ion on the *apparent* reduction potential of thallous ion is demonstrated in Fig. VI-7. Curve 1 was obtained with a solution of thallous chloride in dilute potassium chloride, and curve 2 resulted when an excess of potassium cyanide was added. At first glance it appears that the reduction potential of thallous ion is shifted to a more negative value in the presence of cyanide ion, but this is not true because thallous ion does not form a complex with cyanide ion. What actually occurs is that at -0.6 v. and more positive potentials cyanide ion produces its anodic current and curve 2 actually corresponds to reaction 36 above, and not to the reduction of thallous ion. The thallous ion wave occurs in the anodic part of the polarogram of the mixture, and does not appear in Fig. VI-7 because the concentration of cyanide ion is excessively large.

Another example of the compensation of anodic and cathodic currents is shown by the polarograms in Fig. VI-8 obtained by Lingane[12] with mixtures of $+2$ copper and $+2$ tin in an air-free tartrate supporting electrolyte of pH = 4.3. Curve 1 without added copper shows an anodic wave at -0.35 v. due to the 2-electron oxidation of the stannous tartrate complex to the stannic complex, and a cathodic wave at -0.6 v. resulting from the 2-electron reduction of the stannous tartrate complex to the metal. The other curves were obtained with increasing additions of $+2$ copper, which produces a cathodic wave at -0.09 v. *vs.* S.C.E. corresponding to the 2-electron reduction of the cupric tartrate complex to the metal.

---

[12] J. J. Lingane, *J. Am. Chem. Soc.*, **65**, 870 (1943).

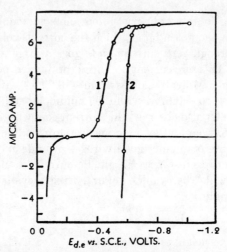

Fig. VI-7. Influence of cyanide ion on the position of the thallous ion wave. Curve *1* is a cathodic wave of thallous ion, and curve 2 was obtained after adding cyanide ion.

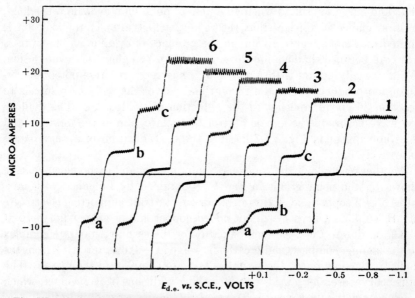

Fig. VI-8. Polarograms of mixtures of +2 copper and +2 tin in acidic tartrate supporting electrolyte, demonstrating simultaneous cathodic and anodic reactions.[12] Curve *1* recorded with 2 millimolar stannous tin alone, and others after addition of increasing amounts of copper.

From the relative half-wave potentials the stannous tartrate complex *should* reduce the cupric tartrate complex directly, but actually this reaction does not occur with a measurable speed when the solutions are mixed. However, at potentials between -0.1 and -0.3 v. the cathodic diffusion current of the cupric tartrate complex compensates the anodic diffusion current of the stannous tartrate complex.   The cathodic copper wave occurs in the anodic part a to b of the polarogram of the mixture, and with an excess of copper the anodic stannous wave is shifted to the cathodic part of the polarogram.   That no direct reaction occurs is proven by the fact that the height of the cathodic stannous wave at c, and the anodic stannous diffusion current at potentials more positive than a, are exactly the same in the mixtures as in the stannous solution alone.

A stannous solution can be titrated amperometrically with a cupric solution by measuring the net current between -0.1 and -0.3 v.   The end point is obtained when the net current becomes zero, *i. e.*, equal to the residual current of the supporting electrolyte alone, and this occurs when

$$\frac{C_{Cu}}{C_{Sn}} = \left(\frac{D_{Sn}}{D_{Cu}}\right)^{1/2} = \frac{I_{Sn}}{I_{Cu}} \tag{37}$$

The end point may also be detected potentiometrically because the zero current potential of the d.e. undergoes an abrupt positive shift of nearly 0.2 v. in going from a solution containing a slight excess of stannous tartrate complex to one containing a slight excess of the cupric tartrate complex.

CHAPTER VII
Electrical Migration Current

1. INFLUENCE OF THE CONCENTRATION OF SUPPORTING ELECTROLYTE ON LIMITING CURRENTS

In general, reducible ions reach the surface of the dropping electrode under the influence of two more or less independent forces, a diffusive force, proportional to the concentration gradient at the electrode surface, and an electrical force, proportional to the electrical potential gradient at the electrode. When an excess of supporting electrolyte is present in the solution the electrical force on the reducible ions is nullified, because the ions of the added salt carry practically all the current, and the potential gradient is shortened or compressed to a region so very close to the electrode surface that is it no longer operative to attract reducible ions. Under these conditions the limiting current is solely a diffusion current. On the other hand, when no supporting electrolyte is present the limiting current is governed by the rate of supply of reducible ions to the electrode surface by both electrical migration and diffusion. Heyrovsky[1] coined the name "migration current" to denote that fraction of the limiting current due to electrical migration of the reducible ions.

In the reduction of cations it has been found experimentally that the limiting current without any supporting electrolyte present is generally about twice as large as the diffusion current obtained after an excess of supporting electrolyte is added to the solution. When an indifferent salt is added in small amounts to a pure solution of a salt of a reducible cation the limiting current decreases most rapidly with the first small additions, and then more slowly, until it finally becomes constant and independent of further additions of the supporting electrolyte when the concentration of the latter is about 50 times larger than that of the reducible salt. This behavior is exemplified by the typical data shown in Table VII-1 for the limiting current of lead ion in various concentrations of potassium chloride, potassium nitrate, and hydrochloric acid. These data were obtained by Lingane and Kolthoff[2] and are in agreement with similar data obtained by Slendyk[3] for a variety of reducible cations.

---

[1] J. Heyrovsky, *Archiv Hem. i Farm.*, **8**, 11 (1934).

[2] J. J. Lingane and I. M. Kolthoff, *J. Am. Chem. Soc.*, **61**, 1045 (1939).

[3] I. Slendyk, *Collection Czechoslov. Chem. Communs.*, **3**, 385 (1931).

On the other hand, in the reduction of anions, *e. g.*, iodate, chromate, etc., it is found that the limiting current without supporting electrolyte present is much *smaller* than the diffusion current obtained after an excess of supporting electrolyte has been added.

In order to account for these experimental facts, Heyrovsky (*loc. cit.*) and Ilkovic[4] assumed that the total limiting current, i_l, is the algebraic sum of a diffusion current, i_d, and a migration current, i_m. In the case of cation reduction the limiting current is increased by the electrical migra-

TABLE VII-1

INFLUENCE OF VARIOUS CONCENTRATIONS OF POTASSIUM CHLORIDE POTASSIUM NITRATE, AND HYDROCHLORIC ACID ON THE LIMITING CURRENT OF LEAD CHLORIDE

50 ml. of 0.00095 M PbCl$_2$ plus 0.2 ml. of 0.1 per cent sodium methyl red, with various concentrations of added electrolytes. Temp. = 25°, $h = 21.8$ cm., $m^{2/3}t^{1/6} = 2.28$ mg.$^{2/3}$ sec.$^{-1/2}$.

Added salt, equiv. liter^{-1}	Limiting current, microamp,		
	KCl	KNO$_3$	HCl
0	17.6	17.6	17.6
0.0001	16.3	16.2	15.7
0.0002	14.9	15.0	14.6
0.0005	13.3	13.4	12.7
0.001	11.8	12.0	11.2
0.005	9.8	9.8	9.5
0.1	8.35[a]	8.45[a]	[b]
1.0	8.00[a]	8.45[a]	[b]

[a] Corrected for the residual current.
[b] Maxima present, and diffusion currents not well defined.

tion, and Heyrovsky and Ilkovic write

$$i_l = i_d + i_m \qquad \text{(cation reduction)} \qquad (1)$$

In the reduction of anions the direction of the electric field is such that anions are repelled from the electrode, and we have

$$i_l = i_d - i_m \qquad \text{(anion reduction)} \qquad (2)$$

That is, anion limiting currents are decreased by the electrical migration. In the *oxidation* of cations and anions the foregoing relations are reversed.

Heyrovsky and Ilkovic assumed that the migration current is given by the product of the transference number of the reducible ion and the *total* limiting current:

$$i_m = T_i i_l \qquad (3)$$

[4] D. Ilkovic, *Collection Czechoslov. Chem. Communs.*, **6**, 498 (1934).

where T_i is the transference number of the reducible ion in the particular solution. When no supporting electrolyte is present, the transference number will be designated by the superscript $(^0)$, $i.\ e.$, T_i^0. When indifferent electrolyte is added to the solution the transference number is decreased from T_i^0 to some smaller value, T_i, which depends on the *relative* concentrations of the reducible ions and the added electrolyte, and to a lesser degree on the charges and mobilities of all the ions concerned.

The transference number of the reducible ion decreases rapidly as indifferent salt is added, and approaches zero when the supporting electrolyte is present in large excess. For example, in a pure 0.001 molar solution of lead chloride the transference number of the lead ion is 0.48, whereas if the solution also contains 0.002 N potassium chloride $T_{Pb^{++}}$ is only about 0.25, and in the presence of 0.2 N potassium chloride it is reduced to only about 0.05. This accounts for the rapid decrease of the migration current —and hence the limiting current—when increasing concentrations of supporting electrolytes are added to a solution of a reducible cation (Table VII-1).

Heyrovsky and Ilkovic assumed that the diffusion component, i_d, of the limiting current is the same in a pure solution of a reducible salt as in a solution containing an excess of supporting electrolyte. If the initial limiting current in the complete absence of supporting electrolyte is represented by i_l^0, then on the basis of their assumption the following relations are obtained by combining eqs. 1 and 2 with eq. 3.

$$\frac{i_l^0}{i_d} = \frac{1}{1 - T_+^0} = \frac{1}{T_-^0} \qquad \text{(cation reduction)} \qquad (4)$$

$$\frac{i_l^0}{i_d} = \frac{1}{1 + T_-^0} \qquad \text{(anion reduction)} \qquad (5)$$

If the transference number of the reducible ion is exactly 0.5 the foregoing relations predict that the initial limiting current in cation reduction without supporting electrolyte present should be exactly twice as large as the diffusion current obtained in the presence of an excess of supporting electrolyte. These relations are shown schematically in Fig. VII-1.

However, the assumption of Heyrovsky and Ilkovic that the diffusion component of the limiting current is independent of the presence of supporting electrolyte is not strictly justified. Actually the diffusion current may change appreciably when the supporting electrolyte is added, due to a change in the *effective* diffusion coefficient of the reducible ions. According to the Ilkovic equation (see Chap. II)

$$i_d = 607nCm^{2/3}t^{1/6}D^{1/2} = kD^{1/2} \qquad (6)$$

From the discussion of this equation in Chapter IV it is evident that the constant k is independent of whether or not supporting electrolyte is present, provided that all other conditions are kept constant. When an excess of supporting electrolyte is present the effective diffusion coefficient, D, is the characteristic diffusion coefficient of the reducible ions

$$D_{ion} = \frac{RT}{zF_y^2} \lambda_i^0 \qquad (7)$$

However in a pure solution of a reducible salt the reducible ions are not

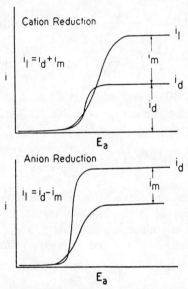

Fig. VII-1. Schematic representation of limiting currents without supporting electrolyte and diffusion currents in presence of excess supporting electrolyte for cases in which $T_i^0 = 0.500$.

free to diffuse independently of the ions of opposite sign, and consequently the effective diffusion coefficient is that of the salt itself

$$D_{salt} = \frac{RT}{F_y^2} \left(\frac{\lambda_+^0 \lambda_-^0}{\lambda_+^0 + \lambda_-^0} \right) \left(\frac{1}{z_+} + \frac{1}{z_-} \right) \qquad (8)$$

The derivation of these relations has been discussed in Chapter III.

In a pure solution of a reducible salt the diffusion current component of the limiting current, which may be designated by i_d^0, should be given by

$$i_d^0 = kD_{salt}^{1/2} \qquad (9)$$

whereas in the presence of an excess of supporting electrolyte

$$i_d = kD_{\text{ion}}^{1/2} \tag{10}$$

Since in general D_{ion} will not be equal to D_{salt} (except in the case of a salt like thallous chloride where $\lambda_+^0 = \lambda_-^0$, and $z_+ = z_-$), it is evident that in general i_d^0 should differ more or less from i_d.

By combining eqs. 9 and 10 with eqs. 1, 2, and 3, we obtain the following relations between the initial limiting current without supporting electrolyte present and the diffusion current in an excess of indifferent electrolyte

$$\frac{i_l^0}{i_d} = \left(\frac{D_{\text{salt}}}{D_{\text{ion}}}\right)^{1/2} \left(\frac{1}{1 - T_+^0}\right) \qquad \text{(cation reduction)} \tag{11}$$

$$\frac{i_l^0}{i_d} = \left(\frac{D_{\text{salt}}}{D_{\text{ion}}}\right)^{1/2} \left(\frac{1}{1 + T_-^0}\right) \qquad \text{(anion reduction)} \tag{12}$$

These equations should be more exact than eqs. 4 and 5.

MacGillavry[5] has also derived an equation for the ratio i_l^0/i_d in cation reductions. In the present notation his equation is

$$\frac{i_l^0}{i_d} = \left(1 + \frac{z_+}{z_-}\right)^{1/2} \left(1 + \frac{z_+ \delta_+^0}{z_- \delta_-^0}\right)^{1/2} \left(\frac{\delta_+^0}{\delta_+}\right)^{1/2} \left(\frac{t^0}{t}\right)^{1/6} \tag{13}$$

where δ_+^0 and δ_-^0 are the mobilities at infinite dilution of the cation and anion of the reducible salt, δ_+ is the mobility of the reducible cation in the presence of an excess of supporting electrolyte, and t^0 and t are the drop times at constant pressure without and with supporting electrolyte. Since

$$\delta_+^0 = \frac{\lambda_+^0}{z_+ F_y^2}$$

$$D_{\text{ion}} = \frac{RT}{z_i F_y^2} \lambda_i^0$$

and

$$T_+^0 = \frac{\lambda_+^0}{\lambda_+^0 + \lambda_-^0}$$

it can be shown that the *first two* terms in MacGillavry's equation are identical with eq. 11. The third term is a correction for the decrease in the mobility of the reducible cation, and the last term is a correction for the change in drop time, when supporting electrolyte is added. The change

---

[5] D. MacGillavry, *Rec. trav. chim.*, **56**, 1039 (1937); **57**, 33 (1938).

in t when the supporting electrolyte is added is small, unless the added salt is strongly capillary active, and therefore the ratio t^0/t will usually be so close to unity that the last term in eq. 13 can be neglected. The essential difference between MacGillavry's equation and eq. 11 is the correction term $(\delta_+^0/\delta_+)^{1/2}$ for the decrease in the mobility of the reducible ion when supporting electrolyte is added to the solution. This correction is justified, but for reasons already given in Chapter III our knowledge of the effect of ionic strength on ion mobilities is too incomplete at the present time to

TABLE VII-2

COMPARISON OF INITIAL LIMITING CURRENTS AND DIFFUSION CURRENTS OF VARIOUS
REDUCIBLE IONS

Reducible salt	i_l^0, microamp.	i_d, microamp.	T_i^0, calcd.	Ratio i_l^0/i_d		
				Obs.	Calcd. 1 (eq. 4)	Calcd. 2 (eq. 11)
0.001 M TlCl	11.6	6.10[a]	0.500	1.90	2.00	2.00
	11.6	5.95[b]	0.500	1.95	2.00	2.00
0.0013 M TlOH	13.9	8.15[a]	0.277	1.71	1.39	1.66
0.0026 M TlOH	26.7	15.85[a]	0.277	1.69	1.39	1.66
0.0026 M TlC$_2$H$_3$O$_2$	34.2	15.85[a]	0.646	2.16	2.83	2.37
0.0005 M TlIO$_3$	6.55 (Tl$^+$)	3.30[a]	0.646 (Tl$^+$)	1.99	2.83	2.37
0.00095 M PbCl$_2$	17.6	8.35[a]	0.483	2.11	1.93	2.39
	17.6	8.00[b]	0.483	2.20	1.93	2.39
0.001 M CdSO$_4$	12.7	8.00[a]	0.400	1.59	1.67	1.83
0.00015 M KIO$_3$	2.40 (IO$_3^-$)	3.70[a]	0.356 (IO$_3^-$)	0.65	0.74[c]	0.84[d]

[a] In 0.1 N KCl corrected for the residual current.
[b] In 0.9 N KCl corrected for the residual current.
[c] Equation 5.
[d] Equation 12.

permit a reliable calculation of the correction. It should also be realized that eqs. 11 and 12 are theoretically just as exact as eq. 13, provided that experimentally determined values of D_{ion} and D_{salt}, rather than the ideal values at infinite dilution, are used.

In order to test the foregoing equations, Lingane and Kolthoff[2] determined the initial limiting currents with no supporting electrolyte present, i_l^0, and the diffusion currents in 0.1 N or 0.9 N potassium chloride, i_d, of various thallous salts, lead chloride, cadmium sulfate, and potassium iodate (reduction of IO$_3^-$). The various thallous salts were chosen so that the transference number of the thallous ion would differ as much as possible in the various cases, and thus provide a better test of the theory. A trace of sodium methyl red was added to the solutions to eliminate maxima, and special experiments showed that this very small amount of methyl red had no appreciable effect on the limiting or diffusion currents. The results obtained are given in Table VII-2.

The transference numbers of the reducible ions in the pure solutions of the reducible salts, T_i^0, given in the fourth column of Table VII-2 were calculated from the familiar relation

$$T_i^0 = \frac{\lambda_i^0}{\lambda_+^0 + \lambda_-^0} \qquad (14)$$

where λ_+^0 and λ_-^0 are the equivalent conductances at infinite dilution of the positive and negative ions of the reducible salt. The fifth column contains the observed ratios of the initial limiting current to the diffusion current in as excess of potassium chloride. The values of this ratio computed according to the simple eqs. 4 and 5 are tabulated in the sixth column, while the last column contains the values of i_l^0/i_d computed according to eq. 11 or eq. 12.

The values of i_l^0/i_d computed according to eq. 11 or eq. 12 are in most cases in better agreement with the observed values of this ratio than the values calculated by means of eq. 4 or eq. 5. Cadmium sulfate and potassium iodate are exceptions; in these cases eq. 4 and eq. 5 gave better results. The observed values of i_l^0/i_d are in most cases smaller than the calculated values. Nevertheless, the agreement is sufficiently good to show that Heyrovsky's theory of the migration current is fundamentally sound.

It is evident from the foregoing data that the concentration of supporting electrolyte must be made at least 25 times larger than the concentration of the reducible ions in order to eliminate the migration current completely. Provided that a sufficiently large excess is present, even relatively large variations in the concentration of the supporting electrolyte do not appreciably influence the diffusion current. Hence in practical work the concentration of the supporting electrolyte need only be controlled to 25 or 50 per cent.

Finally it should be mentioned that the limiting current of an uncharged substance should be entirely a diffusion current, since neutral molecules are not subject to electrical migration. Hence the limiting current of an uncharged substance should be constant and independent of the presence of foreign salt. No experimental data on this point are available.

2. INCREASE, OR "EXALTATION," OF THE MIGRATION CURRENT BY SIMULTANEOUS DISCHARGE OF AN UNCHARGED SUBSTANCE

The migration current is equal to the product of the *total* limiting current and the transference number of the reducible ions (eq. 3). If some uncharged substance, which is reduced at a more positive potential than the reducible ion in question, is added to a pure solution of a reducible salt, the resulting total limiting current (at potentials at which the reducible ions are discharged) will be the sum of that due to the reduction of the uncharged substance and that of the reducible ions:

$$i_{total} = i_u + i_l \qquad (15)$$

where i_u is the limiting current (a diffusion current) of the uncharged substance. Under these conditions the migration current of the reducible ions will be increased, or "exalted."[6] The exalted migration current should be given by

$$i_m = (i_u + i_l)T_i \qquad (16)$$

The effect of this exaltation of the migration current will be to increase the limiting current in cation reductions, and to decrease it in anion reductions. The exaltation effect was first demonstrated by Heyrovsky and Bures[6] who found that the initial limiting currents of potassium and sodium ions in very dilute pure solutions of the alkali chlorides were increased by the preceding discharge of oxygen. The effect is shown by the curves in Fig. VII-2. Curve 1 was obtained by electrolyzing a pure $9.4 \times 10^{-4} N$ solu-

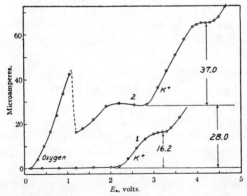

Fig. VII-2. Exaltation of the limiting current of potassium ion by the preceding discharge of oxygen.

tion of potassium chloride, from which the air had been completely removed with nitrogen, and curve 2 was obtained after saturating the solution with pure oxygen. It is seen that the limiting current of the potassium ions was increased more than twofold by the preceding discharge of the oxygen.

6 J. Heyrovsky and M. Bures, *Collection Czechoslov. Chem. Communs.*, **8**, 446 (1936).

If we represent the initial limiting current in the absence of foreign salts and without any reducible nonelectrolyte present by i_l^0, and the original migration current under the same conditions by i_m^0, then

$$i_m^0 = i_l^0 T_i^0 \tag{17}$$

The migration current during the simultaneous discharge of the uncharged substance, i_m, is given by eq. 16, and hence the exaltation of the migration current should be given by

$$i_m - i_m^0 = (i_u + i_l - i_l^0)T_i^0 \tag{18}$$

where i_l is the exalted limiting current. However, if we assume that the diffusion component of the limiting current is unaffected by the discharge of the uncharged substance, we have

$$i_m - i_m^0 = i_l - i_l^0 \tag{19}$$

and hence the exaltation of the limiting current will be equal to the exaltation of the migration current, and should be given by

$$i_l - i_l^0 = i_m - i_m^0 - i_u \left(\frac{T_+^0}{1 - T_+^0} \right) \tag{20}$$

in cation reductions. On the other hand, in anion reductions the limiting current should be *decreased* by the same amount that the migration current is increased.

It is evident from eq. 20 that the exaltation should be independent of the concentration of the reducible ions, and should increase in direct proportion to the diffusion current of the uncharged substance. In the special case that T_i^0 is exactly 0.5, the exaltation should be equal simply to the diffusion current of the uncharged substance. It should be possible to increase cation limiting currents many fold (in the complete absence of supporting electrolyte) by simply increasing the concentration of the uncharged substance (increasing i_u), and entirely to suppress anion limiting currents. However, when the total limiting current is made very large compared to the concentration of the reducible ions the electrical potential gradient at the surface of the dropping electrode will become correspondingly very large; under these conditions it is probable that the ordinary laws of ionic transfer will no longer apply.

In curve *2* of Fig. VII-2 the limiting current of oxygen, i_u, is 28.0 micro-amp. Since the transference number of the potassium ion in potassium chloride is 0.493, one calculates from eq. 20 that the exaltation of the potassium ion limiting current by the preceding discharge of oxygen should be

$$28.0 \times \frac{0.493}{0.507} = 27.2 \text{ microamp.}$$

The observed exaltation is $37.0 - 16.2 = 20.8$ microamp., and hence considerably less than the calculated value.

Lingane and Kolthoff (*loc. cit.*) found that the exaltation of the limiting current of sodium ions by the preceding discharge of oxygen was also considerably smaller than the calculated value. They attributed the discrepancies to the fact that hydroxyl ions are a product of the reduction of oxygen, and when the latter is discharging simultaneously with the alkali ions the solution close to the surface of the mercury drops is actually equivalent to a mixture of the alkali chloride and hydroxide. Hence the transference numbers of the alkali ions in the solution close to the surface of the dropping electrode are considerably less than in the pure solutions of the alkali chlorides, and the exaltation is decreased correspondingly. From the observed exaltation in the case of potassium ion (Fig. VII-2), the *effective* transference number of the potassium ion is calculated to be 0.443, instead of the value 0.493 in pure potassium chloride. From eq. 20 it will be evident that a relatively small change in the effective transference number produces a relatively large change in the exaltation effect.

Heyrovsky and Bures apparently did not recognize the necessity of correcting for the decrease in the effective transference numbers of the reducible ions due to the accumulation of hydroxyl ions, probably because they saturated their solutions with air instead of pure oxygen, in which case the correction is smaller. The reduction of uncharged molecules practically always involves hydrogen ions, which in neutral solutions must be furnished by the dissociation of water molecules, with the consequent accumulation of hydroxyl ions at the surface of the dropping electrode. Hence with practically all uncharged substances, the formation of hydroxyl ions must be taken into account in the interpretation of exaltation phenomena. Von Stackelberg[7] has recently recommended that the transference number of the alkali ions in the *pure alkali hydroxides* be used to calculate the exaltation effect. However, it is evident from the experimental data described above, and also from the data obtained by Heyrovsky and Bures, that this would lead to a large overcorrection. The effective transference number is actually intermediate between that in the pure alkali chloride and in the alkali hydroxide, and its value also depends on the rela-

---

[7] M. von Stackelberg, Z. *Elektrochem.*, **45**, 466 (1939).

tive values of i_u and the initial limiting current, $i.$ $e.$, on the relative concentrations of the uncharged substance and the reducible ions.

Heyrovsky and Bures state that they also obtained the exaltation effect with barium and manganous ions, and by using other reducible nonelectrolytes in place of oxygen, $e.$ $g.$, quinone.

From the foregoing relations it is evident that the exaltation of the sodium and potassium ion limiting currents should be directly proportional to the equivalent conductances of the two alkali ions, when the anion in both cases is the same. The exaltation of the potassium ion limiting current will therefore be considerably greater than that of the sodium ion, at a given value of i_u. The exaltation effect in individual pure solutions of potassium and sodium chlorides should be in the ratio of the equivalent conductances of the two alkali ions, namely 74/50.5 at 25°. In a mixture of potassium and sodium chlorides the observed exaltation is intermediate between the characteristic exaltations of the two alkali ions, and is directly proportional to the ratio of the two salts in the mixture. Heyrovsky and Bures recommended this behavior as a means of determining the ratio of the two alkali chlorides in a mixture of the pure salts.

3. EXALTATION OF THE MIGRATION CURRENT BY SIMULTANEOUS DISCHARGE OF ANOTHER REDUCIBLE ION

Lingane and Kolthoff[8] found that the migration current (and hence the limiting current) of a reducible cation can be exalted by the simultaneous discharge of another reducible ion, as well as by the discharge of a nonelectrolyte. This is shown by the curves in Fig. VII-3. Curve 1 was obtained with a pure 9.4×10^{-4} N potassium chloride solution, from which the air had been displaced by nitrogen. Curve 2 was obtained after addition of sufficient thallous chloride solution to make the concentration of the latter 8.3×10^{-4} N (the concentration of the potassium chloride being reduced to 8.6×10^{-4} N by the increase in volume).

Without thallous chloride present the potassium ion limiting current was 15.8 microamp. (curve 1), and it was increased to 20.1 microamp. by the preceding discharge of the thallous ion (curve 2). Without thallous chloride present the calculated diffusion current of the potassium ion was 15.8 $(1 - 0.493) = 8.0$ microamp., but it was decreased to $8.0 (8.6/9.4) = 7.3$ microamp. by the increase in volume when the thallous chloride solution was added.

Since the mobilities of the thallous, potassium, and chloride ions are practically all equal, and since the mixed solution contained practically equal concentrations of thallous chloride and potassium chloride, the trans-

---

[8] J. J. Lingane and I. M. Kolthoff, $J.$ $Am.$ $Chem.$ $Soc.$, **61**, 1045 (1939).

ference numbers of the thallous and potassium ions in the mixed solution were each equal to 0.25, while that of the chloride ions was 0.50.   Hence the diffusion current of the thallous ion in the mixed solution was 6.1 $(1 - 0.25)$ = 4.6 microamp.   Since the diffusion current of the potassium ion was 7.3 microamp., the *total* diffusion current was $4.6 + 7.3 = 11.9$ microamp. Hence the *total* observed migration current when both thallous and potassium ions were discharging was $26.2 - 11.9 = 14.3$ microamp.   Since the total cation transference number in the mixed solution was 0.50, and since the concentrations of the thallous and potassium ions were practically equal, the calculated total migration current in the mixed solution is 0.50×26.2

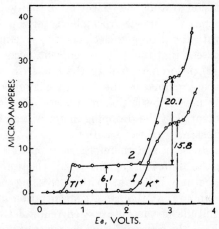

Fig. VII-3. Exaltation of the limiting current of potassium ion by the preceding discharge of thallous ion.

= 13.1 microamp., which is in fair agreement with the observed value 14.3 microamp.

It should be noted that when the potential corresponding to the limiting current of potassium ion was reached in the mixed solution, the thallous ion migration current as well as that of the potassium ion was increased by the increased current.   Hence only a part of the apparent increase in the potassium ion limiting current was actually due to the exaltation of the potassium ion migration current, and the remainder was due to the exaltation of the migration current of the thallous ions themselves when they were discharging simultaneously with the potassium ions.

It will also be noted that the calculated diffusion current of potassium ion in the above experiment (7.3 microamp.) is abnormally large compared to that of the thallous ion (4.6 microamp.).   This discrepancy needs further investigation.

CHAPTER VIII

The Electrocapillary Curve of Mercury

1. SIGNIFICANCE OF THE ELECTROCAPILLARY CURVE IN POLAROGRAPHIC WORK

The curve which expresses the relation between the potential of mercury and the surface tension at a mercury electrolyte solution interface is called the *electrocapillary curve*. The electrocapillary curve is of interest in voltammetric work with the dropping electrode for several reasons. In the first place, we have seen that the diffusion current, according to the Ilkovic equation (Chap. II), is proportional to the one-sixth power of the drop time, t. As a close approximation the drop time is proportional to the surface tension at the mercury–solution interface. The latter, in turn, depends upon the potential of the dropping mercury, and on the presence of capillary-active substances in the solution.

Since the surface tension, and therefore the drop time, changes with the applied potential, the diffusion current of an electroreducible substance does not remain entirely constant with increasing negative potential. Moreover, if we compare, at the same concentration and with the same capillary, the magnitude of the diffusion currents of two electroreducible substances which have the same diffusion coefficient but which are reduced at different potentials the two diffusion currents will not be identical. Their ratio will be equal to the ratio of the one-sixth powers of the drop times at the potentials at which the comparison is made (see Chap. IV). Also, when an electroreducible substance yields two waves both of which involve the same number of electrons the two diffusion currents will not be exactly equal, due to the difference in drop times. Let AB in Fig. VIII-1 represent the diffusion current, i_{d_1}, of the first wave (after correction for the residual current) and CD the total diffusion current (corrected for the residual current) after the second reduction is complete. Without further consideration we would conclude that $i_{d_2} = CD - AB$. However, the value thus obtained will not be exactly equal to i_{d_1}, because at the potential D the drop time t_D is different from that (t_B) at B. Hence, the value of i_{d_1} at D is not equal to AB, but

$$i_{d_1} \text{ at } D = AB \left(\frac{t_D}{t_B}\right)^{1/6}$$

Then we find for i_{d_2}

$$i_{d_2} \text{ at } D = CD - AB \left(\frac{t_D}{t_B}\right)^{1/6}$$

The values thus found for i_{d_1} at D and i_{d_2} at D should be equal after correction for the residual current. The relation between the electrocapillary curve and the diffusion current is discussed in detail in Chapter IV.

Also in connection with the magnitude of the condenser current (Chap. IX) and the appearance and suppression of maxima in current–voltage curves (see Chap. X), an understanding of electrocapillary phenomena is of great importance. For these reasons a discussion of the electrocapillary curve is given in this chapter.

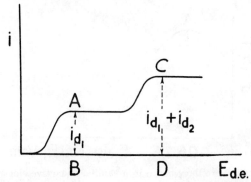

Fig. VIII-1. Schematic polarogram of a substance which is reduced in two stages both of which involve the same number of electrons.

2. THE ELECTROCAPILLARY CURVE

Lippmann[1] was the first to measure and interpret the relation between the surface tension σ and the potential difference at a mercury–electrolyte solution interface. An excellent thermodynamic discussion of the electrocapillary curve has been given by Frumkin.[2]

Lippmann had found that the surface tension of cathodically polarized mercury first increases, and then decreases again with increasing negative potential, so that the electrocapillary curve has a parabolic shape. In air-free solutions of capillary-inactive electrolytes such as potassium nitrate, the electrocapillary curve has the shape shown in Fig. VIII-2. The inter-

[1] G. Lippmann, *Pogg. Ann.*, **149**, 547 (1873); *Ann. chim. phys.*, (5) **5**, 494 (1876); **12**, 265 (1877); *Wiedemann's Ann.*, **11**, 316 (1880).

[2] A. Frumkin, *Ergeb. exakt. Naturw.*, **7**, 235 (1928). For a more modern review see D. C. Grahame, *Chem. Revs.*, **41**, 441 (1947).

facial tension σ is plotted on the ordinate and the potential of the mercury, referred to the normal calomel electrode, on the abscissa.

The total surface tension, in general, is due to two effects: (1) attractive van der Waals forces on the surface atoms or molecules which act contractively to decrease the surface area, and (2) an electrical contribution to the surface energy, due to the repulsive coulomb force between fixed surface charges, which acts to increase the surface area, and hence counteracts the van der Waals forces. As a result of this electrical effect the net interfacial tension is decreased. The change in the total surface tension according to the electrocapillary curve in the absence of capillary active substances is due entirely to the change in magnitude and sign of the electrical forces with changing applied potential. At the beginning of the curve (applied poten-

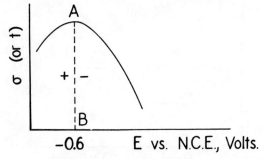

Fig. VIII-2. Electrocapillary curve in a capillary-inactive electrolyte solution.

tial equal to zero) the mercury has a positive charge which decreases the surface tension. Cathodic polarization of the mercury decreases the positive charge, and the surface tension increases until at the maximum the mercury is uncharged. In solutions of capillary-inactive electrolytes this so-called *electrocapillary maximum*, or *electrocapillary zero*, or *isoelectric point*, of mercury is at a potential of -0.56 v. against the normal calomel electrode.

The electrocapillary maximum has been the subject of extensive discussions in electrochemistry in connection with the magnitude of "absolute" or "single" potential differences at the interface electrode–solution. If the mercury at the maximum of the electrocapillary curve has a "zero potential" the absolute potential of the normal calomel electrode would be $+0.56$ v., *i. e.*, the potential difference between the positively charged mercury and the negatively charged solution. It is beyond the scope of this monograph to attempt a more elaborate discussion of the significance of the "absolute" potential.

However, it is of importance to emphasize that in the absence of capillary-active substances the surface tension has a maximum value at a potential of -0.56 v. *vs.* the N.C.E., and the *electrokinetic potential at the mercury-solution interface is zero at the maximum.* When the potential of the mercury is made more negative than -0.56 v. the metal acquires a negative charge, and consequently the surface tension decreases. Summarizing then, the mercury is positively charged to the left of AB (Fig. VIII-2), it is uncharged at the electrocapillary maximum, and it is negatively charged to the right of AB. The part of the electrocapillary curve obtained with increasing negative potential, to the left of AB, is often called the ascending part (or positive branch), and at the right of AB, the descending part (or negative branch) of the curve.

A curve almost idential with that in Fig. VIII-2 is obtained when we plot the drop time of the mercury t, instead of the surface tension σ, against the potential of the dropping mercury. The same arrangement is used as in the polarographic determination of current–voltage curves. The mercury drops into the air-free electrolyte solution (say, 0.1 N potassium chloride) and a large layer of mercury on the bottom of the cell serves as a depolarized anode. Since the solution around the anode becomes saturated with calomel, the potential of the large layer of mercury is that of the 0.1 N calomel electrode. The drop time is determined with the aid of a stop watch at various potentials. The values of the drop time plotted against the potential yield an electrocapillary curve like that in Fig. VIII-2.

At first sight it may be hard to understand why the drop time obtained at an applied potential of zero is much smaller than that at the electrocapillary maximum. The mercury in the reservoir and in the capillary is uncharged, and hence the interfacial tension of the mercury dropping into the air-free solution should have a maximum value. This is actually the case when the mercury drops freely and no short circuit is made with the anode. Henry and Jackson[3] measured the interfacial tension of mercury in the complete absence of oxygen and found at 20° C. a value of 427 dynes cm.$^{-1}$. This is in very good agreement with the value 426.4 dynes cm.$^{-1}$ found by Gouy[4] at the electrocapillary maximum.

However, when the dropping electrode is short-circuited with the large anode the large electrode impresses its potential upon the dropping electrode. Hence, positive charges flow from the anode through the external circuit to the dropping electrode, and the latter acquires almost the same positive charge (and potential) as the anode, and the interfacial tension

[3] D. C. Henry and J. Jackson, *Nature*, **142**, 616 (1938).
[4] G. Gouy, *Ann. phys.*, (9) **6**, 5 (1916).

corresponds approximately to that of the mercury in a 0.1 N calomel electrode. This matter will be mentioned again in connection with the condenser current.

Investigators who report the value of the drop time of the mercury in polarographic work should mention whether the value is obtained with or without short circuit with the large anode. If the value is determined when the system is short-circuited at an applied e.m.f. of zero, the kind of anode used should also be reported. Under such conditions the drop time will be smaller the more positive the potential of the reference electrode. When the latter has the potential of the 0.1 N or 1 N calomel electrode the drop time is about 1.14 to 1.10 times smaller with short circuit than without short circuit. For example, we found a drop time of 2.75 sec. in 0.1 N potassium chloride on short circuit, while the value at the maximum was 3.08 sec.

3. EFFECT OF CAPILLARY-ACTIVE IONS ON THE ELECTROCAPILLARY CURVE

Several inorganic anions and many organic anions and cations are capillary-active at the mercury–solution interface. Such ions lower the interfacial tension as a result of their adsorption at the surface of the mercury. Moreover, they cause a shift of the location of the electrocapillary zero. Inorganic cations are capillary-inactive, but several anions, such as bromide, thiocyanate, cyanide, iodide, and sulfide, are increasingly capillary-active in the order given. In general, anions which form slightly soluble salts or stable complex ions with mercury are the most strongly capillary-active. Chloride is only slightly capillary-active, and many other anions, such as nitrate, perchlorate, sulfate, carbonate, hydroxide, and phosphate, are practically capillary-inactive. The effect of several inorganic anions in 1 N solutions on the shape of the electrocapillary curve is shown in Fig. VIII-3.

Frumkin[5] gives the following values for the potential of the electrocapillary maximum in 1 N solutions of the following sodium or potassium salts: perchlorate, -0.55 v.; chloride, -0.56 v.; nitrate, -0.56 v.; bromide, 0.65 v.; thiocyanate, -0.72 v.; iodide, -0.82 v.; and sulfide, -0.92 v. *vs.* the N.C.E.

A few words may be said about the interpretation of the shift of the maximum by capillary-active ions, as this matter is of importance with regard to the maxima in c.v. curves. We will consider the change of the electrical potential in going from the mercury phase to the other liquid phase and start at the isoelectric point in the absence of capillary-active substances. For the sake of convenience we assume that at the isoelectric

---

[5] A. Frumkin, *Ergeb. exkat. Naturw.*, **7**, 254 (1928).

point the potential E of the mercury is equal to that of the liquid E_0. Hence the potential line has the simple shape[6] shown in Fig. VIII-4.

At the electrocapillary maximum the mercury is uncharged, and there is no electrokinetic potential. While keeping the potential of the mercury constant at -0.56 v. (*vs.* the N.C.E.), suppose that iodide is added to the air-free solution, which is devoid of mercury ions. The iodide ions are adsorbed on the surface of the mercury, and simultaneously an equivalent number of potassium ions is dragged along with the iodide ions. Only the iodide ions are capillary-active and they accumulate in the adsorbed state

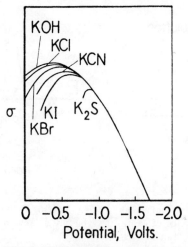

Fig. VIII-3. Electrocapillary curve in the presence of various anions (according to Gouy).

very close to the mercury surface as shown in Fig. VIII-5. The potassium ions which are capillary-inactive and which are dragged along with the iodide ions cannot come as close to the surface as the iodide ions. They are located in the so-called "diffuse double layer." The primary adsorption of iodide ions causes the establishment of a negative electrokinetic potential ζ, which is represented by ab in Fig. VIII-5. (The effective thickness of the double layer depends greatly upon the kind and concentration of ions present in the solution.)

Since mercury is a metallic conductor the presence of the negatively charged adsorbed iodide ions gives rise to considerable image forces in the mercury phase. Electrons are repelled from the surface of the mercury to the interior, and consequently the surface will contain an excess of positive

---

[6] Comp. E. J. W. Verwey, *Chem. Revs.*, **16**, 363 (1935).

charges (Fig. VIII-5). Due to the repulsion of electrons from the surface
to the interior the mercury phase would attain a potential which is more
negative than E, were it not for the fact that E is kept constant at -0.56
v. by an outside source of e.m.f.

From the above it appears that the surface of the mercury becomes positively charged in the presence of adsorbed iodide or other adsorbed anions
at a potential of -0.56 v. However, the electrocapillary zero (maximum)
can no longer be located at this same potential because the positive charge
counteracts the surface tension. Consequently, a more negative potential

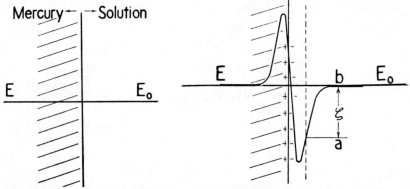

Fig. VIII-4. Potential curve at
isoelectric point in absence of capillary-active substances; the electrical potential of the mercury is assumed equal to that of the solution.

Fig. VIII-5. Potential curve at -0.56 v.
vs. the N.C.E. in the presence of iodide ion.

has to be applied to the mercury to remove the positive charge, and the
electrocapillary maximum is shifted to more negative potentials (see Fig.
VIII-3).

When the potential is made less negative than -0.56 v., the excess of
positive charge in the mercury surface will promote the adsorption of iodide
ions. The deviation of the new electrocapillary curve from the normal one,
i. e., in the absence of capillary-active substances, will become most pronounced at the extreme end of the positive branch of the curve as shown
in Fig. VIII-3. On the other hand, if the potential is made more negative
than -0.56 v. it becomes increasingly more difficult for the iodide ions to
be adsorbed. With increasing negative potential a point is finally reached
where the surface tension has a maximum and where the surface charge
has again become equal to zero. At this electrocapillary maximum in the

presence of capillary-active anions there are still adsorbed anions as shown in Fig. VIII-6. Consequently, the surface tension does not coincide with that on the normal electrocapillary curve at the same potential, but it is smaller than the latter. The potential curve is represented in Fig. VIII-6. At this potential the new electrocapillary maximum occurs; in this case the potential curve crosses the interface at E_0.

There are still some iodide ions adsorbed, and there is still a slight negative electrokinetic potential at the electrocapillary maximum in the presence of capillary active ions. If the potential of the mercury is made still more negative, it becomes increasingly more difficult for the iodide ions

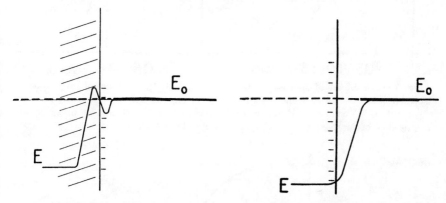

Fig. VIII-6. Potential curve at the electrocapillary maximum in the presence of capillary-active anions.

Fig. VIII-7. Potential curve to the right of the electrocapillary maximum in the presence of capillary-active anions.

to be adsorbed. Soon, the electrocapillary curve coincides with the normal one and the potential curve becomes as shown in Fig. VIII-7. At this point, where there is complete desorption of iodide ions, the entire potential drop occurs in the liquid. The surface of the mercury carries an excess of negative charges at the right side of the maximum, and the value of the negative electrokinetic potential increases. Under the latter condition, the capillary-inactive cations from the solution are drawn close to the surface by the electric field and the anions are located in the diffuse double layer.

It can easily be shown that capillary-active cations shift the location of the electrocapillary zero to less negative potentials. Inorganic cations are capillary-inactive but several organic cations (substituted amines, alkaloids) are capillary-active.

4. EFFECT OF CAPILLARY-ACTIVE NONELECTROLYTES ON THE ELECTROCAPILLARY CURVE

Several organic nonelectrolytes are capillary-active at the mercury-solution interface, and they lower the surface tension and change the electrocapillary curve. Dependent upon the nature of the capillary-active

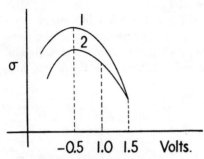

Fig. VIII-8. Effect of sucrose on the electrocapillary curve: (1) electrocapillary curve in 1 N sodium sulfate; (2) in the presence of sucrose.

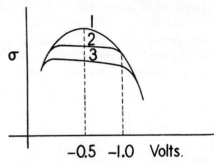

Fig. VIII-9. Influence of amyl alcohol on the electrocapillary curve: (1) normal curve; (2) and (3) in the presence of amyl alcohol.

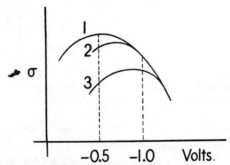

Fig. VIII-10. Electrocapillary curves in the presence of thiourea (2 and 3).

substances the shape of the electrocapillary curve may be affected in different ways.

(a) The maximum may not be shifted by the capillary-active substances and the shape of the curve remains unchanged. At a given potential the surface tension is smaller in the presence of the capillary-active substance than in its absence. As an example the electrocapillary curve in 1 N sodium sulfate, and in the latter solution in the presence of sucrose,[7] is given in Fig. VIII-8.

---

[7] Taken from A. Frumkin, *Ergeb. exakt. Naturw.*, **7**, 257 (1928).

In many instances the top part of the electrocapillary curve becomes very flat in the presence of capillary-active substances. This, for example, is the case in the presence of higher alcohols. The effect of amyl alcohol is shown in Fig. VIII-9 (according to Frumkin).

(b) The adsorbed substances are dipoles which are oriented with the negative side to the mercury. In this case the adsorbed substances induce a positive charge on the mercury (image force). The maximum of the electrocapillary curve will be shifted to more negative potentials for the same reason as in the case of iodide. Many sulfur-containing organic substances have such an effect. Electrocapillary curves in the presence of thiourea are shown in Fig. VIII-10.

(c) The dipoles of the adsorbed substances are oriented with the positive side to the mercury. In such cases, e. g., caffeine and camphor, the maximum is shifted to a more positive potential.

All curves coincide with the normal electrocapillary curve at more or less negative potentials, indicating that the capillary-active substances are desorbed at such potentials.

It is beyond the scope of this monograph to discuss the electrocapillary curves of amalgams. As this may be of some importance in polarographic work reference is made to the review paper of Frumkin.[8]

In conclusion attention should be called to the fact that capillary-active ions and nonelectrolytes change the drop time of mercury. As the drop time has some effect upon the diffusion current, the latter may be smaller in the presence than in the absence of capillary-active substances.

---

[8] A. Frumkin, *Ergeb. exakt. Naturw.*, **7**, 235 (1928).

CHAPTER IX

Condenser or Charging Current. Residual Current

1. THE POTENTIAL OF DROPPING AND QUIET MERCURY IN VARIOUS SOLUTIONS

In the previous chapter it was mentioned that mercury freely dropping into a solution is uncharged. When the solution contains a capillary-inactive electrolyte the dropping mercury should adopt the potential corresponding to the electrocapillary zero, *i. e.*, -0.56 v. *vs.* the N.C.E. Careful experiments carried out by Erdey-Gruz and Szarvas[1] with systems from which air was completely removed showed this to be true. In 1 N sodium perchlorate they measured a potential of -0.583 v., in 0.01 N perchlorate -0.529 v., in 1.4 N sodium nitrate -0.612 v., in 0.13 N nitrate -0.572 v., etc. The measurements were reproducible within a few millivolts. When oxygen is not completely excluded from the system less negative potentials are found. In solutions of 0.1 N potassium chloride from which air was displaced by hydrogen or nitrogen, we have often measured potentials of -0.4 to -0.45 v., while Erdey-Gruz and Szarvas in *completely* oxygen-free solutions found a value of -0.55 v.

When potential measurements were made with a quiet mercury electrode, Erdey-Gruz and Szarvas found a very poor reproducibility in solutions of *capillary-inactive* electrolytes. The values were of the order of 0.0 to -0.1 v., but fluctuated several tenths of a volt. On the other hand, in solutions of *capillary-active* electrolytes, such as bromide, thiocyanate, iodide, cyanide, and sulfide, reproducible potentials were obtained with the quiet electrode. In general, these potentials were more positive than those obtained with the dropping electrode. The potentials obtained with the latter electrode always corresponded to the potential of the electrocapillary zero in the particular electrolyte solution. A few representative figures are given in Table IX-1 in which the values are compared with those reported by Frumkin[2] at the electrocapillary maximum.

The fact that the dropping mercury adopts the potential of the electrocapillary zero in solutions of capillary-active electrolytes is easily explained.

---

[1] T. Erdey-Gruz and P. Szarvas, *Z. physik. Chem.*, **A177**, 277 (1937).

[2] A. Frumkin, *Ergeb. exakt. Naturw.*, **7**, 235 (1928).

When the uncharged mercury drops into a solution, say of iodide, it adsorbs iodide ions at its surface.   As a result of the image forces electrons are repelled from the surface and the latter contains an excess of positive charges.   The bulk of the mercury in the reservoir will acquire a negative charge.   A second drop, therefore, is negatively charged and adsorbs less iodide ions.   These newly adsorbed iodide ions not only neutralize the negative charge in the surface but again cause a repulsion of electrons. When the potential of the dropping electrode has become equal to that at the electrocapillary zero in an iodide solution, only a few iodide ions are adsorbed but the surface of the mercury remains uncharged.   The potential of the dropping mercury then remains constant upon further dropping.

TABLE IX-1

POTENTIALS AT MAXIMUM OF ELECTROCAPILLARY CURVES (FRUMKIN) AND OF FAST DROPPING MERCURY (ERDEY-GRUZ AND SZARVAS) IN ELECTROLYTE SOLUTIONS *vs.* THE N.C.E.

Electrolyte	Approximate concentration, molar	E, electrocapillary maximum	E, dropping electrode
$NaClO_4$	1	−0.60	−0.583
$KCl(NaCl)$	1	−0.61	−0.610
$KNO_3(NaNO_3)$	1	−0.61	−0.612
$KBr(NaBr)$	1	−0.70	−0.681
$KCNS$	1	−0.77	−0.770
$KI(NaI)$	1	−0.87	−0.875
$K_2S(Na_2S)$	0.5	−0.97	−1.124

From the polarographic viewpoint it is of importance to emphasize that the potential of the dropping mercury always corresponds to that at the electrocapillary zero in the particular solution when the latter is completely free of oxygen and other reducible substances.

2. CONDENSER OR CHARGING CURRENT

Let us first consider the cell, 0.1 N calomel electrode–dropping mercury, in air-free 0.1 N potassium chloride.   When the cell is not short-circuited the dropping electrode adopts a potential which is about −0.53 v. more negative than that of the 0.1 N calomel electrode.[3]   When the cell is short-circuited the calomel electrode impresses its potential upon the dropping electrode.   This causes a flow of positive electricity through the external circuit from the calomel electrode to the dropping electrode, or an electric current passes through the solution in a direction opposite to that

---

[3] D. Ilkovic, *Collection Czechoslov. Chem. Communs.*, **8**, 170 (1936).

obtained upon cathodic electrolysis at the dropping cathode. A current in this direction is called a negative current. Upon polarizing the dropping electrode cathodically by an impressed e.m.f. this negative current decreases and becomes zero when the applied e.m.f. is equal to the potential of the mercury at the electrocapillary zero. At this point the opposing applied e.m.f. balances the e.m.f. of the cell calomel electrode–dropping electrode. When the applied e.m.f. is further increased the dropping electrode acquires a negative charge, and a positive current results. Hence, when the applied e.m.f. is smaller than that corresponding to the electrocapillary maximum the mercury is charged positively and a negative current passes through the cell. At the other side of the maximum the mercury is charged negatively and a positive current flows through. If the mercury electrode were stationary the current would become equal to zero almost instantaneously, as only a minute amount of electricity flows at the moment when short circuit is made. With the dropping electrode each new drop takes up a charge sufficient to counteract the applied potential, and, consequently, a continuous current flows. This current, which is nonfaradaic, is called the *condenser* or *charging* current and is represented by i_c. In the absence of electroreducible substances i_c is equal to the *residual current*. The order of magnitude of the condenser current in practically air-free 0.1 N potassium chloride solution with a capillary of normal size and drop time is a few tenths of a microampere.

In Fig. IX-1 is shown a condenser current curve obtained by Maas[4] in an air-free solution of pure 0.1 N sodium chloride. The curve was recorded with a polarograph, using the full sensitivity of the galvanometer. The electrocapillary maximum in 0.1 N chloride is at about −0.56 v. so the condenser current should have been zero at this potential. Actually, it is seen that the current was zero at a somewhat less negative potential, at about −0.35 v. This is probably due to the presence of a trace of oxygen. (It is very difficult to remove the last traces of oxygen.) It is significant to note that the current oscillations during the formation of the individual mercury drops decreased with increasing potential and practically disappeared at potentials of −0.45 to −0.55 v. near the isoelectric point (electrocapillary maximum). As the potential was increased above −0.55 v., the oscillations reappeared and their magnitude increased with increasing negative potential. The current oscillations are an approximate measure of the magnitude of the charging current during the formation of the individual mercury drops, the minimum oscillations being found at the electrocapillary zero.

[4] J. Maas, *De Polarografische Methode met de Druppelende Kwikelectrode ten Dienste van het Pharmaceutisch Onderzoek*, Amsterdam, 1937.

Ilkovic[3] measured the potential–time curves of individual mercury drops falling into a very pure, air-free solution of 0.1 N potassium chloride.   At potentials more positive than the electrocapillary maximum he found that the potential of an individual drop became more positive during its growth. At the potential of the electrocapillary maximum the potential remained practically constant during the life of a drop, while at more negative potentials it became more negative during the life of each drop.   These results confirm the concept that the double layer changes sign at the electrocapillary maximum and that no double layer exists at the maximum itself.

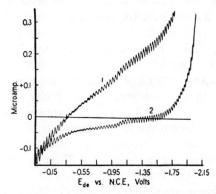

Fig. IX-1. Condenser current curves in air-free 0.1 N sodium chloride according to Maas.   Curve 2 was obtained by the compensation technique (Chap. XIV).

3. RELATION BETWEEN MAGNITUDE OF THE CONDENSER CURRENT AND CAPACITY OF THE DOUBLE LAYER AT A MERCURY-SOLUTION INTERFACE

If the double layer at a mercury–solution interface behaves as a condenser, the average condenser current during the life of a drop should be given by

$$i_c = kq\psi \tag{1}$$

where k is the capacity per unit area of the double layer, q is the average rate at which fresh mercury surface is being exposed to the solution (cm.^{2} sec.$^{-1}$), and ψ is the potential difference between the mercury and solution. Since i_c is zero at the potential corresponding to the electrocapillary maximum, and since k remains fairly constant for small changes in the potential, eq. 1 can be written as

$$i_c = kq(\psi_{max.} - \psi) = kq(E_{max.} - E) \tag{2}$$

where $\psi_{\text{max.}}$ is the absolute potential difference between the mercury and the solution at the electrocapillary maximum, and i_c is the condenser current at some other potential ψ. Since the potential of the quiet electrode remains constant during the electrolysis, and since the electrical potential of the solution is constant $(\psi_{\text{max.}} - \psi)$ can be replaced by $(E_{\text{max.}} - E)$, where E is the potential of the dropping electrode with respect to an external reference electrode. Since q and k can be measured easily, this equation allows us to calculate i_c at various potentials of the dropping electrode.

Ilkovic[3] calculated the capacity of the double layer in specially purified 0.1 N potassium chloride from his measurements of the potential–time curves of individual mercury drops. On the negative branch of the electrocapillary curve $(-1.3$ v.$)$ he found a value for k of 22.3 microfarad. cm.$^{-2}$, while on the positive side of the electrocapillary maximum $(-0.18$ v.$)$ he found a value for k of 42.2 microfarad. cm.$^{-2}$. These results are in agreement with the measurements of Philpot,[5] who found values for k of 21.8 and 48.8 microfarad. cm.$^{-2}$ on the negative and the positive sides of the electrocapillary maxiumu, respectively.

It is interesting to compare the value of i_c computed by means of eq. 2 with the data for the residual current in 0.1 N potassium chloride given in Table IV-5 in Chapter IV. It is readily derived that the area exposed per second by the growing mercury drops is given by

$$q = (4\pi)^{1/3}(3/d)^{2/3}m^{2/3}t^{-1/3} = 0.0085m^{2/3}t^{-1/3} \text{ cm.}^2 \text{ sec.}^{-1} \tag{3}$$

where d is the density of mercury and m is expressed in mg. sec.$^{-1}$. From the data in Table IV-5 in Chapter IV we find that m was equal to 2.67 mg. sec.$^{-1}$ and t was 2.18 sec. at -1.5 v., and hence q was 0.0126 cm.^{2} sec.$^{-1}$. Since $E_{\text{max.}}$ is equal to -0.56 v. with respect to the N.C.E., and k is equal to 22 microfarad. cm.$^{-2}$, we calculated from eq. 2 for i_c at -1.5 v.,

$$i_c = 22 \times 0.0126 \times (-0.56 + 1.5) = 0.26 \text{ microamp.} \tag{4}$$

This agrees reasonably well with the experimentally observed value, 0.38 microamp., in Table IV-5.

The capacity of the double layer can also be computed approximately from the slope of the condenser current curve. From eq. 2 we see that the capacity is given by

$$k = (di_c/dE)/q \tag{5}$$

---

[5] Y. St. L. Philpot, *Phil. Mag.*, (7) **13**, 775 (1932).

that is, k is equal to the slope of the condenser current curve divided by the area exposed per second. Even if the residual current includes a small faradaic current, it may be assumed that the latter will be practically constant over a small range of potentials, and the slope of the residual current curve will be practically equal to di_c/dE. For example, the slope of curve 1 in Fig. IX-1 is approximately 0.20 microamp. volt^{-1}, and q in this experiment of Maas[6] was 0.0086 cm.^{2} sec.$^{-1}$. The value of k calculated from these data is $0.20/0.0086 = 23$ microfarad. cm.$^{-2}$, in good agreement with the values found by Ilkovic and Philpot by different methods.

Since the condenser current curve in Fig. IX-1 is approximately a straight line at potentials more negative than the electrocapillary maximum, it is evident that the capacity of the double layer is approximately constant between about -0.4 and -1.4 v. It will be noted that the slope of the curve (and hence the capacity of the double layer) is larger on the positive side of the electrocapillary maximum, in agreement with the results of Ilkovic, and Philpot, and Proskurnin and Frumkin.[7]

The capacity of the double layer, and hence the magnitude of the condenser current, depends on the nature of the ions in the solution. Capillary-active ions which are strongly adsorbed at the mercury–solution interface increase the capacity of the double layer, on one or the other branch of the electrocapillary curve. For example, the capacity of the double layer is about twice as great in a solution containing iodide ions as it is in a chloride solution on the positive side of the electrocapillary curve.[8] This corresponds to a decrease in the thickness, or a compression, of the double layer acting as a condenser.

Grahame[9] distinguishes between *static* capacity and *differential* capacity. The static capacity C is defined by the equation $C = -q/E$. The differential capacity C' is the rate of change of the charge with respect to the potential. The increase in the capacity at potentials more positive than that at the isoelectric point is attributed by Grahame to a preformation of the mercurous salt (through deformation) of the anion which is present in the solution. Anions at the surface of the mercury attach themselves by chemical forces identical with those which cause precipitation of the

[6] J. Maas, *De Polarografische Methode met de Druppelende Kwikelectrode ten Dienste van het Pharmaceutisch Onderzoek*, Amsterdam, 1937; *Collection Czechoslov. Chem. Communs.*, **10**, 42 (1938).

[7] M. Proskurnin and A. Frumkin, *Trans. Faraday Soc.*, **31**, 110 (1935); T. Borissowa and M. Proskurnin, *Acta Physicochim. U. R. S. S.*, **4**, 819 (1935); A. Ksenofontov, M. Proskurnin, and A. Gorodetzka, *Acta Physiochim. U. R. S. S.*, **9**, 39 (1938).

[8] A. Frumkin, *Ergeb. exakt. Naturw.*, **7**, 235–275 (1928).

[9] D. C. Grahame, *J. Am. Chem. Soc.*, **63**, 1207 (1941).

corresponding mercurous salt.   In confirmation of this view it is found that
nitrates and perchlorates require the largest positive potential before the
capacity starts to increase rapidly, iodides the least, while the other anions
show the effect approximately in the order of the solubilities of their respective mercurous salts.   In an excellent review paper Grahame[10] presents graphically the differential capacity found with different electrolytes
at varying concentrations.   In the same paper (loc. cit., p. 498) he states
that the apparent capacity of the mercury electrode increases enormously
when the reduction of an ion occurs reversibly.   The reason is that the
reduced form of the ion acts as a reservoir of charge.   The concentration
of the reduced form of the ion is fixed either by the potential or by the rate
of diffusion of the ions to the surface depending upon whether the current
is smaller or greater than that at the half-wave potential.

When the potential of the metallic electrode is made so strongly negative
that the concentration of the reduced form of the ion is limited by diffusion,
changes of potential cause no further change in the concentration of the
reduced form of the ion, and the differential capacity becomes normal.
This is a particularly good illustration of an electrode which is not ideally
polarized acting like one which is.   The enhanced capacity caused by the
reversible reduction of ions has been called by Grahame a "pseudo-capacity," since it does not correspond to any bound charge except in the
sense that neutral metallic atoms represent bound charge.   For example,
the differential capacity observed in the polarographic reduction of 0.002
M cadmium chloride in 0.1 M sodium chloride solution was found to increase from about 25 (at the beginning of the wave) to more than 90 μF
cm.$^{-2}$ and then dropped sharply to about 20 after the diffusion current was
reached.   The pseudo-capacity is observed on extreme cathodic polarization of alkali ions, and ammonium and tetramethylammonium salts, and
presumably will be found with practically all cations.   Hydronium ions,
oxygen, and nitrate are reduced irreversibly which is characterized by the
absence of pseudo-capacity.   *It would be interesting to know whether absence of pseudo-capacity is a general criterion of irreversible electrode reactions.*

Grahame states that as an analytical tool, the measurement of the
pseudo-capacity at a dropping electrode might be found to possess the
advantage of high sensitivity in the presence of small amounts of substances which are reducible but not reversibly.   The technique would be a
modified form of polarography, but its greater complication would limit
its usefulness to cases where ordinary polarographic methods fail.

[10] D. C. Grahame, *Chem. Revs.*, **41**, 441 (1947).

In order to eliminate as far as possible the uncertainty in the measurement of very small diffusion currents, due to the residual current, Ilkovic and Semerano[11] recommend that the residual current be "compensated" by sending a current of equal magnitude through the current-measuring galvanometer in a direction opposite to that of the residual current (see Chap. XVI). Recent models of the polarograph are equipped with a device for automatically compensating, or balancing out, the residual current, at all values of the applied e.m.f.[12] Curve *2* in Fig. IX-1 was obtained by compensating (actually by slightly overcompensating) the residual current in this way.

4. SIGNIFICANCE OF THE RESIDUAL CURRENT IN POLAROGRAPHIC WORK

In the complete absence of electroreducible substances the residual current is equal to the condenser current. The magnitude of the latter depends upon the potential of the dropping mercury, the area of mercury exposed per second (which depends in turn upon the characteristics of the capillary), and the presence of capillary-active substances in the solution.

In ordinary, practical work the residual current, i_r, as a rule is greater than the condenser current, i_c, because it also includes a slight "faradaic" current, i_f, due to the reduction of traces of reducible impurities in the solution:

$$i_r = i_c + i_f$$

It is very difficult to remove the last traces of oxygen from a solution by bubbling an inert gas through it. Therefore, the trace of oxygen left contributes to the residual current. Ordinary distilled water often contains traces of copper which is easily reduced at the dropping electrode. Another source of impurity which contributes to the residual current is dissolved mercury. Although not necessary, a large layer of mercury is often used as anode in polarographic work. When the mercury is added to the solution to be investigated, before the oxygen is removed, the metal reacts more or less rapidly with the oxygen, with the formation of mercurous or mercuric ions and hydrogen peroxide (the latter is electro-reduced at about -1.0 v.). Especially when the solution contains ions which have a great affinity for mercury (sulfide, iodide, thiosulfate, large amounts of chloride and bromide, etc.) relatively large amounts of mercury

---

[11] D. Ilkovic and G. Semerano, *Collection Czechoslov. Chem. Communs.*, **4**, 176 (1932).

[12] Cf. H. Hohn, *Chemische Analysen mit dem Polarographen*, Berlin, 1937.

may dissolve in a relatively short time and it becomes difficult or impossible to obtain reproducible results in duplicate experiments. In such cases it is necessary to remove the oxygen from the solution and cell before the layer of mercury is placed on the bottom, or, better still, to use an outside anode (Chap. XVII).

When measuring diffusion currents, a correction must be applied for the residual current, by subtracting it from the "apparent" diffusion current. This correction often amounts to several tenths of a microampere, and it becomes greater the more negative the potential at which the substance in question is reduced. It is obvious, therefore, that the accuracy with which small diffusion currents can be determined is greatly dependent on the accuracy of the correction for the residual current. In testing the proportionality between the concentration and the diffusion current many authors have overlooked this correction for the residual current. It is evident that the deviations from proportionality become greater with increasing dilution when the correction is not applied. It is also evident that minimum detectable concentration of a reducible substance will depend on the accuracy with which the residual current can be measured. In accurate polarographic work it is essential to determine the residual current in the particular supporting electrolyte solution that is used whenever this is possible.

5. COMPENSATION OF CONDENSER CURRENT BY A DIFFUSION CURRENT. APPLICATION TO POTENTIOMETRIC DETERMINATION OF OXYGEN WITH DROPPING MERCURY AS INDICATOR ELECTRODE

A highly specific analytical application of the difference in sign between the condenser current and a reduction current at the positive side of the isoelectric point has been made by Laitinen[13] et al. in the "potentiometric" estimation of traces of oxygen, using the dropping electrode as indicator electrode. For very small concentrations of oxygen, it is evident that at some value of the potential the diffusion and charging currents will be equal in magnitude but opposite in direction and hence will cancel. Since the instantaneous value of the diffusion current varies with the one-sixth power of the time and is independent of the potential, while the charging current at a constant potential varies with the two-thirds power of time (q), it is evident that the null potential must vary with time in such a way that the instantaneous current will be zero at all times.

To calculate the magnitude of the effect, Laitinen et al. equate the total charge, $(q_c)_t$ held by the drop at any time, t, with the number of coulombs

[13] H. A. Laitinen, T. Higuchi, and H. Czuha, J. Am. Chem. Soc., 70, 561 (1948).

$(q_d)_t$, lost by the drop through electroreduction of oxygen molecules from the beginning of drop formation to time t, or

$$(q_c)_t = (q_d)_t$$

By a consideration of the factors determining $(q_c)_t$ and $(q_d)_t$ the following relation is arrived at:

$$(E - E_{\text{max.}})_t = \frac{6}{21\pi} \cdot \frac{nF_yCD^{1/2}t^{1/2}}{k} = 7.12 \times 10^4 \frac{nCD^{1/2}t^{1/2}}{k}$$

in which k is the capacity of the double layer per unit area, and E_{max}. the potential at the isoelectric point.   Using known values for D(oxygen) and k we find

$$E - E_{\text{max.}} = 17.2Ct^{1/2} \; (25°\text{C.}) \tag{6}$$

where $E - E_{\text{max}}$. is the shift in the potential when the current is zero as referred to the potential at the isoelectric point.   For the observed current to be zero at every instant, the potential difference must fluctuate with time.   The voltage fluctuation should be directly proportional to the oxygen content of the electrolyte, but independent of the rate of flow of mercury (m).

By inserting a high-capacity condenser into the circuit to lower the voltage fluctuation to a negligible value, the observed potential will correspond to the maximum potential difference of the undamped system just before the drop breaks.   The observed nonfluctuating e.m.f. (damped system) was found to be identical (within 2 mv.) with the maximum e.m.f. in the undamped system.   It was found more convenient to measure the latter.   A Beckman Research Model G pH meter, operated as a millivoltmeter was used to measure the e.m.f. of the cell.   This instrument is particularly suitable because of its sensitivity and its rapid response.   In an undamped system, the meter was permitted to remain continuously in the circuit and the maximum e.m.f. developed during the formation of each drop was determined by balancing the slide wire so that the galvanometer showed zero deflection at the end of drop formation.

Cell for Continuous Measurement.   A cell suitable for this type of investigation must fulfill the following requirements: Arrangements must be made to bring the electrolyte rapidly in equilibrium, with respect to its oxygen content, with the sample gas.   The dropping electrode must be shielded from any turbulence caused by flow of gas through the solution.   The reference electrode must have constant reversible potential and possess relatively low resistance.   It must be placed so that the reducible products, if any, of the electrode cannot affect the dropping electrode.   The mercury from the dropping electrode must be removed in such a manner as to minimize contact with the electrolyte.   Any mercurous chloride formed through interaction of the mercury with the electrolyte might affect the dropping electrode potential. To permit continuous operation, it is advisable to construct the cell in such a manner as to permit continuous partial replacement of the electrolyte. This prevents accumulation of contaminants over a long period of time. A schematic diagram of the apparatus which was employed is shown in Fig. IX-2.

Operation of the Unit.   The electrolyte in a 1-liter stoppered flask (reservoir A) in Fig. IX-2 is maintained at constant head in scrubbing vessel B. The solution is allowed to flow at a predetermined rate of 1.1 ml. per minute through capillary tube

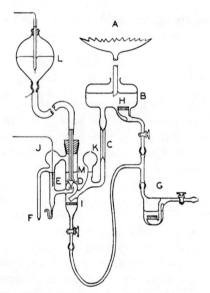

Fig. IX-2. Cell for measurement of oxygen.

C into the dropping mercury electrode cell D, past the silver–silver chloride reference electrode E, to the outlet F.

The gas sample is first saturated with water vapor from the electrolyte solution in vessel G and then part of the gas stream is forced through the fritted glass disc H into the scrubbing vessel B where the electrolyte receives a preliminary scrubbing with the gas sample. The final solubility equilibrium between the oxygen in the sample and the electrolyte solution is obtained by passing another portion of the gas stream through the fritted disc I into the dropping mercury electrode cell. The gas is allowed to escape through two spray trap bulbs J and K, on either side of the cell.

Mercury from reservoir L is forced through the dropping mercury electrode capillary M. A funnel-shaped shield surrounding the tip of the capillary serves to protect the slowly forming mercury drops from agitation of the rising gas bubbles, and also to direct mercury drops into the siphon, thus removing them from the cell.

An important feature of the design of the equipment is the continuous removal of any reducible materials such as mercurous chloride and silver chloride which would form at the electrodes in small concentrations in a stationary system. The flow of electrolyte is in such a direction as to prevent the accumulation of calomel around the dropping electrode. For the same reason, the reference electrode is situated in the outflowing stream of electrolyte.

In the absence of oxygen the e.m.f. at zero current in 0.1 N potassium chloride was found to be 0.500 v. against the silver–silver chloride electrode (in 0.1 N KCl) as compared with the expected value of 0.558 v. The value of 0.500 v. was taken as the potential corresponding to the electrocapillary zero maximum. In order to find strict proportionality between ($E - E_{max}$.) and the oxygen concentration the solution was made 2×10^{-4} per cent in methyl red to suppress the oxygen maximum. The proportionality then holds until ($E - E_{max}$.) is about 0.300 v. When this value exceeds 0.300 v., no proportionality can be found since the diffusion current of oxygen is then not reached. Methyl red undergoes reduction at the dropping electrode at a potential slightly more positive than the electrocapillary maximum. Methyl red, therefore, behaves like oxygen. This is considered in making the calibration curves. Using 0.1 N potassium chloride as supporting electrolyte with a trace of methyl red, the method was found to be sensitive to 0.01 per cent of oxygen in a gas. A linear relation was found over the range from zero to 1 per cent of oxygen. In agreement with the theoretical postulates the potential was found to vary with the square root of the drop time and to be independent of the rate of flow of mercury through the capillary at a constant drop time.

The method is useful for the determination of oxygen in polarographically inert gases, like nitrogen, hydrogen, hydrocarbons, etc. Substances which are reduced before the electrocapillary maximum or which depolarize the mercury anodically (hydrogen sulfide or hydrogen cyanide) interfere. Capillary-active substance (naphthalene or iodide) change the capacity of the double layer and therefore affect the potential. For the reasons mentioned the method is more useful for the determination of oxygen in gases than in aqueous solutions.

CHAPTER X

Polarographic Maxima

1. CHARACTERISTICS OF MAXIMA

One of the general characteristics of the current–voltage curves with the dropping mercury electrode is the more or less pronounced maximum, which is often observed unless special measures are taken to prevent its occurrence. Maxima also may occur with quiet mercury electrodes[1] but they are not reproducible, in contradistinction to those obtained with the dropping mercury electrode, which are perfectly reproducible.[2] The shapes of maxima vary from very acute peaks, with a rapid and almost discontinuous decrease of the current after the maximum, to rounded humps with a gradual decrease in current following the maximum (see Fig. X-1).

The shapes of the maxima are generally independent of the direction in which the applied e.m.f. is changed; if, after the maximum has been passed by increasing the e.m.f. in the usual way, the e.m.f. is then decreased gradually, the curve will in most cases retrace itself exactly over the maximum (see Fig. X-2). In certain cases, when the maxima are very acute, the potential at which the peak of the maximum is reached may be somewhat different with decreasing than with increasing e.m.f. For example, Heyrovsky and Vascautzanu (loc. cit.) found that the peak of the oxygen maximum was about 50 mv. more negative with increasing applied e.m.f. than with decreasing applied e.m.f., but the height of the maximum was practically the same in the two cases.

Just as on other parts of a c.v. curve, the current at the maximum is practically independent of the time of electrolysis. If the applied e.m.f. is kept constant at a value at or near the peak of a maximum the current remains constant indefinitely.

The maximum due to a given electroreducible substance may be either

---

[1] A. Frumkin and B. Burns, Acta Physicochim. U. R. S. S., 1, 232 (1934). P. Herasymenko, Trans. Faraday Soc., 24, 257 (1928). P. Herasymenko, J. Heyrovsky, and K. Tancakivsky, ibid., 25, 152 (1929). S. Jofa and A. Frumkin, Compt. rend. acad. sci. U. R. S. S., 20, 293 (1938).

[2] J. Heyrovsky and E. Vascautzanu, Collection Czechoslov. Chem. Communs., 3, 418 (1931).

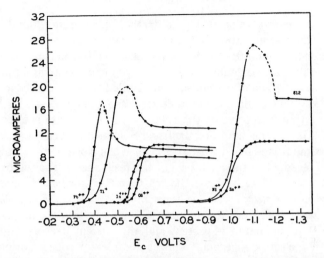

Fig. X-1. Various types of maxima obtained, from left to right, with lead, thallous, indium, cadmium, nickel, and zinc ions. The waves of indium and cadmium ions do not show maxima because their locations coincide with the potentials of the electrocapillary maxima.

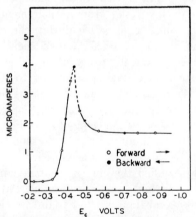

Fig. X-2. Independence of the shape of the lead ion maximum on the direction in which the e.m.f. is applied: 2.75×10^{-4} M lead nitrate in 0.1 N potassium chloride.

acute or rounded, depending on the composition of the solution. For example, Varasova[3] found that the acute maximum of oxygen was very small in extremely dilute potassium chloride solutions, but it became more pronounced with increasing potassium chloride concentration, and

---

[3] E. Varasova, *Collection Czechoslov. Chem. Communs.*, **2**, 8 (1930).

attained its greatest value in about 0.001 N potassium chloride. With increasing salt concentration the oxygen maximum decreased and became more rounded. Qualitatively, we have been able to confirm these results. Quite generally, a maximum will be most pronounced at a certain intermediate concentration of foreign salt; in distilled water and in concentrated salt solutions the oxygen maximum disappears.[4]

An interesting feature when the maximum is very acute is that the c.v. curve is a straight line, and not the usual S-shaped curve, before the peak of the maximum is reached. In such a case the slope of the straight line appears to be equal to the reciprocal of the resistance of the cell in accordance with Ohm's Law.[5] This indicates that *the potential of the dropping electrode remains constant from the beginning of the discharge until the maximum is reached,* and that no concentration polarization occurs. Immediately after the maximum is passed, and the current decreases suddenly, the dropping electrode becomes almost completely concentration polarized. In weakly acid mercurous nitrate solutions this sudden increase in polarization may amount to as much as 1 volt.[6] Conclusive proof that the electrode remains depolarized during the discharge of mercurous ions until the peak of the maximum is reached, and that polarization sets in at the peak, was obtained by Heyrovsky[7] from measurements of the interfacial tension at the mercury–solution interface during the electrolysis. Heyrovsky found that the interfacial tension, in a slightly acid mercurous nitrate solution, remained practically constant until the peak of the maximum was reached, instead of changing according to the electrocapillary curve. As soon as the maximum was passed the interfacial tension changed abruptly and followed the electrocapillary curve.

It is still problematical whether the slope of the straight part of the c.v. curve preceding an acute maximum always corresponds to the reciprocal of the cell resistance. In this connection reference is made to investigations of Hoekstra,[8] who studied the current–voltage curves with scraped electrodes. He found a constant apparent resistance, at various values of the current, which was several times greater than that calculated from the dimensions of the cell and the specific conductance of the solutions. Large

---

[4] J. Heyrovsky and R. Simunek, *Phil. Mag.*, **7**, 951 (1929).

[5] D. Ilkovic, *Collection Czechoslov. Chem. Communs.*, **4**, 480 (1932).

[6] J. Heyrovsky and M. Dillinger, *Collection Czechoslov. Chem. Communs.*, **2**, 626 (1930).

[7] J. Heyrovsky, *A Polarographic Study of the Electrokinetic Phenomena of Adsorption, Electroreduction and Overpotential Displayed at the Dropping Mercury Cathode,* Actualités scientifiques et industrielles, No. 90, Paris, 1934.

[8] H. Hoekstra, *Collection Czechoslov. Chem. Communs.*, **6**, 17 (1934).

apparent resistances were also observed by Laitinen and Kolthoff[9] in electrolyses with stationary and rotated platinum microelectrodes (see Chap. XIX). When dealing with the dropping electrode it seems that resistance of the surface film can be neglected when the electrode reaction is reversible and the potential of the electrode is in equilibrium with the surrounding liquid. If the latter condition is not fulfilled and we are deal-

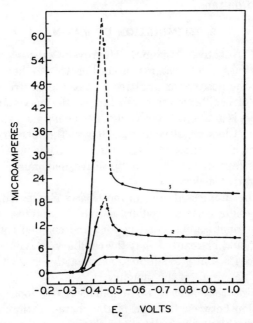

Fig. X-3. Relative heights of maxima obtained with various concentrations of lead ion in 0.1 N potassium chloride. Concentrations of lead nitrate were: (1) 3.3 × 10⁻⁴, (2) 1 × 10⁻³, and (3) 2.3 × 10⁻³ M.

ing with a case of "chemical polarization" the slope of the straight part of the c.v. curve preceding an acute maximum certainly will not correspond to the reciprocal of the cell resistance.

The height of the maximum of a given electroreducible substance is greatly dependent on its concentration. For example, reducible metal ions in dilute alkali chloride solutions usually do not yield maxima when the concentration of the metal ion is very small, but maxima appear and become more and more pronounced as the metal ion concentration is increased. As a rule, there is no simple relation between the height of a

[9] H. A. Laitinen and I. M. Kolthoff, *J. Phys. Chem.*, **45**, 1061, 1079 (1941).

maximum and the concentration of the reducible substance. In the electrolysis of nickel chloride solutions, without any foreign salt present, Emilianova and Heyrovsky[10] found that the ratio $i_{max.}/i_l$ was equal to 1:1 in a 0.0005 N solution, to 2.7:1 in a 0.0025 N solution, to 6:1 in a 0.0062 N solution, and to 6.5:1 in a 0.01 N solution.

The magnitudes of maxima depend on the drop time, becoming smaller the slower the drop time.[7]

2. ELIMINATION OF MAXIMA

Positive and Negative Maxima. Heyrovsky[7] distinguishes between "positive" and "negative" maxima, according to whether a given maximum occurs on the positive or negative side of the electrocapillary curve. In the absence of capillary-active substances, the maximum in the electrocapillary curve is at about -0.6 v. against the normal calomel electrode. If the potential is less negative than -0.6 v. the mercury is positively charged, whereas if it is more negative the mercury is negatively charged. In Fig. X-1 the lead maximum is a "positive maximum," while that of nickel is a "negative maximum."

Maxima can be suppressed, and in most cases eliminated, by adding to the solution traces of certain capillary-active electrolytes and nonelectrolytes, and various non-capillary-active ions and charged colloids. In this connection, it should be realized that the capillary activity of a given substance, and hence its ability to suppress maxima, depends on the charge on, and also on the potential of, the mercury.

Considering first the effect of non-capillary-active ions, there seems to be a close relation between the sign of the charge of the mercury on the one hand, and the signs and valences of the ions on the other. Thus, in the suppression of positive maxima trivalent anions are considered to be much more effective than divalent, and the latter more so than univalent anions, while the valence of the cation is practically without effect. The converse is true for negative maxima, in which case the valence of the cation plays the predominant role. Heyrovsky[7] states, "The dilutions in which cations of different valency cause the same degree of suppression of a negative maximum are in the same ratio as their power of precipitating (flocculating) a negative lyophobic colloid, say, arsenic trisulfide. Indeed, the Schulze-Hardy rule has been found to hold strictly for the suppression of maxima; thus, the dilutions at which ions of potassium, calcium, and lanthanum, respectively, produce suppression to the same extent were found to be in the ratio 1:160:10,000." However, it seems very doubtful

---

[10] N. V. Emilianova and J. Heyrovsky, *Trans. Faraday Soc.*, **24**, 257 (1928).

whether the Schulze-Hardy rule holds strictly in the suppression of maxima. For example, Emelianova and Heyrovsky[10] found the negative maximum of nickel was just suppressed in 0.11 N potassium chloride, or in 2.2 $\times$ 10^{-3} N magnesium chloride, in 1.1 $\times$ 10^{-3} N calcium chloride, in 3 $\times$ 10^{-5} N barium chloride, in 2 $\times$ 10^{-5} N aluminum chloride, and in 1 $\times$ 10^{-6} N lanthanum chloride. It is not clear why barium ions in this respect behave as trivalent cations, quite differently from calcium and magnesium ions.

C. S. Miller (University of Minnesota) found the difference in the suppressive effect of barium ions, on the one hand, and calcium and magnesium ions, on the other, much smaller. He also studied the effect on the maxima of additions of a deficiency of sodium hydroxide to the nickel chloride solution. The alkali causes the partial separation of basic nickel salt presumably as a positively charged colloid. One would expect, therefore, that the negative nickel maximum would be suppressed completely in the presence of this colloid. Actually it was found that the ratio of the maximum current to the limiting current remained practically unchanged in the presence of various amounts of the positive colloid. Another striking exception to the rule given by Heyrovsky was found in the case of the positive oxygen maximum.[11] In 0.001 N potassium chloride a very pronounced, acute maximum occurs, the maximum current being several times greater than the limiting current. Addition of potassium ferrocyanide to this solution, in concentrations ranging between 10^{-5} and 6 $\times$ 10^{-5} M, hardly affected the maximum, and at a concentration of 0.001 M ferrocyanide the maximum was even slightly more pronounced instead of suppressed. Also at other concentrations of potassium chloride no pronounced effect of ferrocyanide ions was found. Nor did the trivalent citrate ion have a greater effect than chloride ion upon the oxygen maximum. It is evident, therefore, that care must be exercised in generalizing Heyrovsky's rule. From Herasymenko's study[12] of the effect of salts on the maximum in the reduction of uranyl ions (first wave), cations of various charge (K^+, Na^+, Mg^{++}, Al^{+++}) were found to have the same effect, and, furthermore, there was hardly any difference between the effect of chloride and sulfate ions. Since the uranyl ions (first wave) are reduced on the positive side of the electrocapillary maximum, one would expect that sulfate ions would be much more effective in suppressing the maximum than chloride ions.

The following peculiar phenomenon is also hard to explain on the basis

---

11 I. M. Kolthoff and C. S. Miller, *J. Am. Chem. Soc.*, **63**, 1013 (1941).
12 P. Herasymenko, *Trans. Faraday Soc.*, **24**, 257 (1928).

of Heyrovsky's rule. Heyrovsky and Dillinger[6] found that in a mixture of nickel and manganous chloride two pronounced negative maxima occurred. The nickel maximum was suppressed by addition of barium ions, but that of manganese was less affected. On the basis of Heyrovsky's rule, both maxima should have been equally suppressed.

From a practical point of view the effect of *capillary-active* ions on maxima is of much greater importance than that of capillary-inactive ions. Heyrovsky[13] states that acid dyes and negative colloids (he used a negative colloidal solution of a barium soap) suppress the positive thallium maximum very easily, whereas basic dyes and positively charged colloids cause a suppression of negative maxima. For example, the positive maximum of thallium is easily suppressed by acid fuchsine (anion), but that of nickel is hardly affected. On the other hand, basic fuchsine (cation) suppresses the negative nickel maximum completely.

In practical analytical work, the occurrence of maxima is a nuisance, but fortunately they can generally be eliminated by the addition of suitable capillary-active ions. We have found, for example, that the positive maxima of thallium and lead in neutral solutions are completely suppressed by traces of the sodium salt of the ordinary indicator methyl red (Fig. X-4). However, the positive lead maximum is not suppressed by the cation form of methyl red in acid medium, which is in accordance with Heyrovsky's rule. On the other hand, the negative maximum of nickel in neutral medium was found to be unaffected by the anion form of methyl red, but in acid medium the maximum was completely eliminated by the cation form of the dye; this is also in accord with Heyrovsky's rule.

Methyl red is itself reduced at the dropping electrode, but the concentrations of the dye used to suppress maxima are so small (less than 0.001 per cent) that they have no appreciable effect on the diffusion current of the substance to be determined.

As an example of the analytical significance of the elimination of maxima we give in Fig. X-5 the c.v. curve of a mixture of lead and cadmium ions without and with methyl red present. In the absence of the dye, no definite measure of the diffusion current of the lead ion can be obtained, but a well-defined diffusion current for lead results when the maximum is eliminated by the addition of methyl red.

One should not infer from the foregoing examples that strongly capillary-active anions only suppress positive maxima, and capillary-active cations

---

[13] J. Heyrovsky, "Polarographie," in W. Böttger's *Die physikalischen Methoden der Chemischen Analyse* (Vol. 2, pp. 260–332), Leipzig, 1936. See also Heyrovsky, *loc. cit.*, 1934.

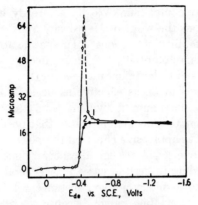

Fig. X-4. Suppression of the positive lead ion maximum by anionic methyl red in neutral solution: (1) 50 ml. of 2.3 × 10^{-3} M lead nitrate in 0.1 N potassium chloride; (2) 0.1 ml. of 0.1 per cent sodium methyl red added.

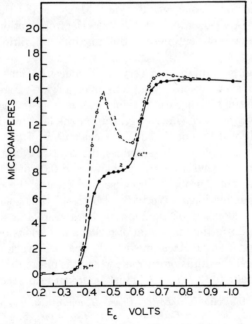

Fig. X-5. (1) 0.001 M lead and cadmium ions in 0.1 N potassium chloride in the absence of a maximum suppressor. (2) 0.1 ml. of 0.1 per cent sodium methyl red added to 50 ml. of solution.

only suppress negative maxima. We have already cited several exceptions to this rule from the work of Heyrovsky and Dillinger.[6] Probably the degree of polarizability of the ions, their specific ability to be adsorbed on mercury at various potentials, and their effect of shifting the electrocapillary zero also have to be taken into account.

That positive dyes can be as effective as negative dyes in suppressing the positive oxygen maximum is evident from the work of Rayman.[14] Furthermore, Hamamoto[15] has demonstrated that positively charged alkaloid ions have a great suppressive effect on the positive oxygen maximum.

Capillary-active nonelectrolytes can also be very effective in suppressing and eliminating maxima in certain cases. In general, it is not to be expected that a certain capillary-active substance will be able to suppress maxima over the entire voltage range, because the adsorbability of these substances usually reaches a maximal value at a certain potential of the mercury. It is to be expected that sulfur-containing organic substances should be effective in eliminating maxima, since such substances are usually capillary active. Heyrovsky[7] mentions the great effect of traces of α-naphthol in suppressing maxima, and Maas[16] found that naphthalene was effective. Oxygen, which in its own electroreduction gives a very pronounced maximum, suppresses the maxima of various metal ions, e. g., nickel ions.

We found that gelatin, even in very small concentrations, is able to suppress the maxima of various metal ions over a wide range of potentials. The use of gelatin to suppress maxima has also been recommended by Hohn.[17] The suppressive effect of gelatin on the lead maximum is shown in Fig. X-6. It will be noted that a concentration of gelatin of 0.02 per cent was ample completely to suppress the lead maximum. When the concentration of the gelatin is greater than about 0.01 per cent it decreases the diffusion currents, probably because it decreases the diffusion coefficient of the reducible ions. We have also found that gelatin completely eliminates the maximum of thallium in both acid and alkaline media, and that it eliminates the maximum of nickel and various other metal ions in both neutral and ammoniacal media. In practical work the suppressive effect of gelatin on the diffusion current, when it is present at concentrations greater than about 0.01 per cent, must be taken into account. Buckley

[14] B. Rayman, *Collection Czechoslov. Chem. Communs.*, **3**, 314 (1931).

[15] E. Hamamoto, *Collection Czechoslov. Chem. Communs.*, **5**, 427 (1933).

[16] J. Maas, *De Polarographische Methode met de Druppelende Kwikelectrode ten Dienste van het Pharmaceutisch Onderzoek*, Amsterdam, 1937; *Collection Czechoslov. Chem. Communs.*, **10**, 42 (1938).

[17] H. Hohn, *Chemische Analysen mit dem Polarographen*. Berlin, 1937.

and Taylor[18] concluded that the complete suppression of a maximum and the appearance of a "well-defined" wave is not indicative that the observed (apparent) diffusion current is entirely diffusion controlled. Streaming phenomena may still be operative.   According to these authors a reliable criterion that the observed diffusion current is diffusion controlled is that slopes of the segments of the current–voltage curve preceding and

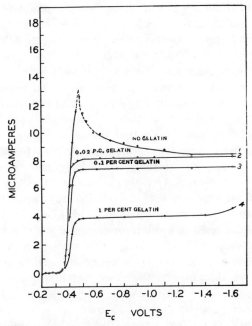

Fig. X-6. Suppression of the maximum, and lowering of the diffusion current, of lead ion by gelatin.   0.001 M lead nitrate in 0.1 N potassium chloride with (1) none, (2) 0.02, (3) 0.1, and (4) 1 per cent gelatin.

following the wave do not differ by more than a few per cent.   Quite generally, it seems wise to determine for each particular substance the minimum concentration of gelatin or other maximum suppressor at which not only the maximum is completely suppressed but also the proportionality between diffusion current and concentration is found.   For the use of maximum suppressors in specific cases the reader is referred to the practical part of this book.   In general, unnecessarily large concentrations of suppressors should be avoided because some of them in large concentration produce undesirable effects.

[18] F. Buckley and J. K. Taylor, *J. Research Natl. Bur. Standards,* **34,** 97 (1945).

3. PHENOMENA AT THE ELECTROCAPILLARY ZERO

Heyrovsky[7] claims that no maximum occurs when the electroreduction of a substance takes place at the potential corresponding to the electrocapillary zero (maximum in the electrocapillary curve), where the mercury is apparently uncharged and the interfacial tension has its maximal value. This statement may be correct so far as the electroreduction of capillary-inactive ions and molecules is concerned, but it is doubtful in the electroreduction of capillary-active substances.[19] For example, no maximum occurs in the discharge of cadmium ion from chloride solutions, because the discharge potential of cadmium ion under these conditions is very close to the electrocapillary zero (-0.6 v. in chloride solutions). Cadmium iodide, on the other hand, gives a very pronounced maximum, even though the half-wave potential of cadmium in very dilute iodide solutions is practically the same as in chloride solutions. The occurrence of the (positive) maximum is explained by the fact that the iodide ions are strongly capillary active, and they shift the electrocapillary zero to a more negative potential so that it no longer coincides with the discharge potential of the cadmium ions. Other capillary active anions, such as S^{--}, CN^-, CNS^-, etc., shift the electrocapillary zero in a similar way, while capillary-active cations shift it to a more positive potential (see Chap. VIII).

Care must be exercised in the interpretation of the effect of these capillary ions on maxima. The capillary-active anions are adsorbed on the positively charged and uncharged mercury (increasing adsorption with increasing positive charge), and they therefore attract an almost equivalent amount of cations to the surface in a triple layer.[20] For this reason the total effect of capillary-active ions may be very complicated. For example, Lingane[21] found that the positive maximum due to lead ions in 0.1 N potassium chloride was almost completely suppressed when the solution was made 0.001 N with respect to iodide ions. On the other hand, in the absence of potassium chloride, the lead maximum was considerably accentuated in 0.001 N and 0.005 N potassium iodide, and was not completely eliminated even in 1 N potassium iodide (in the latter case the lead was present chiefly as PbI_4^{--} anions). It is probable that a similar effect of iodide ions will be found in the case of cadmium and other metal ions.

Heyrovsky and Vascautzanu[22] have demonstrated the effect of thio-

[19] See, e. g., A. Winkel and H. Siebert, Z. Elektrochem., **44,** 402 (1938).

[20] E. J. W. Verwey, Chem. Revs., **16,** 374 (1937).

[21] J. J. Lingane, Ph.D. Thesis, University of Minnesota (1938).

[22] J. Heyrovsky and E. Vascautzanu, Collection Czechoslov. Chem. Communs., **3,** 418 (1931).

cyanate ions in shifting the electrocapillary zero, and the resultant effect on the slight negative maximum of cadmium nitrate. They found that the slight negative maximum in a 0.005 M cadmium nitrate solution was eliminated by the addition of sufficient potassium thiocyanate to make its concentration 0.001 N. With further additions of thiocyanate ions, the electrocapillary zero was shifted to more negative potentials and the cadmium maximum reappeared on the positive side of the electrocapillary zero.

Similar phenomena were observed by these authors in the electroreduction of (undissociated) maleic acid. The c.v. curve of 0.02 M maleic acid in 1 N hydrochloric acid shows a pronounced maximum, which Heyrovsky and Vascautzanu classify as a negative maximum, although the reduction starts at -0.58 v. When the maleic acid solution was made about 0.002 N with respect to potassium iodide the maximum disappeared, but reappeared again as a positive maximum when the electrocapillary zero was shifted to still more negative potentials by further addition of iodide.

Instead of changing the location of the electrocapillary zero, use can be made of complex formation to shift the discharge potentials of metal ions which are normally reduced on the positive side of the electrocapillary zero to more negative values, until they coincide with the electrocapillary zero, and the maxima then disappear. By adding a large excess of the complex-forming salt, the discharge potentials can in certain cases be shifted to such negative values that the maxima are changed from positive to negative maxima. For example, Heyrovsky and Vascautzanu found that the positive maximum of lead was eliminated by adding small amounts of potassium hydroxide to the lead solution, which converted the simple lead ions to complex biplumbite ions, $HPbO_2^-$. By adding a large excess of potassium hydroxide the discharge potential of the lead was shifted to such a negative value that the maximum reappeared on the negative side of the electrocapillary zero. Heyrovsky and Vascautzanu obtained a similar effect by adding potassium cyanide to a solution of cadmium nitrate containing a trace of iodide. In the presence of the small amount of iodide the c.v. curve of cadmium shows a prominent positive maximum, due to the negative shift of the electrocapillary zero by the iodide ions. When cyanide was added to this solution the discharge potential of the cadmium was shifted to more negative values, due to the complex formation, and the positive maximum disappeared. By adding a large excess of cyanide the discharge potential of the cadmium was shifted to such a negative value that the maximum reappeared as a negative maximum.

4. INTERPRETATION OF MAXIMA

The Adsorption Theory of Heyrovsky and Ilkovic. The interpretation of maxima is one of the most difficult problems in polarography. It is not yet possible to present a single theory which will account for all the observed phenomena described in previous sections. Heyrovsky[23] attributes the maximum to an adsorption of the electroreducible substance on the growing mercury drops, whereby the concentration of the reducible substance is increased above its value in the body of the solution and the normal concentration polarization is prevented. This adsorption is supposed, by Heyrovsky, to be caused by the unhomogeneous electric field around the charged drops, which he assumes is identical with the electrokinetic potential at the mercury–solution interface. Since pronounced maxima are only found with the dropping electrode, and since the adsorptive force must be established sooner than the electrokinetic potential can be built up, Ilkovic[24] assumes that the unhomogeneous field responsible for the adsorption is caused by the charging current (not the total current), rather than the electrokinetic potential. The drop in potential around a mercury drop caused by the charging current, i_c, is $i_c R$, where R is the resistance in the surface film surrounding the drop. From fairly involved calculations, Ilkovic concludes that the electric field created by the charging current is much greater than the electrokinetic potential. If the electric field due to the charging current were homogeneous, i. e., $d(i_c R)/dx$ constant and independent of the distance x from the surface of the electrode, it would cause only a motion of ions, and particles subject to dielectric polarization would simply become polarized and oriented, but would undergo no movement in such a field. However, the field created by the charging current is not homogeneous, because R varies greatly with x, and hence the unhomogeneous field causes a motion of dipoles as well as ions. Ilkovic assumes that the attraction of dipolar molecules to the surface of the mercury drop by the unhomogeneous electric field takes place to an appreciable extent only when the concentration of the reducible substance has been reduced to a small value by the discharge process.

To clarify Ilkovic's view the following citation from his paper is given. "Let us now, from this viewpoint, explain the case of a maximum due to the depolarizing action of a solution which contains only one electrolyte, e. g., that due to the deposition of nickel from the solutions of its chloride. At voltages at which the rate of the deposition of nickel ions is smaller than the rate of their adsorption, the current is an 'adsorption' one and can in-

---

[23] J. Heyrovsky, Actualités scientifiques et industrielles, No. 90, Paris, 1934.
[24] D. Ilkovic, *Collection Czechoslov. Chem. Communs.*, **8**, 13 (1936).

crease with increasing voltage.   However, as soon as the voltage is reached at which at the *very beginning* of the formation of the drop the rate of deposition of the ions exceeds the rate of their adsorption, the exhaustion of the surface layer starts.   At this instant a large electric force acts at the cathode, which cannot be depolarized, there being no reducible matter present in the exhausted surface film.   However, the water molecules of the surface film are polarizable owing to their dipole character.   They must be, therefore, polarized in the strong field, their oriented polarized layer thus constituting the increase of the 'back e.m.f.' observed at the fall of the maximum.   Under such conditions now the electric field in the solution is considerably shortened so that no more ions can be attracted to the surface by adsorptive force.   The current due to the deposition of nickel ions is now furnished only by the penetration of these cations through the polarized layer of water molecules and thus becomes a 'diffusion' current.   The suppressivé action of adsorbable particles on the maximum is similar to that of water molecules, *viz.*, in that they increase the polarization owing to their dipole moment and thus counterbalance the unhomogeneous electric field due to the charge of the small mercury electrode.''

The Heyrovsky-Ilkovic interpretation of the maxima involves certain difficulties.   We have seen in previous chapters that both the charging current and the charge of the double layer (electrokinetic potential) change sign at the maximum in the electrocapillary curve.   It is evident, therefore, that the *direction* of the electric field responsible for the adsorption must also change at the electrocapillary maximum, regardless of whether this field is due to the electrokinetic potential (Heyrovsky) or to the charging current (Ilkovic).   Hence, reducible ions of a given sign should only be adsorbed, by electrical attraction, on one side or the other side of the electrocapillary maximum, but not on both sides.   On the negative side of the electrocapillary maximum, the field is in the proper direction to cause adsorption of positive ions, but on the positive side of the electrocapillary maximum the field is in the opposite direction, and hence positive ions should be repelled, not attracted and adsorbed.   Actually it is found, in contradiction of the Heyrovsky-Ilkovic theory, that the discharge of positive ions gives rise to maxima on *both* sides of the electrocapillary maximum, *e. g.*, lead and nickel ions are discharged on opposite sides of the electrocapillary curve, but the c.v. curves of both of these ions show prominent maxima.

The Electrokinetic Theory of Antweiler and von Stackelberg.   The adsorption theory of Heyrovsky and Ilkovic has been strongly opposed on

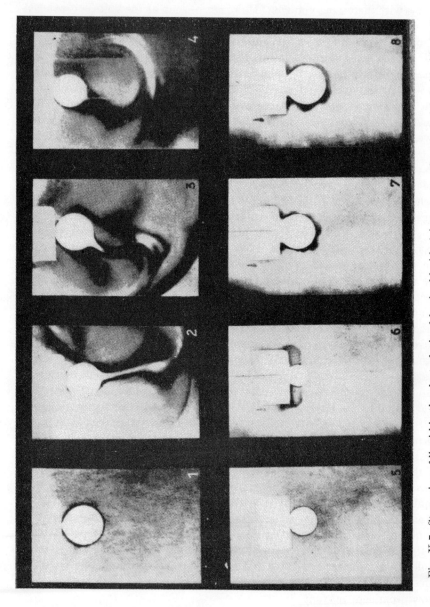

Fig. X-7. Streaming of liquid in the electrolysis of ferric chloride (pictures *1* to *5*) and of nickel chloride (*6, 7, 8*) (Antweiler).

both theoretical and practical grounds by Frumkin and his co-workers.[25] Working with a quiet mercury cathode these authors showed experimentally that at relatively large current densities the surface of the mercury is in active motion and that the potential and the surface tension of the mercury are different at the center of the pool than at the periphery. Consequently, local currents flow between spots of different potential, and—combined with the difference in surface tension—this causes a stirring effect in the solution close to the surface of the electrode. Jofa and Frumkin[26] noticed that maxima observed with quiet electrodes and the dropping mercury electrode disappear if the solution is subjected to vigorous stirring.

The ingenious experiments of Antweiler[27] showed conclusively that there is a more or less pronounced streaming of the liquid around the dropping mercury on the part of the current–voltage curve which shows a maximum. Antweiler made diffusion layers and stirring visible microphotographically by applying Toepler's "Schlierenmethod," and making an ingenious use of the optical interference method. Some typical photographs given in his first paper are reproduced in Fig. X-7. The first four pictures were taken during the electrolysis of a 0.02 N ferric chloride solution. At potentials at which the limiting current is obtained no streaming is observed and a well-defined diffusion layer is clearly visible. The same is true at the limiting current of 1/50 N nickel chloride in picture 5. Pictures 2, 3, and 4 show the violent streaming of the liquid from the top, i. e., where the drop is formed, to the bottom on the part of the c.v. curve which shows a pronounced maximum. In the case of nickel chloride, which is reduced at the negative side of the isoelectric point, the type of stirring (pictures 6, 7, and 8) is quite different, the streaming of the liquid (picture 6) often being in a direction opposite to that noticed in the case of ferric chloride. Whenever maxima were suppressed streaming ceased on the waves and photographs of a quietly developing diffusion layer (as in pictures 1 and 5) were obtained.

Detailed studies were carried out by Antweiler with solutions of copper chloride, ferric chloride, mercuric nitrate, nickel, manganese, zinc, and calcium chlorides in which the metal concentration varied between 1/30 to 1/300 N. Potassium chloride was used as supporting electrolyte in concentrations between 1 and 0.01 N, except in the case of mercuric nitrate

[25] A. Frumkin and B. Burns, *Acta Physicochim. U. R. S. S.*, **1**, 232 (1934). B. Burns, A. Frumkin, S. Jofa, L. Vanjukova, and S. Zolotarevskaja, *ibid.*, **9**, 359 (1938).

[26] S. Jofa and A. Frumkin, *Compt. rend. acad. sci. U. R. S. S.*, **20**, 293 (1938).

[27] H. J. Antweiler, *Z. Elektrochem.*, **43**, 596 (1937); **44**, 719, 831, 888 (1938). See also M. von Stackelberg, H. J. Antweiler, and L. Kieselbach, *ibid.*, **44**, 663 (1938).

when potassium nitrate was used. Antweiler not only determined the polarograms of a great number of solutions but also made photographs of the stirring at various potentials and recorded a great number of current–time curves, *i. e.*, the change of the current during the growth of a drop, with the aid of an oscillograph. No abnormalities were noticed in the formation of the mercury drops except in the case of mercuric nitrate. Here there was a distinct pulsation of the drop during its formation which was also noticed microscopically by Kolthoff and Miller.[28] We believe that this pulsation may be due to the interaction between mercury and mercuric ions: $Hg^{++} + Hg \rightarrow Hg_2^{++}$ Kolthoff and Miller showed that this reaction occurs very rapidly at the dropping electrode. At fairly high negative potentials the pulsation of the drops ceases. This is probably due to the fact that at high negative potentials the mercuric ions are reduced to mercury before they have a chance to form mercurous ions. The large number of observations made by Antweiler can be classified as follows. In general two types of streaming can be distinguished on waves with maxima: one is directed from the top to the bottom of the mercury drop (see diagrammatic picture in Fig. X-8) and occurs quite generally at the positive side of the isoelectric point; the other type of stirring is directed sideward and usually accompanies negative maxima. The *downward* streaming of liquid is divided by Antweiler into the following three classes:

(1) A *very rapid*, smooth streaming, without pulsation. The speed of this streaming can be relatively great; Antweiler reports cases in which the speed amounted to 5 cm. per second (ferric iron); while von Stackelberg[29] states that speeds of 10 cm. per second have been found. This kind of streaming has been observed with solutions of ferric iron, oxygen, copper chloride (with small concentrations of indifferent electrolyte), and mercuric nitrate (in the absence of indifferent electrolyte). In general, then, this type of streaming is observed on waves with "positive maxima." E. Orlemann (University of Minnesota) succeeded in making the streaming visible microscopically by adding a little talcum powder to the solution under investigation.

(2) A *rapid* streaming with pulsation of the drop. When there is pulsation the oscillogram (current–time curve) shows irregular fluctuations. The case occurs with not too dilute mercuric nitrate solutions in the presence of potassium nitrate.

(3) A *slow* streaming which is branched sideways and which causes great

---

[28] I. M. Kolthoff and C. S. Miller, *J. Am. Chem. Soc.*, **63,** 1013 (1941).

[29] M. von Stackelberg, *Z. Elektrochem.*, **45,** 466 (1939).

fluctuations in the oscillograms. It occurs in not too dilute copper chloride solutions the polarograms of which show rounded maxima.

The above types of stirring are portrayed in Fig. X-9. The long "Schlieren" are caused by the fall of the previous drop. The irregularities in the oscillograms corresponding to streaming according to cases (2) and (3) are quite pronounced. Antweiler usually worked with fairly concentrated solutions of the reducible cations and it is doubtful whether such large fluctuations occur at concentrations normally used in polarographic work.

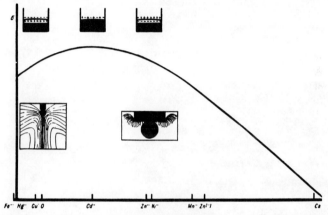

Fig. X-8. Diagrammatic pictures of two main types of stirring as related to electrocapillary curve (and reduction potential of some cations) (Antweiler).

The *sideward* streaming is divided by Antweiler into the following three classes:

(1) A sideward streaming in which the liquid is ejected from between the base of the capillary and the top of the drop. A diagrammatic picture of this kind of streaming is seen in Fig. X-8. It has been observed by Antweiler in solutions, of nickel, manganese, calcium, and zincate ions which yield negative maxima, and also in mixtures of mercuric and potassium nitrates in which the ratio of KNO_3 to $Hg(NO_3)_2$ was greater than 100.

(2) A sideward streaming emanating from the side of the drop itself. This type of streaming was found to occur in the case of zinc.

(3) A turbulent disturbance of the diffusion layer. A distinction can be made between fine whorls (calcium, zinc, and zincate) and coarse whorls (manganese and nickel); the latter are relatively small in number but bring larger volumes of liquid into motion.

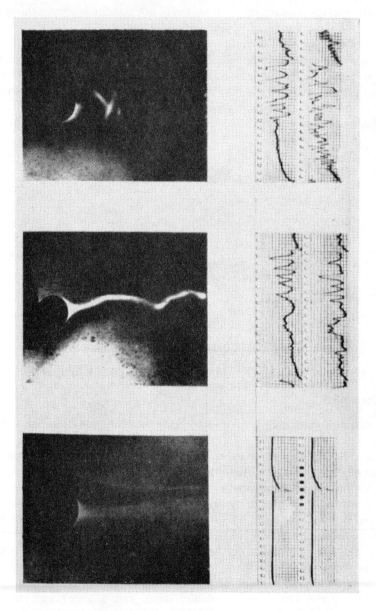

Fig. X-9. Different types of stirring and corresponding current–time curves (Antweiler).

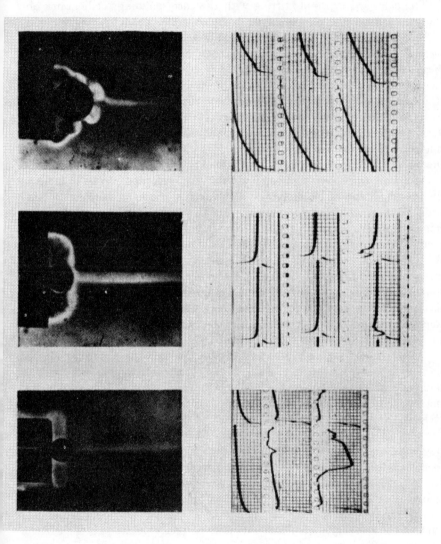

Fig. X-10. Sideward streaming and corresponding current–time curves (Antweiler).

The sideward types of stirring with the corresponding oscillograms obtained by Antweiler are portrayed in Fig. X-10.

It is of importance to emphasize that in general the *downward streaming occurs when dealing with positive maxima* and *sideward streaming when dealing with negative maxima*. In agreement with Heyrovsky and his school no maxima were found when the reduction potential was close to the isoelectric point of mercury and no stirring was noticed. Diagrammatically the situation is shown in Fig. X-8.

Antweiler infers from the phenomena observed by him that the streaming is an electrokinetic phenomenon. Electrical double layers can migrate under the influence of potential gradients. However, in electroosmotic experiments the speed of streaming has never been found to be as large as in the streaming of electrolyte at the mercury drop. According to Antweiler the great difference between the two cases is that in the case of mercury we are not dealing with a solid–liquid interface, but a liquid–liquid one. When a liquid streams past a solid wall the friction between the body of the liquid and the liquid film firmly attached to the wall is very great and it counteracts the driving electrokinetic force. When the second phase is a liquid, and a good electrical conductor (mercury), the double layer can move very easily, because it can take along the top layers of the mercury phase. In our case this may be promoted by a slight difference in surface tension between the top and the bottom of the drop.[29]

When dealing with a positive maximum the mercury surface carries an excess of positive charges. As a result of electrical attraction an excess of anions from the aqueous phase will accumulate close to the surface of the mercury. The direction of streaming of the liquid (double layer) suggests that it moves under a potential gradient which has its positive pole at the bottom and its negative pole at the top of the mercury drop. When dealing with a negative maximum an excess of cations from the aqueous phase accumulates close to the surface of the mercury. Since it has the same potential gradient in the same direction as before, the double layer will now move from the bottom to the top of the mercury drop. The chief difficulty is to account for the potential gradient between the top and the bottom of the mercury. As Antweiler quite correctly points out, the current density at the bottom of the drop is greater than at the top. The tip of the capillary exerts a screening effect and prevents and counteracts the free diffusion of the reducible particles to the surface of the mercury, while at the bottom the reducible particles have free access to the surface. The difference in current density causes an unequal distribution of the ions in the double layer at the bottom and at the top of the mercury drop and consequently a tangential potential gradient in the double layer around the drop. Antweiler calls the double layer at positively charged mercury (positive side of isoelectric point) a negative double layer and states that "a negatively charged double layer moves from a place with higher cation concentration to a place with lower cation concentration, while a positively charged double layer moves away from it. One can assume, therefore, that the potential gradient is caused by a small cation concentration of the double layer at the top and a large cation concentration at the bottom of the drop. The radial potential gradient, *i. e.*, the gradient perpendicular to the surface of the mercury, is larger at the bottom than at the top of the drop; under the influence of this potential gradient more cations in the double layer arrive at the bottom than at the top, the latter having only a small potential gradient. The cations concerned are mainly 'indifferent' cations which are not reduced at the applied potential but which can accumulate in the double layer and cause an increase of the cation concentration in the latter."

In the above we have quoted Antweiler freely. Although we agree with Antweiler that the streaming undoubtedly is due to an electrokinetic force in the double layer, we are not able to give a clear picture of the distribution of the indifferent ions in the double layer at the bottom and at the top of the drop.

Mercury is an excellent conductor, and, since the currents ordinarily involved in polarographic work are small, the iR drop between the top and the bottom of the drop is also negligibly small. Hence, even though the current density at the top is smaller than at the bottom, the potential of the mercury is the same over the entire surface of the drop. Von Stackelberg,[29] in whose laboratory Antweiler's work has been carried out, states in his excellent review paper that the top of the drop behaves as if it has a more positive potential than the bottom, although it is more exact to say that the solution, *i. e.*, the adsorption layer, is more negative at the top of the drop than at other parts of the surface. If the drop behaves as if it has a more positive potential at the top than at the bottom the surface tension at the top is smaller than at the bottom when dealing with positive maxima (see electrocapillary curve, Fig. VIII-2). The interface, therefore, is pulled from top to bottom, which is the direction of streaming observed by Antweiler. When dealing with negative maxima the top with the more positive potential has a greater surface tension than the bottom, and the direction of streaming is reversed. Near the isoelectric point the electrocapillary curve is very flat and a slight difference in potential between the top and the bottom does not cause a streaming of the interface.

The sudden change from the maximal current to the diffusion current is attributed by von Stackelberg to a blocking effect by the indifferent cations in the double layer at spots of higher current density. The accumulated cations cover the surface and make it more difficult for the reducible substance to reach to the surface; the effect, therefore, results in a more equal distribution of the current lines over the surface of the mercury drop.

Antweiler's experimental work contributes greatly to our practical knowledge of maxima. However, an exact interpretation of many of the involved phenomena cannot be given at present. For example, specific effects of the reducible substance itself have not been accounted for. In addition, it is well known that different substances which are reduced at about the same potential do not give maxima of equal height at the same concentration in the same medium. It seems quite possible that the adsorbability of the reduced substance at the surface of mercury also has to be considered and that a theory which accounts for all the phenomena involved in the occurrence of maxima should include the effect of adsorptive forces (Heyrovsky, Ilkovic) and electrokinetic forces (Antweiler, von Stackelberg).

Extensive theoretical and experimental studies on the cause of polarographic maxima and the factors which determine the stirring have been carried out by Frumkin and his associates.[30] Expressions have been derived for the rates of both electrokinetic and electrocapillary motions. The electrocapillary motion is due to the difference in surface tension between the top and the bottom of the mercury as discussed above. Application of an external field produces a dissymmetry of field strength within the double layer. Studies of the mobility of mercury droplets in a viscous medium of glycerol[31] gave results in agreement with the theoretical postulates. The electrocapillary mobility decreases with decreasing electrolyte concentration. Systematic investigations on the flow phenomena at a dropping mercury over a wide range of potassium chloride concentrations have been carried out by Kryukova.[32] The nature of the damping effect

[30] A. N. Frumkin, J. Colloid Sci., 1, 277 (1946); Bull. acad. sci. U. R. S. S., Classe sci. chim., 1945, 223; see Chem. Abstr., 40, 2055 (1946). A. N. Frumkin and V. Levich, Acta Physicochim. U. R. S. S., 20, 769 (1945). T. A. Kryukova and B. N Kabanov, J. Gen. Chem. U. S. S. R., 15, 294 (1945); Chem. Abstr., 40, 3325 (1946). A. N. Frumkin and V. Levich, J. Phys. Chem. U. S. S. R., 21, 1183, (1947); Chem. Abstr., 42, 3244 (1948).

[31] I. A. Bagotskaya and A. N. Frumkin, Compt. rend. acad. sci. U. R. S. S., 55, 131 (1947); see Chem. Abstr., 41, 7202 (1947).

[32] T. A. Kryukova, Zavodskaya Lab., 9, 699 (1940); see J. Phys. Chem. U. S. S. R., 20, 1179 (1946); 21, 365 (1947); Chem. Abstr., 41, 3004, 6160 (1947).

exercised by the charges of the double layer on the movement of the liquid–metal surface is considered.

5. INFLUENCE OF EXTERNAL RESISTANCE IN CELL CIRCUIT ON MAXIMA

Brdicka[33] made the discovery that the prominent maximum on the c.v. curve of the reduction of mercurous ions from a slightly acid mercurous nitrate solution was greatly suppressed by inserting a high resistance in series with the cell. Lingane[34] was able to confirm Brdicka's results, and he also showed that the introduction of an external resistance had a similar effect on the maxima of oxygen, lead, zinc, and nickel. The effect, there-

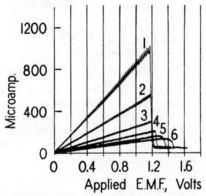

Fig. X-11. Influence of external resistance in the cell circuit on the maximum of 0.05 M mercurous nitrate in 0.005 N nitric acid. External resistance was: (1) none, (2) 1000 ohms, (3) 3000 ohms, (4) 5000 ohms, (5) 7000 ohms, and (6) 9000 ohms.

fore, appears to be a general one. To illustrate the effect a few polarograms obtained by Lingane with mercurous nitrate, oxygen, and lead are given in Figs. X-11, X-12, and X-13. In these polarograms the *total applied e.m.f.* is plotted against the current. In the case of mercurous nitrate the value of the *total applied e.m.f.* at which the peak of the maximum occurred remained practically constant when the external resistance R_e was smaller than about 5000 ohms, but with larger values of R_e the peak of the maximum was shifted to larger values of the applied e.m.f. These results are in agreement with those of Brdicka.

The suppression of the oxygen maximum required a much larger external

[33] R. Brdicka, *Collection Czechoslov. Chem. Communs.*, **8**, 419 (1936). See also W. Kemula, *ibid.*, **2**, 347 (1930).

[34] J. J. Lingane, *J. Am. Chem. Soc.*, **62**, 1665 (1940).

resistance than in the case of the mercurous ions. Moreover, the peak of the maximum shifted uniformly from 0.46 to 0.62 v. applied e.m.f. when the external resistance was increased from zero up to 20,000 ohms. In the

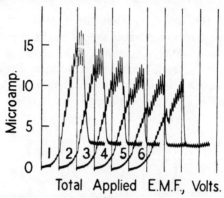

Fig. X-12. 0.02 N potasium chloride saturated with air. Start at $E_a = 0$ v. in all cases, and the distance between each vertical line is 0.200 v. External resistance in series with the cell was: (1) none, (2) 3000 ohms (3) 6000 ohms, (4) 10,000 ohms, (5) 15,000 ohms, and (6) 20,000 ohms. The values of the total applied e.m.f. at the peaks of the maxima are: (1) 0.46 v., (2) 0.48 v., (3) 0.52 v., (4) 0.57 v., (5) 0.60 v., and (6) 0.62 v.

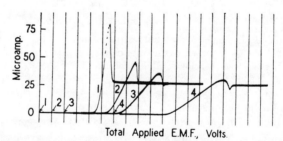

Fig. X-13. 3.5 × 10⁻³ M lead nitrate in 0.09 N potassium chloride. Start at $E_a = 0$ in all cases at points marked by arrows. the distance between each vertical line being 0.100 v. External resistance was: (1) none, (2) 3000 ohms, (3) 6000 ohms, and (4) 10,000 ohms. The values of the total applied e.m.f. at the peaks of the maxima are: (1) 0.56 v., (2) 0.68 v., (3) 0.78 v., and (4) 0.90 v.

other cases investigated the peak of the maximum was also found to shift with increasing external resistance. Lingane showed that this shift was due to the increased ohmic potential drop in the circuit as the external resistance is increased. The total e.m.f., E_a, applied to the circuit is distributed across the cell and the external resistance:

$$E_a = E_{cell} + iR_e$$

In all the cases, except that of mercurous nitrate, the shift of the location of the maximum was found to correspond to the ohmic potential drop iR_e. That is, *the peak of the maximum occurred at the same average value of E_{cell}, or at the same potential of the dropping electrode.* In the case of mercurous ions (Fig. X-11) the currents were very large and the slope of line *1* in Fig. X-11 is inversely proportional to the resistance of the cell itself (1200 ohms). The fact that the peaks of the maxima in Fig. X-11 are at the same value of E_a when R_e was less than 5000 ohms is merely a coincidence. When the external resistance was increased the maximal current decreased just enough to keep the total iR drop approximately constant until the external resistance exceeded 5000 ohms. Hence, the mercurous ion maximum also occurs at the same potential of the dropping electrode with various values of the external resistance. At first glance it is difficult to understand that the current, dependent upon the external resistance, can have different values at the same potentials of the dropping mercury. Such an effect could not occur with a quiet mercury electrode.

In order to interpret the peculiar effect of the external resistance we must realize that the measured values of the current and of E_c are average values; the actual values of i and E_c may vary during the growth of the drop. In the extreme case in which the external resistance is zero, the applied e.m.f. is equal to E_c. Under these conditions the latter is constant during the growth of the drop and, as will be shown below, the current during the formation of a drop when the electrode is *depolarized* will increase with the area of the drop. In the other extreme case, in which the internal resistance is negligibly small with regard to the external resistance, E_c will increase during the growth of the drop when the electrode is depolarized but the current will remain practically constant after the very early stage of the formation of the drop (see Fig. X-14). Hence, the fluctuation of the galvanometer when dealing with a depolarized dropping electrode should decrease with increasing external resistance and should finally disappear.

Let us now compare the change of the current during the formation of a drop (depolarized electrode) in the two extreme cases when the average E_{cell} is the same, but when the external resistance in one case is equal to zero and in the other case is infinitely great. Naturally, with the same average E_{cell} the average current measured will be nearly the same. In the absence of an external resistance the current should increase during the formation of the drop, but, on the other hand, with a large external resistance in the circuit the current remains practically constant after the early stages of formation of the drop. As the average current is the same in both cases the *current density* during the early stages of the formation of the drop in the presence of a large external resistance is much greater than in the absence of external resistance. It has been stated earlier in this section that an acute maximum is characterized by a sudden polarization due to an exhaustion of depolarizer in the immediate vicinity of the growing drop. The drop then remains polarized, and the current drops from the maximum to the value of the diffusion current. Since the current density during the early stages of the formation of the drop is, with the same average E_{cell}, much greater with a large external resistance in the circuit than in the absence of an external resistance, the critical exhaustion of the depolarizer (maximum) will be obtained at a smaller average current when the external resistance is great than when there is no external resistance in the circuit. From this it follows that the height of the maximum must also decrease with increasing external resistance. Brdicka[33] has calculated the change of the current with time as a function of the external resistance. His derivations are given below in a condensed form.

When the dropping electrode is depolarized and the external resistance is equal to zero the current is determined by Ohm's Law

$$i = \frac{E_{appl.}}{R_i} \tag{1}$$

in which R_i is the internal resistance and E_a is equal to the applied e.m.f. The internal resistance changes with the size of the mercury drop. According to Ilkovic[35]

$$R_i = \frac{\rho}{4\pi r} \tag{2}$$

in which ρ denotes the specific resistance of the electrolyte and r the radius of the mercury drop considered to be spherical. It is easily seen that r is a simple function of the time t

$$r = at^{1/3} \tag{3}$$

in which a is a function of the characteristics of the capillary used. From eqs. 1, 2, and 3 it follows that

$$i_t = \frac{E_a 4\pi a t^{1/3}}{\rho} \tag{4}$$

---

[35] D. Ilkovic, *Collection Czechoslov. Chem. Communs.*, **8**, 13 (1936).

The average current, $\bar{\imath}$, according to Ilkovic[36] is

$$\bar{\imath} = \frac{4\pi E_a a}{t_{max.}} \int_0^{t_{max.}} t^{1/3} dt = \frac{E_a}{\bar{R}} = \frac{E_a}{\frac{4}{3}R_{min.}} \tag{5}$$

in which $\bar{R}$ is the mean resistance. The resistance $R_{min.}$ is equal to the minimum resistance at the moment when the drop falls. When the drop is depolarized and the external resistance in the circuit is equal to R_e the current at any time t is given by

$$i_t = \frac{E_a}{R_i + R_e} = E_a \frac{4\pi a t^{1/3}}{\rho + 4\pi a t^{1/3} R_e} \tag{6}$$

and the mean current $\bar{\imath}$

$$\bar{\imath} = \frac{E_a 4\pi a}{t_{max.}} \int_0^{t_{max.}} \frac{t^{1/3} dt}{\rho + 4\pi a t^{1/3} R_e}$$

$$= \frac{E_a}{R_e} \left\{ 1 - \frac{3}{2} \frac{R_{min.}}{R_e} + 3 \left(\frac{R_{min.}}{R_e} \right)^2 - 3 \left(\frac{R_{min.}}{R_e} \right)^3 \ln \left(1 + \frac{R_e}{R_{min.}} \right) \right\} \tag{7}$$

The mean resistance, $\bar{R}$, is given by the expression

$$\bar{R} = \frac{R_e}{1 - \frac{3}{2} \frac{R_{min.}}{R_e} - 3 \left(\frac{R_{min.}}{R_e} \right)^2 - 3 \left(\frac{R_{min.}}{R_e} \right)^3 \ln \left(1 + \frac{R_e}{R_{min.}} \right)} \tag{8}$$

Brdicka writes this expression in a simplified form

$$\bar{R} = R_e + \alpha R_{min.} \tag{9}$$

in which α depends upon the ratio $R_{min.}/R_e$ as shown in the following table:

$\dfrac{R_{min.}}{R_e}$	1/1000	1/100	1/10	1	10	100
α	1.499	1.493	1.457	1.378	1.336	1.334

In the electrolysis of a slightly acid mercurous nitrate solution the minimum resistance of which was 1008 ohms, Brdicka found that eq. 9 was valid within 2 per cent when the external resistance was varied from 26 to 8026 ohms.

From eq. 4 it is evident that with the depolarized electrode the current should increase with $t^{1/3}$ during the formation of a drop when the external resistance is zero. On the other hand, it is seen from eq. 6 that the current should not change during the formation of the drop when the external re-

---

[36] D. Ilkovic, *Collection Czechoslov. Chem. Communs.*, **4**, 480 (1932).

sistance becomes so great that ρ is negligibly small compared to $4\pi a t^{1/3} R_e$. If this extreme condition is fulfilled we can write, instead of eq. 6, $i_t = (E_a/R_e)$.

Brdicka (*loc. cit.*) determined current–time curves during the formation of a drop in the neighborhood of the maximum in slightly acid mercurous nitrate solutions with the aid of a galvanometer of extremely short period with various external resistances in the circuit. In the absence of an external resistance the current increased continuously and rapidly during the formation of each drop. With increasing external resistance the rate of

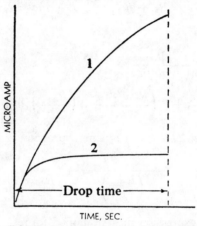

Fig. X-14. Schematic representation of current–time curves during the formation of a single mercury drop: (*1*) with no external resistance, and (*2*) with a large external resistance, in a series with the cell.

increase of the current during the growth of the drop became increasingly less. Indeed, with a large external resistance the current became almost constant after the early stages of drop formation. Diagrammatically, this is shown in Fig. X-14. The current–time curves obtained by Ilkovic[35] in the electrolysis of oxygen in 0.002 N potassium chloride solutions in the immediate neighborhood of the maximum are also of interest in this connection and can be interpreted in a similar way.

6. ANALYTICAL USE OF SUPPRESSION OF MAXIMA. ADSORPTION ANALYSIS

We have seen that maxima which occur on current–voltage curves of reducible substances like oxygen can be suppressed and in many instances eliminated by the addition of capillary-active substances. The suppression increases with increasing concentration of the capillary-active substances and this effect can be made the basis for the quantitative determination of these substances. Since, in many instances, even traces of capillary-active substances exert a suppressing effect, the method should be useful for trace analysis. Moreover, it can be used for the determination of the relative adsorbabilities of substances which are capillary active at the interfac mercury–water.[37]

From the analytical viewpoint the method has serious disadvantages. The height of a maximum in the absence of a capillary-active substance depends on the concentration of the electroreduced substance. This can be taken care of by keeping the concentration of this substance constant. The kind and concentration of the supporting electrolyte, the drop time, the mass of mercury, the temperature, and the pH affect the height of the maximum more seriously. In addition, many maxima are suppressed even by extremely small traces of capillary-active substances; for example, an oxygen maximum is greatly suppressed by filtration of the solution through quantitative filter paper or by contact with a cork stopper.

Analytical use of suppression of maxima for a quantitative determination of the concentration of the suppressor was introduced by Heyrovsky[38] under the name of "adsorption analysis."

The suppression of the oxygen maximum has been utilized by Veldstra and Havinga[39] for the determination of the capillary activity of sulfonamide and derivatives at the interface mercury–water. Czechoslovak workers[40] have studied the effect of impurities in refined sugars on the suppression of the oxygen maximum and use the method for the evaluation of refined sugars. Trusov[41] evaluates the photographic activity of gelatin by its effect on the oxygen maximum. Schwarz et al.[42] used the suppression of the oxygen maximum for the estimation of surface-active constituents in natural and effluent waters. As stated elsewhere, the height of the oxygen

[37] Compare J. Heyrovsky, *Polarography*, Springer, Berlin, 1941, p. 171.

[38] See especially J. Heyrovsky, *loc. cit.*, p. 408 ff.

[39] E. Havinga, H. W. Julius, H. Veldstra, K. C. Winkler, *Modern Development of Chemotherapy*, Elsevier, New York-Amsterdam, 1946, p. 76. H. Veldstra and E. Havinga, *Rec. trav. chim.*, **66**, 273 (1947).

[40] K. Sandera and B. Zimmermann, *Z. Zuckerind. Czechoslovak. Rep.*, **53**, 373 (1929). I. Vavruck, *Z. Zuckerind. Böhmsen-Mähren*, **66**, 43, 161 (1942); *Chem. Abstr.*, **38**, 5099, 5100 (1944).

[41] V. V. Trusov, *Zavodskaya Lab.*, **13**, 303 (1947).

[42] K. E. Schwarz, H. J. Schröder, and M. von Stackelberg, *Z. Elektrochem.*, **48**, 6 (1942).

maximum varies with the concentration of supporting electrolyte. However, the above authors found that a plot of the height of the maximum at various electrolyte concentrations (potassium chloride was used) against the ratio of the concentrations of electrolyte and oxygen yields a curve which is not affected by the electrolyte concentration. In measuring the suppression of the maximum they added to 10 ml. of "base" solution, which was 0.01 N in potassium chloride and air-saturated, varying amounts of the water to be tested. The ratio of the volume of "base" solution to the volume of water necessary to reduce the maximum height to half of the original value is called the "degree of impurity." If relatively large volumes of water must be added it is necessary to make the water also 0.01 N in potassium chloride, in order to work at a fairly constant electrolyte content. At the recommended electrolyte concentration the oxygen maximum is rounded and occurs in a fairly constant potential region. Therefore, it is not necessary to measure the entire current–voltage curve, but only the height of the wave at the potential corresponding to the maximum.

The suppressing effects on the oxygen maximum of Twitchell's reagent (sulfonaphthylstearic acid) and of lauric acid have been investigated by Capitanio and Pittoni.[43] Thiesse and Belon[44] studied the relation between wetting power of seven wetting agents and the activation energy necessary for their adsorption on a mercury–water interface by determining the suppression of the oxygen maximum.

Von Stackelberg and Schütz[45] recommend the use of the cupric copper maximum for the determination of the concentration of maximum suppressors. A solution of 0.01 M cupric chloride in 0.1 N sulfuric acid yields an acute maximum which is not affected by small amounts of salts.

In order to keep the technique as simple as possible von Stackelberg and Schütz do not determine the decrease in height of the maximum, but the potential at which the new maximum occurs ("Abbruch Potential"). When working with an automatic Heyrovsky type of polarograph it is not necessary to make a photographic record of the current–voltage curve, but only to observe the potential on the rotating slide wire at which the current suddenly drops.

The potential E_c at which the maximum occurs is

$$E = -E_c + E_a + iR$$

[43] V. Capitano and A. Pittoni, *Atti ist. Veneto sci.*, Pt. 2, **100**, 290 (1941); *Chem. Abstr.*, **19**, 5660 (1943).

[44] X. Thiesse and S. Belon, *Compt. rend.*, **223**, 794 (1946).

[45] M. von Stackelberg and H. Schütz, *Kolloid Z.*, **105**, 20 (1943).

in which E is the measured e.m.f., E_c the potential of the dropping electrode, and E_a that of the anode.

With the standard electrolyte proposed by von Stackelberg and Schütz large currents (of the order of 1000 μa.) may flow through the cell. In order to keep E_a constant it is necessary to use an anode which is not polarized under these conditions. A calomel electrode is not satisfactory for this purpose and von Stackelberg and Schütz recommend the use of a mercury–mercurous sulfate electrode (saturated with Hg_2SO_4 in 0.1 N sulfuric acid) in which the mercury occupies a surface of the order of 10 cm.^{2} The electrolysis cell is connected with the reference electrode by

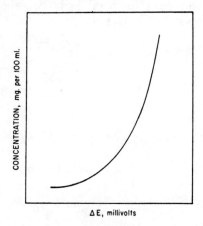

Fig. X-15. Change of ΔE with concentration of maximum suppressor.

the aid of two sintered glass (G^4, Schott and Gen. Jena) diaphragms, the salt bridge being filled with 0.1 N sulfuric acid. The drop time is about 1.5 seconds and must be kept constant.

Before using the method for the determination of the concentration of a given maximum suppressor a calibration curve must be made. Since the resistance R is kept constant and E_a is also a constant it is only necessary to plot the change of the applied e.m.f. at which the maximum occurs (ΔE) against the concentration of the maximum suppressor. The curve obtained has the general appearance shown in Fig. X-15.

The largest values of ΔE are found at the smallest concentrations. When the concentrations become relatively large ΔE changes only very little with the concentration, because the surface becomes saturated with the suppressor. Therefore it would be most advantageous to measure ΔE at the smallest concentrations. However, at very small concentrations

ΔE becomes poorly reproducible and it is best to select an intermediate concentration range in which ΔE can be measured reproducibly. It is recommended that the calibration curve be determined every day.

Von Stackelberg and Schütz apply the method to the determination of the concentration of the detergent Mersolate (an alkyl sulfonate) in commercial products. They also give calibration curves for an alkyl polyglycol ether sulfonate, an alkyl polyglycol ether and an alkyl naphthalene sulfonate. It should be realized that the method is highly unspecific, because all capillary-active substances exert the same effect. When commercial detergents are mixtures of varying composition, e. g., ordinary soaps, an investigation should be made as to how the calibration curves change with the composition of the sample.

CHAPTER XI

Polarographic Waves of Simple Metal Ions. Significance of the Half-Wave Potential

1. INTRODUCTION

The steeply rising part of a current–voltage curve between the decomposition potential and the potential at which a constant limiting or diffusion current is reached is called a "polarographic wave." In this and the following chapters we shall consider the relations that exist between the potential of the dropping electrode and the corresponding current at each point on a polarographic wave, that is, the equation of the wave.

In the analysis of the waves of metal ions it is necessary to distinguish between reactions involving simple and complex metal ions. The waves of simple metal ions will be discussed in this chapter and in the following chapter the analysis of the waves of complex metal ions will be treated. The term "simple metal ion" is actually somewhat of a misnomer, because the existence of simple ions is only possible in a gas phase, and in polar solvents the ions of metals are more or less strongly combined with molecules of the solvent. In many cases these solvation complexes are of such definite composition that they may properly be called "aquo complex ions," or simply "aquo ions." For example, chromic ion in dilute aqueous solution exists chiefly as complex hexaquo chromic ion, $Cr(H_2O)_6^{+++}$. Although such aquo ions are true complexes, they constitute a unique class and it is convenient to classify them separately from other complex ions, and to refer to them as "simple metal ions." This nomenclature will be used in the following discussion, and for simplicity's sake the aquo ions will usually be written as if they were free ions, $e. g.$, Cr^{+++}.

There are four possibilities to consider in the reduction and oxidation of simple metal ions at the dropping electrode: (1) Reduction to the metallic state of the ions of metals that are soluble in mercury, resulting in the formation of an amalgam on the surface of the dropping electrode. (2) Reduction to the metallic state but the metal is insoluble in mercury and is deposited in the solid state at the dropping electrode. (3) Reduction or oxidation from one soluble oxidation state to another, $e. g.$, Cr^{+++} to Cr^{++}. (4) Combination of case 3 with either case 1 or case 2, so that stepwise reduction occurs and the polarogram consists of two or more waves, *e. g.*, Cr^{+++} to Cr^{++} followed by Cr^{++} to Cr.

2. CASE 1. REDUCTION OF SIMPLE IONS OF METALS THAT ARE SOLUBLE IN MERCURY

In this case the electrode reaction is

$$M^{n+} + ne + Hg = M(Hg) \tag{1}$$

where $M(Hg)$ symbolizes the amalgam formed at the surface of the mercury drops.   If this reaction is reversible, and very rapid compared to the rate of diffusion of the metal ions up to the electrode surface, the dropping electrode will be subject only to concentration polarization, and accordingly its potential at every point on the polarographic wave should be given by[1, 2]

$$E_{d.e.} = E_a^0 - \frac{RT}{nF_y} \ln \frac{C_a^0 f_a}{a_{Hg} C_s^0 f_s} \tag{2}$$

where C_a^0 is the concentration of the amalgam formed on the surface of the mercury drops, C_s^0 is the concentration of the reducible metal ions in the layer of solution *at the surface of the drops*, f_a and f_s are the corresponding activity coefficients, and a_{Hg} is the activity of mercury in the amalgam. E_a^0 is the standard potential of the amalgam, that is, the e.m.f. of the cell

$$\text{Reference electrode}/M^{n+}/M(Hg)$$

when the quantity $C_a^0 f_a / a_{Hg} C_s^0 f_s$ is equal to 1.   Since the amalgams formed at the dropping electrode are very dilute, a_{Hg} will be virtually the same as the activity of pure mercury, and can be regarded as a constant.   Equation 2 may then be written

$$E_{d.e.} = \epsilon - \frac{RT}{nF_y} \ln \frac{C_a^0 f_a}{C_s^0 f_s} \tag{3}$$

where the constant ϵ is equal to $E_a^0 + RT/nF_y \ln a_{Hg}$.

The signs of $E_{d.e.}$ and E_a^0 will be taken to be positive when the dropping electrode is positive to the particular reference electrode used, and *vice versa*.   In polarographic work calomel electrodes are usually used as refer-

---

[1] J. Heyrovsky and D. Ilkovic, *Collection Czechoslov. Chem. Communs.*, **7**, 198 (1935).

[2] J. J. Lingane, *J. Am. Soc.*, **61**, 2099 (1939).

ence electrodes.   It should also be noted that $E_{d.e.}$, C_a^0, and C_s^0 vary during the growth of each mercury drop, due to the periodic change in area and current as each drop grows and falls.   Unless stated to the contrary, the *average* values of these quantities during the life of each drop will be understood in the following discussion.

When an excess of supporting electrolyte is present to eliminate the migration current, the reducible ions reach the surface of the dropping electrode only by diffusion, and the values of C_s^0 and the current are governed by the rate of diffusion.   In order to express C_s^0 as a function of the current, Heyrovsky and Ilkovic (*loc. cit.*) assumed that the rate of diffusion was directly proportional to the difference in concentration between the depleted surface layer and the body of the solution.   On this basis the current at any point on the wave should be given by

$$i = k_s(C_s - C_s^0) \tag{4}$$

where C_s is the constant concentration of the metal ions in the body of the solution.   The proportionality constant k_s is defined by the Ilkovic equation and at 25° C. is equal to $607nD^{1/2}m^{2/3}t^{1/6}$ (see Chaps. II and IV).   The average concentration of the metal ions at the surface of the drops, C_s^0, decreases with increasing current along the wave.   When a constant diffusion current, i_d, is attained, C_s^0 has decreased to a value which is negligibly small compared to the concentration of the metal ions in the body of the solution.   In other words, at potentials corresponding to the diffusion current the metal ions are reduced as rapidly as they diffuse up to the electrode surface, C_s^0 in eq. 4 can be neglected and we have

$$i_d = k_s C_s \tag{5}$$

The general validity of this relation has already been demonstrated in Chapter IV.   By combining eqs. 4 and 5 we obtain the following expressions for C_s^0 at any point on the polarographic wave

$$C_s^0 = C_s - \frac{i}{k_s} = \frac{i_d - i}{k_s} \tag{6}$$

or

$$C_s^0 = C_s \frac{i_d - i}{i_d} \tag{7}$$

The value of C_s^0 decreases in direct proportion to the increase in the current.   At the midpoint of the wave where $i = i_d/2$, C_s^0 is equal to one-half of C_s , and so forth for other points on the wave.   These relations are based on the assumption that the concentration gradient between the electrode and the solution is linear, and from the discussion in Chapter II of the theory underlying the Ilkovic equation it is evident that this is not strictly correct.   However, the diffusion layer around the mercury drops is so thin (about 0.05 mm.), and the diffusion time so short, that the curvature of the concentration gradient is negligible and no serious error results from assuming that it is linear.

The concentration of the amalgam formed at any point on the wave is directly proportional to the current:

$$C_a^0 = k'i = \frac{i}{k_a} \qquad (8)$$

where the constant k_a has the same form as k_s and depends in the same way on the properties of the capillary and the rate of flow of mercury, except that it is a function of the diffusion coefficient of the metal atoms in the amalgam rather than that of the metal ions in the solution.

When the relations expressed by eqs. 6 and 8 are substituted into eq. 3 we obtain

$$E_{\mathrm{d.e.}} = \epsilon - \frac{RT}{nF_y} \ln \frac{f_a k_s}{f_s k_a} - \frac{RT}{nF_y} \ln \frac{i}{i_d - i} \qquad (9)$$

where $E_{\mathrm{d.e.}}$ and i are corresponding values at any point on the wave. The half-wave potential, $E_{1/2}$, is defined as the value of $E_{\mathrm{d.e.}}$ at the midpoint of the wave where $i = i_d/2$.   The last log term in eq. 9 becomes zero when $i = i_d/2$, and hence we have

$$E_{1/2} = \epsilon - \frac{RT}{nF_y} \ln \frac{f_a k_s}{f_s k_a} \qquad (10)$$

and eq. 9 simplifies to

$$E_{\mathrm{d.e.}} = E_{1/2} - \frac{0.0591}{n} \log \frac{i}{i_d - i} \qquad (11)$$

This fundamental equation of the polarographic wave was first derived by Heyrovsky and Ilkovic.[1]

It is common practice to employ a stationary layer of mercury on the bottom of the cell as a second nonpolarizable electrode.   When this technique is used the value $E_{1/2}$ is obtained by measuring the e.m.f. of this quiet electrode against an external reference electrode and algebraically subtracting the value obtained from the half-wave value of the *total* applied e.m.f.

If there is any appreciable iR drop in the cell circuit it must be subtracted from the total applied e.m.f. before computing $E_{1/2}$. Methods of determining the cell resistance have been discussed by Ilkovic.[3] The cell resistance is usually less than 1000 ohms, and hence negligibly small, when a sufficient excess of supporting electrolyte is present.

It is evident from eq. 11 that a plot of $E_{\text{d.e.}}$ *versus* $\log i/(i_d - i)$ should

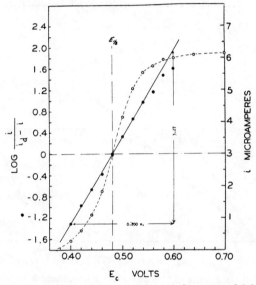

Fig. XI-1. Test of the equation of the wave of 0.001
M thallous ion in 0.9 N potassium chloride.

produce a straight line with a slope equal to $0.0591/n$ v. at 25° C., and the potential where the log term becomes zero should be the half-wave potential. These predictions and the general validity of eq. 11 in the reduction of various metal ions have been verified experimentally by Tomes[4] and Kolthoff and Lingane.[5] As a typical example the current–voltage curve of 0.001 M thallous chloride in 0.9 N potassium chloride, and the straight line obtained by plotting $E_{\text{d.e.}}$ against $\log i/(i_d - i)$, are shown in Fig. XI-1, in which the circles are experimental points. The reciprocal of the

[3] D. Ilkovic, *Collection Czechoslov. Chem. Communs.*, **4**, 480 (1932).

[4] J. Tomes, *Collection Czechoslov. Chem. Communs.*, **9**, 12, 81, 150 (1937).

[5] I. M. Kolthoff and J. J. Lingane, *Chem. Revs.*, **24**, 1–94 (1939).

slope of the straight line is 0.061 v., in good agreement with the theoretical value 0.059 v. for the reduction of a unipositive metal ion. The potential corresponding to the value of zero for the log term is the half-wave potential (vertical broken line).

A similar good agreement between experiment and theory is shown by the log plots of the c.v. curves of thallous, lead, and indic ions[2] given in Fig. XI-2. The experimental points of the log plots form good straight lines with slopes of 0.059, 0.033, and 0.023 v., in close agreement with the

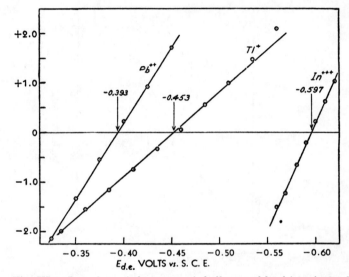

Fig. XI-2. Log plots of the waves of thallous and lead ions in 0.1 N potassium chloride, and of indic ion in 1 N potassium chloride. The slopes of the three lines are Tl[+] 0.059 v., Pb[++] 0.033 v., and In[+++] 0.023 v. Ordinate, log $[i/(i_d - i)]$.

theoretical values which are 0.059, 0.030, and 0.020 v., respectively, for the thallous, lead, and indic ions.

By differentiating eq. 11 we obtain

$$\frac{dE}{di} = -\frac{RT}{nF_y}\left(\frac{1}{i} + \frac{1}{i_d - i}\right) \tag{12}$$

and

$$\frac{d^2E}{di^2} = \frac{RT}{nF_y}\left[\frac{1}{i^2} - \frac{1}{(i_d - i)^2}\right] \tag{13}$$

Since the slope of the polarographic wave is di/dE, it is evident from eq. 12

that the slope or steepness of the wave depends directly on the value of n, and also on the concentration of the reducible ion, because i and i_d are directly proportional to the concentration. Hence at a given value of $E_{d.e.}$, say at $E_{1/2}$, the slope of the wave is greater the greater the concentration of the reducible ion, and at a given concentration the slope of the wave is greater the greater the value of n. In other words, at a given concentration the wave of a divalent ion rises more steeply than that of a univalent ion. These predicted characteristics of the waves have been verified experimentally.

Although the slope of the wave itself depends on both the concentration of the reducible ion and the value of n, the slope of the log plot of eq. 11 depends only on n and is independent of the concentration, because the ratio $i/(i_d - i)$ is independent of the concentration at any given value of $E_{d.e.}$. This fact can be used to determine the value of n in an "unknown" case from the slope of the log plot. However, although this method is reliable in many instances, it is not infallible.

From eq. 13 it is evident that at the midpoint of the wave, where $i = i_d/2$, the second differential d^2E/di^2 becomes zero, corresponding to the inflection point in the wave. The wave is symmetrical about the midpoint and the half-wave potential coincides with its inflection point and center of symmetry. *The most important characteristic of the half-wave potential is that it is constant and independent of the concentration of the reducible metal ion, provided that the supporting electrolyte concentration and the temperature are kept constant.* This is demonstrated by the polarogram of various concentrations of cadmium ion in 1 N potassium chloride shown in Fig. XI-3, and by some typical data obtained by Kolthoff and Lingane[5] which are given in Table XI-1. With increasing concentration of the reducible ion the wave starts sooner but ends later, so that the width of the wave (in volts) increases and $E_{1/2}$ remains constant.

The thermodynamic equations which describe a reversible polarographic wave are identical with those of a potentiometric titration curve; the current axis of the polarographic curve corresponds to the "volume of titrant" axis of the potentiometric curve. The only difference is that in the polarographic case the "titration" is performed by direct electron transfer at the electrode rather than by electron transfer to or from an added reagent. The polarographic half-wave potential is identical with the potential at the 50 percent point in a potentiometric titration where one-half the equivalent amount of titrant has been added. In both cases the potential at these corresponding points is constant because the ratio of activities of the oxidized and reduced forms at the electrode surface is unity regardless of the total amount of substance reduced or titrated.

Prior to the recognition by Heyrovsky and Ilkovic of the significance of the half-wave potential it was the common custom to measure "reduction

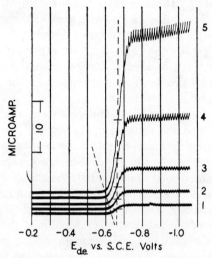

Fig. XI-3. Independence of the half-wave potential on the concentration of a reducible ion: (1) 2.8×10^{-4}, (2) 5.6×10^{-4}, (3) 1.1×10^{-3}, (4) 2.5×10^{-3}, (5) 5×10^{-3} M CdSO$_4$ in 1 N KCl.

TABLE XI-1

CONSTANCY OF THE HALF-WAVE POTENTIALS OF SEVERAL METAL IONS AT VARIOUS CONCENTRATIONS IN 0.1 N POTASSIUM CHLORIDE

Half-wave potentials at 25° C. in volts, referred to the saturated calomel electrode.

| | $E_{1/2}$ | | | |
C, millimolar	Tl$^+$	Pb^{++}	Cd^{++}	Zn^{++}
0.05	−0.45	—	—	—
0.1	−0.462	−0.396	—	—
0.2	—	—	−0.594	−0.990
0.5	−0.457	−0.396	−0.593	−0.989
1.0	−0.460	−0.392	−0.594	—
2.0	−0.456	−0.397	−0.601	−0.999
5.0	−0.459	−0.394	−0.598	−0.992
10.0	—	−0.398	−0.605	−1.003
Av.........	−0.459 ± 3	−0.396 ± 3	−0.599 ± 5	−0.995 ± 6

potentials" as the point of contact of a 45° tangent drawn to the foot of the wave. However the "reduction potential" measured in this way depends on the concentration of the reducible or oxidizable substance (compare

Fig. XI-3), and also on the properties of the dropping electrode capillary and the galvanometer sensitivity, and its use is now obsolete.

The half-wave potential of a metal ion is usually not influenced by the preceding discharge of other ions or other reducible substances, and as a general rule the $E_{1/2}$ values of various ions in a mixture are the same as in their single solutions.

Heyrovsky and Ilkovic have shown experimentally that the half-wave potential is constant and independent of the particular capillary that is used, and of the rate of mercury flow, the drop time, and the galvanometer sensitivity. It is evident from this fact and eq. 10 that the ratio k_s/k_a must be constant and independent of these factors. This is good justification for assuming that k_a depends on these factors in the same way as k_s, and is given by $607nD_a^{1/2}m^{2/3}t^{1/6}$, which is identical with the expression for k_s except that it contains the diffusion coefficient of the metal in the amalgam, D_a, instead of that of the metal ions in the solution. In this connection it may be mentioned that Lingane[6] and von Stackelberg and Freyhold[7] studied c.v. curves with dropping amalgam electrodes, in which case the electrode reaction is simply eq. 1 from right to left, and the anodic diffusion currents that they obtained were of the order of magnitude to be expected on the basis of this assumption. It appears logical, therefore, to conclude that the ratio k_s'/k_a is equal simply to $(D_s/D_a)^{1/2}$, where D_s is the diffusion coefficient of the metal ions in the solution. Further evidence for the validity of this assumption is presented below (Table XI-2).

Influence of Ionic Strength on the Half-Wave Potential. We see from eq 10 that $E_{1/2}$ should depend on the activity coefficient of the metal in the amalgam, f_a, and on that of the metal ions in the solution, f_s. The amalgams formed at the dropping electrode are so very dilute (usually much less than 0.01 M) that we are justified in assuming that they behave ideally and that f_a is practically equal to 1. However, since the solution ordinarily contains a relatively large excess of supporting electrolyte, f_s will usually be considerably smaller than 1. Since f_s is a function of the total ionic strength of the solution it is evident that it should be decreased, and that $E_{1/2}$ should be shifted to a more negative value, by increasing the concentration of supporting electrolyte. This effect, although small, has been demonstrated by Lingane[8] who obtained the data given in Table XI-3.

[6] J. J. Lingane, *J. Am. Chem., Soc.*, **61**, 976 (1939). See also J. Heyrovsky and M. Kalousek, *Collection Czechoslov. Chem. Communs.*, **11**, 464 (1939).

[7] M. von Stackelberg and H. von Freyhold, *Z. Elektrochem.*, **46**, 120 (1940).

[8] J. J. Lingane, *J. Am. Chem. Soc.*, **61**, 2099 (1939).

TABLE XI-2

COMPARISON OF CALCULATED AND OBSERVED HALF-WAVE POTENTIALS OF SEVERAL
METAL IONS

Values of $E_{1/2}$ and E_M^0 in volts with respect to the saturated calomel electrode
at 25° C.   Values of $C_{satd.}$ at 25° C.

Ion	E_M^0	E_s	$C_{satd.}$, moles per l. amalgam	$f_{satd.}$	$E_{1/2}$, calcd.	$E_{1/2}$, obs.
Tl[+]	−0.582	+0.003[c]	27.4[i]	8.3[m]	−0.440	−0.459[a]
Pb[++]	−0.372	0.006[d]	0.96[j]	0.72[j]	−0.371	−0.388[a]
Cd[++]	−0.647	0.051[e]	6.40[i]	1.15[i]	−0.570	−0.578[a]
Zn[++]	−1.008	0[f]	4.37[k]	0.74[k]	−0.993	−0.997[a]
Na[+]	−2.961	0.780[g]	3.52[l]	1.3[k]	−2.14	−2.12[b]
K[+]	−3.170	1.001[h]	1.69[h]	5.6[h]	−2.11	−2.14[b]

[a] In 0.1 N KNO₃; Lingane, J. Am. Chem. Soc., **61**, 2099 (1939).
[b] In tetramethyl ammonium hydroxide; Heyrovsky and Ilkovic, *Collection Czechoslov. Chem. Communs.*, **7**, 198 (1935).
[c] Richards and Daniels, J. Am. Chem. Soc., **41**, 1732 (1919).
[d] Gerke, J. Am. Chem. Soc., **44**, 1684 (1922).
[e] Hulett, *Trans. Am. Electrochem. Soc.*, **7**, 333 (1905).
[f] Clayton and Vosburgh, J. Am. Chem. Soc., **58**, 2093 (1936).
[g] Bent and Forziati, J. Am. Chem. Soc., **58**, 2220 (1936).
[h] Bent and Gilfillan, J. Am. Chem. Soc., **55**, 3989 (1933).
[i] Teeter, J. Am. Chem. Soc., **53**, 3917, 3927 (1937).
[j] Hoyt and Stegeman, J. Phys. Chem., **38**, 753 (1934).
[k] Pearce and Eversole, J. Phys. Chem., **32**, 209 (1928).
[l] Bent and Swift, J. Am. Chem. Soc., **58**, 2216 (1936).
[m] Lewis and Randall, *Thermodynamics*, p. 267.

TABLE XI-3

HALF-WAVE POTENTIALS OF THALLOUS, ZINC, CADMIUM, AND LEAD IONS AS A FUNC-
TION OF THE IONIC STRENGTH

Half-wave potentials in volts referred to the saturated calomel electrode at 25° C.

Supporting electrolyte	$E_{1/2}$			
	Tl[+]	Zn[++]	Pb[++]	Cd[++]
0.02 N KNO₃	−0.451	−0.988	—	−0.572
0.1 N KNO₃	0.459	0.997	−0.388	0.578
1 N KNO₃	0.477	1.012	0.405	0.586
0.02 N KCl	—	−0.988	−0.377	−0.578
0.1 N KCl	−0.459	0.995	0.396	0.599
0.25 N KCl	0.466	—	0.402	—
1 N KCl	0.480	−1.022	0.435	0.642

The $E_{1/2}$ values were measured with special care and were reproducible to
about ±3 mv.

The negative shift of the half-wave potentials is of the order of magnitude predicted by eq. 10 when potassium nitrate is used as the supporting electrolyte. The half-wave potential of thallous ion is the same in potassium nitrate and potassium chloride solutions at the same ionic strength, but with the other metal ions the negative shift is considerably greater in potassium chloride than in potassium nitrate solutions. This is apparently caused by complex formation between the divalent metal ions and chloride ions, or to incomplete dissociation of the heavy metal chlorides. In the case of lead, the excessive shift of $E_{1/2}$ in chloride solutions is actually in agreement with the known value of the dissociation constant of the $PbCl^+$ ion. It should also be noted that k_s, being proportional to $D_s^{1/2}$, varies somewhat with ionic strength, and part of the shift of $E_{1/2}$ is doubtless due to this effect. It is evident from these results that both the kind and concentration of supporting electrolyte used should be specified when reporting half-wave potential data, even when the supporting electrolyte is an "indifferent salt" in the sense that its ions do not participate directly in the electrode reaction.[9]

Thermodynamic Interpretation of the Half-Wave Potentials of Simple Metal Ions. It is evident that the half-wave potential has definite thermodynamic significance. Von Stackelberg[9a] and Lingane[8] independently have shown that $E_{1/2}$ is related in a simple way to the ordinary standard potential of the metal, its solubility in mercury, and its affinity for mercury. From a knowledge of these quantities it is possible to compute quite accurately the $E_{1/2}$ values of metal ions.

We have seen that the half-wave potential of a simple metal ion is expressible by

$$E_{1/2} = E_a^0 + \frac{RT}{nF_y} \ln a_{Hg} - \frac{RT}{nF_y} \ln \frac{f_a k_s}{f_s k_a} \tag{14}$$

The half-wave potential can be expressed in terms of the standard potential of the solid metal, instead of that of its amalgam, by considering the cell

$$M(s)/M^{n+}/M(Hg)_{satd.}$$

in which the left electrode is the solid metal, and the right electrode is its saturated two-phase amalgam. Let $a_{satd.}$ be the activity of the metal in the saturated amalgam in contact with a solid phase which may be either the pure metal or a solid compound or a solid solution of the metal and

[9] In this connection see also D. DeFord and D. L. Andersen, *J. Am. Chem. Soc.*, **72**, 3918 (1950).

[9a] M. von Stackelberg, *Z. Elektrochem.*, **45**, 466 (1939).

mercury. The e.m.f. of this cell, which we designate by E_s, is independent of the concentration of the metal ions in the solution, and is given by

$$E_s = E_a^0 - E_M^0 - \frac{RT}{nF_y} \ln \frac{a_{\text{satd.}}}{a_{\text{Hg}}^*} \qquad (15)$$

where E_M^0 is the ordinary standard potential of the pure metal, that is, the e.m.f. of the cell

$$\text{Reference electrode}/M^{n+}(a = 1)/M(s)$$

and a_{Hg}^* is the activity of mercury in the saturated amalgam, relative to pure mercury.

In the case of metals which do not form solid compounds or solid solutions with mercury, e. g., zinc, the solid phase in equilibrium with the saturated amalgam is simply the pure metal, and E_s is then zero. In general, however, when the metal forms a solid solution or solid compound with mercury, E_s is equal to $-\Delta F/nF_y$ where ΔF is the free energy increase in the reaction

$$xM(s) + yHg = M_xHg_y(s) \qquad (16)$$

Designating the solubility of the metal in mercury by $C_{\text{satd.}}$ (moles of metal per liter of saturated amalgam), and the corresponding activity coefficient by $f_{\text{satd.}}$, we obtain from eq. 15 at 25° C.

$$E_a^0 = E_M^0 + E_s + \frac{0.0591}{n} \log C_{\text{satd.}}.f_{\text{satd.}} - \frac{RT}{nF_y} \ln a_{\text{Hg}}^* \qquad (17)$$

When this expression for E_a^0 is substituted into eq. 14 we obtain

$$E_{1/2} = E_M^0 + E_s + \frac{0.0591}{n} \log C_{\text{satd.}}.f_{\text{satd.}} -$$

$$\qquad (18)$$

$$\frac{0.0591}{n} \log \frac{f_a k_s}{f_s k_a} + \frac{0.0591}{n} \log \frac{a_{\text{Hg}}}{a_{\text{Hg}}^*}$$

For the present purpose it will usually be sufficiently accurate to assume that the activity of mercury in the saturated amalgams, a_{Hg}^*, does not differ in order of magnitude from the activity of mercury, a_{Hg}, in the amalgams actually formed at the dropping electrode. Hence we may neglect the last term in eq. 18, and write

$$E_{1/2} \cong E_M^0 + E_s + \frac{0.0591}{n} \log C_{\text{satd.}}.f_{\text{satd.}} - \frac{0.0591}{n} \log \frac{f_a k_s}{f_s k_a} \qquad (19)$$

There is good reason for believing that the ratio k_s/k_a is equal simply to $(D_s/D_a)^{1/2}$, where D_s is the diffusion coefficient of the metal ions in the solution and D_a is that of the metal in the very dilute amalgam formed at the dropping electrode. In most cases D_a is somewhat larger than D_s, but not greatly so, and it is to be expected that the quantity $(D_s/D_a)^{1/2}$ will ordinarily have a value in the neighborhood of, or somewhat smaller than, unity. For example, in the case of cadmium[10] at 20° C., $D_a = 1.52 \times 10^{-5}$ cm.^{2} sec.$^{-1}$ and $D_s = 0.65 \times 10^{-5}$ cm.^{2} sec.$^{-1}$, and hence $(D_s/D_a)^{1/2} = 0.7$. Since the amalgams formed at the dropping electrode are very dilute f_a will be practically equal to 1, but, on the other hand, f_s is smaller than 1 to an extent dependent on the ionic strength of the solution. Since $(D_s/D_a)^{1/2}$, which we assume is equal to k_s/k_a, will usually be somewhat smaller than 1, and f_a/f_s will be somewhat larger than 1, these two terms tend to cancel each other and the whole term $f_a k_s/f_s k_a$ should have a value of the order of 1 in most cases. Hence it is to be expected that the last log term in eq. 19 will also be of minor importance, and as a good *approximation* $E_{1/2}$ should be given by

$$E_{1/2} \cong E_M^0 + E_s + \frac{0.0591}{n} \log C_{\text{satd}}. f_{\text{satd}}. \qquad (20)$$

The validity of these conclusions is demonstrated in Table XI-2 in which the experimental $E_{1/2}$ values of a number of metal ions are compared with the theoretical values calculated from eq. 20.

The agreement between the observed and calculated half-wave potentials is quite satisfactory. The fact that the observed values are all slightly larger (more negative) than the calculated values is probably due chiefly to the neglect of the activity coefficients of the metal ions in the calculations. The experimental values were obtained at an ionic strength of 0.1 M, at which ionic strength the values of f_s will be considerably smaller than 1, so it is not surprising that the observed values of $E_{1/2}$ are slightly more negative than the values calculated from eq. 20 which correspond approximately to zero ionic strength. By comparing the theoretical values of $E_{1/2}$ with the experimental values at various ionic strengths given in Table XI-3 it is seen that the experimental values approach the theoretical values as a limit at zero ionic strength.

It will be noted that the half-wave potentials of lead and zinc do not differ very much from the ordinary standard potentials of these metals, whereas in the case of thallium, cadmium, and especially the alkali metals, $E_{1/2}$ is much more positive than E_M^0. With regard to thallium the differ-

---

[10] Data on D_a for a number of metals in mercury have been summarized by J. Duclaux, *Diffusion dans les Gels et les Solides*, Paris, 1936, p. 31.

ence between $E_{1/2}$ and E_M^0 is due practically entirely to the unusually large solubility of thallium in mercury and E_s is negligibly small. On the other hand, in the case of the alkali metals the large difference between $E_{1/2}$ and E_M^0 is chiefly caused by the great affinity of these metals for mercury and the corresponding large values of E_s. Roughly speaking, the order of the half-wave potentials of the metals is about the same as that of their standard potentials.

Temperature Coefficient of the Half-Wave Potential. By differentiating eq. 20 with respect to temperature, and neglecting the term $d \log f_{\text{satd.}}/dT$ which is negligibly small, we find that the temperature coefficient of the half-wave potential of a simple metal ion at 25° C. should be given by

$$\frac{dE_{1/2}}{dT} = \frac{dE_M^0}{dT} + \frac{dE_s}{dT} + \frac{0.0591}{n}\frac{d \log C_{\text{satd.}}}{dT} + \frac{0.000198}{n} \log C_{\text{satd.}}f_{\text{satd.}}. \quad (21)$$

Mr. H. Kerlinger, in the University of California laboratory, tested this equation in the case of thallous ion in 0.1 N potassium chloride as supporting electrolyte. He found a value of $dE_{1/2}/dT$ at 25° C. of -0.9 mv. deg.$^{-1}$, which was in reasonably good agreement with the theoretical value -0.7 mv. deg.$^{-1}$ calculated from eq. 21. The negative sign signifies that $E_{1/2}$ becomes more negative with increasing temperature.

Nejedly[11] measured the temperature coefficients of the *reduction potential* (not $E_{1/2}$) of various metal ions in 0.1 N potassium chloride, and he obtained values ranging from a few tenths up to 1 mv. deg.$^{-1}$, except in the case of hydrogen discharge whose temperature coefficient was 3 mv. deg.$^{-1}$. In all cases, except that of the thallous ion, Nejedly found a positive temperature coefficient (easier reduction with increasing temperature). Unfortunately, Nejedly employed the obsolete 45° tangent method for measuring the reduction potentials, and hence his data cannot be used for a serious test of eq. 21. For most practical analytical purposes the temperature coefficient of the half-wave potential is small enough to be neglected.

Irreversible Reductions. The foregoing derivations will only be valid when the electrode reaction is reversible. When the electrode reaction is irreversible a straight line may still result in the plot of $E_{\text{d.e.}}$ *versus* log $i/(i_d - i)$, and $E_{1/2}$ may in certain cases be constant and independent of the concentration of the reducible metal ions. However, the slope of the log plot will differ from the theoretical value if the reduction is irreversible. An additional criterion of reversibility is the fact that $E_{1/2}$ in the reduction

[11] V. Nejedly, *Collection Czechoslov. Chem. Communs.*, **1**, 319 (1929).

of the metal ions should coincide with the half-wave potential of the *anodic* wave of the metal amalgam in the same medium.[12]

The classical example of an electroreduction which involves a large "overvoltage" on mercury is that of hydrogen discharge. This case is discussed in detail in Chapter XIII. Certain aquo complexes of heavy metal ions, such as those of nickel, cobalt, and indium, also require a large overvoltage for their reduction. In such cases the overvoltage can frequently be decreased by the formation of stable complex ions.[13]

3. CASE 2. REDUCTION OF IONS OF METALS THAT ARE INSOLUBLE IN MERCURY

The reduction to the metallic state of the simple ion of a metal that is insoluble in mercury, *e. g.*, Fe^{++}, may be represented by

$$M^{n+} + ne = M(s) \qquad (22)$$

the metal being deposited in the solid state on the surface of the dropping electrode. If we assume that the activity of the deposited metal is constant and independent of the current density (which is still a moot question), then $E_{d.e.}$ at any point on the wave should depend only on the activity of the metal ions in the solution, and should be given by

$$E_{d.e.} = E_M^0 + \frac{RT}{nF_y} \ln C_s^0 f_s \qquad (23)$$

where E_M^0 is the ordinary standard potential of the solid metal, C_s^0 is the concentration of the metal ions at the surface of the dropping electrode, and f_s is the corresponding activity coefficient. As in the previous case, C_s^0 will be given by eq. 6 or eq. 7 and hence the equation of the polarographic wave should be

$$E_{d.e.} = E_M^0 - \frac{RT}{nF_y} \ln \frac{k_s}{f_s} + \frac{RT}{nF_y} \ln (i_d - i) \qquad (24)$$

In this case the half-wave potential should be given by

$$E_{1/2} = E_M^0 - \frac{RT}{nF_y} \ln \frac{k_s}{f_s} + \frac{RT}{nF_y} \ln \frac{i_d}{2} \qquad (25)$$

[12] M. von Stackelberg, *Z. Elektrochem.*, **45**, 466 (1939).
[13] J. J. Lingane, *Chem. Revs.*, **29**, 1 (1941).

or, since $i_d = k_s C$

$$E_{1/2} = E_M^0 + \frac{RT}{nF_y} \ln f_s + \frac{RT}{nF_y} \ln \frac{C}{2} \qquad (26)$$

where C is the concentration of the metal ions in the body of the solution. It is evident that in this case $E_{1/2}$ should not be constant, but should be shifted by $0.059/n$ v. to a more positive value for a ten-fold increase in the concentration of the metal ions.

No systematic studies have yet been made to test eq. 24 or eq. 26. However, Mr. H. Kerlinger, in the University of California laboratory, has investigated the half-wave potential of ferrous iron as a function of concentration in 1 N ammonium perchlorate as supporting electrolyte. He found that $E_{1/2}$ decreased from -1.48 to -1.44 v. *vs.* the S.C.E. when the concentration of ferrous ion was increased from 2×10^{-4} up to $0.01 M$. This shift of 0.04 v. is in fair agreement with the theoretical value of 0.05 v. predicted by eq. 26 for $n = 2$ and a fifty-fold concentration change.

It should be noted that the curve of eq. 24 will not have a point of inflection. Theoretically the slope of the c.v. curve should be infinite at $i = 0$; that is, the curve should start vertically from the voltage axis, and the slope should should gradually decrease until it finally becomes zero when the diffusion current is reached. Actually the slope is not found to be infinite at $i = 0$, and the experimental c.v. curves increase gradually and have an inflection point. This is due to the fact that a certain amount of the solid metal must be deposited on the surface of the mercury drops before its activity becomes constant, a fact which was neglected in deriving eq. 24.

An exact test of eq. 26 is further complicated by the fact that there are very few metals that are sufficiently insoluble in mercury for eq. 22 and eq. 23 to be strictly valid. The ions of those metals that are sufficiently insoluble in mercury (Fe, Cr, Mo, W, V, etc.) are usually present as complexes in aqueous solution and are reduced irreversibly. For example, the reduction of ferrous ion from a 0.01 M solution in 1 N ammonium perchlorate does not start until a potential of about -1.3 v. *vs.* the S.C.E. is reached, which is about 0.5 v. greater than the reversible potential under these conditions. Furthermore, the slope of the ferrous ion wave is much smaller than that predicted by eq. 24. It is still a matter for speculation whether or not a metal like iron when freshly deposited is in its most stable standard state; if not, the activity of the solid metal will probably not be constant and it may depend on the current density.

Equation 24 is also the equation of the wave for the reduction of a simple metal ion at a platinum microelectrode, and it has been tested by Laitinen[14] in the discharge of thallous and lead ions at a stationary platinum wire electrode.   Laitinen found that the plots of $E_{d.e.}$ *versus* log $(i_d - i)$ produced straight lines, whose slopes were 0.070 v. for thallium and 0.060 v. for lead.   These values are considerably larger than the theoretical values 0.059 v. and 0.030 v., respectively, which indicates that other polarization phenomena in addition to concentration polarization come into play in the deposition of the solid metals.   Laitinen's results are in accord with the supposition that the thermodynamic activity of a freshly deposited metal is considerably greater than the activity of the metal in its normal standard state.

4. CASE 3. REDUCTION AND OXIDATION OF METAL IONS FROM ONE OXIDATION STATE TO ANOTHER AT THE DROPPING ELECTRODE

The reduction of a simple metal ion to a lower oxidation state may be represented by

$$M^{n+} + ae = M^{(n-a)+} \tag{27}$$

In this case the dropping electrode should function simply as an indifferent or "noble" electrode, and if the foregoing reaction is rapid and reversible its potential should obey the equation

$$E_{d.e.} = E^0 - \frac{RT}{aF_y} \ln \frac{C^0_{red.} f_{red.}}{C^0_{ox.} f_{ox.}} \tag{28}$$

where $C^0_{red.}$ and $C^0_{ox.}$ are the concentrations of the metal ions in the lower and higher oxidation states at the electrode surface, the f's are the corresponding activity coefficients, and E^0 is the ordinary standard potential of the reaction.

The equation of the polarographic wave will depend on whether or not any of the reduced form is originally present in the solution.   We shall first assume that none of the reduced form is originally present, and hence the concentration of the reduced form produced at the electrode surface at any point on the wave will be directly proportional to the current

$$C^0_{red.} = k'i = \frac{i}{k_{red.}} \tag{29}$$

where $k_{red.}$ is proportional to the square root of the diffusion coefficient of the reduced form.

---

[14] H. A. Laitinen, *Ph.D. Thesis*, University of Minnesota, 1940.

It is readily derived that

$$E_{\text{d.e.}} = E^0 - \frac{0.0591}{a} \log \frac{f_{\text{red.}} k_{\text{ox.}}}{f_{\text{ox.}} k_{\text{red.}}} - \frac{0.0591}{a} \log \frac{i}{i_d - i}. \qquad (30)$$

and

$$E_{1/2} = E^0 - \frac{0.0591}{a} \log \frac{f_{\text{red.}} k_{\text{ox.}}}{f_{\text{cx.}} k_{\text{red.}}} \qquad (31)$$

and hence we have

$$E_{\text{d.e.}} = E_{1/2} - \frac{0.0591}{a} \log \frac{i}{i_d - i} \qquad (32)$$

This equation is identical in *form* with the equation of the wave for case 1 above (eq. 11), and hence the general characteristics of the waves should be the same in the two cases.

The foregoing relations apply when the original solution does not contain any of the reduced form. Under these conditions the wave is entirely cathodic as shown by curve *1* in Fig. XI-4. If the original solution also contains the reduced form the c.v. curve will lie partly above and partly below the zero current line on the polarogram, as shown by curve *2* in Fig. XI-4; provided that the reaction $M^{n+} + ae = M^{(n-a)+}$ is rapid and reversible. Curve *2* represents a case in which the concentrations of the oxidized and reduced forms are about equal in the original solution. The cathodic part of the wave above the zero current line (positive current) is due to the reduction of the oxidized form, while the lower anodic part of the wave (negative current) results from the oxidation of the reduced form. If the original solution does not contain any of the oxidized form the wave will be entirely anodic, as shown by curve *3*. We shall employ the convention of giving a negative sign to an anodic current (electrooxidation).

The anodic limiting diffusion current, indicated in Fig. XI-4 by $(i_d)_a$, is directly proportional to the concentration of the reduced form in the body of the solution:

$$-(i_d)_a = k_{\text{red.}} C_{\text{red.}} \qquad (33)$$

The constant $k_{\text{red.}}$ is the same as that in eq. 29, and according to the Ilkovic equation it is proportional to the square root of the diffusion coefficient of the reduced form.

When the reduced form is present in the original solution, its concentration at the electrode surface at any point on either a cathodic or anodic wave will be given by

$$C^0_{\text{red.}} = C_{\text{red.}} + \frac{i}{k_{\text{red.}}} = \frac{-(i_d)_a + i}{k_{\text{red.}}} \tag{34}$$

For the concentration of the oxidized form at the electrode surface we have

$$C^0_{\text{ox.}} = \frac{(i_d)_c - i}{k_{\text{ox.}}} \tag{35}$$

where $(i_d)_c$ is the cathodic diffusion current.   These are perfectly general

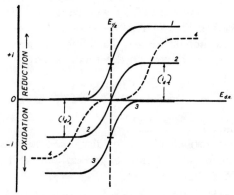

Fig. XI-4. Schematic representation of polarographic waves due to reduction or oxidation of metal ions, or other substances, from one oxidation state to another: (1) cathodic wave of oxidized form; (2) composite cathodic-anodic wave of a mixture of the oxidized and reduced forms; (3) anodic wave of the reduced form; (4) composite cathodic-anodic wave when the electrode reaction is irreversible.

relations that apply to cathodic, anodic, or combined cathodic and anodic waves, when i is given its proper sign of $(+)$ for a cathodic current and $(-)$ for an anodic current.   When these relations are substituted into eq. 28 we obtain the following general equation:

$$E_{\text{d.e.}} = E^0 - \frac{0.0591}{a} \log \frac{f_{\text{red.}} k_{\text{ox.}}}{f_{\text{ox.}} k_{\text{red.}}} - \frac{0.0591}{a} \log \frac{i - (i_d)_a}{(i_d)_c - i} \tag{36}$$

When $C_{\text{red.}} = 0$, and hence $(i_d)_a = 0$, eq. 36 becomes identical with eq. 30 and the wave is entirely cathodic.   On the other hand, when $C_{\text{ox.}} = 0$, so that $(i_d)_c = 0$ and the wave is entirely anodic, eq. 36 becomes

$$E_{\text{d.e.}} = E^0 - \frac{0.0591}{a} \log \frac{f_{\text{red.}} k_{\text{ox.}}}{f_{\text{ox.}} k_{\text{red.}}} - \frac{0.0591}{a} \log \frac{i - (i_d)_a}{-i} \tag{37}$$

or

$$E_{d.e.} = E_{1/2} + \frac{0.0591}{a} \log \frac{i}{(i_d)_a - i} \tag{38}$$

It is seen that this equation of the anodic wave is identical in form with that for the cathodic wave (eq. 32) except for the $(+)$ sign before the log term, which is due to the fact that the potential becomes more positive with increasing current. Furthermore, it is evident that the anodic half-wave potential is given by eq. 31, and hence *it is identical with the cathodic half-wave potential.* This is shown schematically in Fig. XI-4.

It can also be shown that the half-wave potential of a composite cathodic-anodic wave (curve *2* in Fig. XI-4) is the same as that of either a separate cathodic or separate anodic wave. Therefore the general equation for either a cathodic, anodic, or combined cathodic-anodic wave is

$$E_{d.e.} = E_{1/2} - \frac{0.0591}{a} \log \frac{i - (i_d)_a}{(i_d)_c - i} \tag{39}$$

with the same value of $E_{1/2}$ for all three cases.

When the concentrations of the oxidized and reduced forms in the original solution are equal, the ratio of the cathodic and anodic diffusion currents is given by

$$\frac{(i_d)_c}{(i_d)_a} = \frac{k_{ox.}}{k_{red.}} = \left(\frac{D_{ox.}}{D_{red.}}\right)^{1/2} \tag{40}$$

This relation can be used to evaluate experimentally the quantity $k_{ox.}/k_{red.}$ which is required for the calculation of $E_{1/2}$ by means of eq. 31.

It will be evident from the above relations that in the case of a composite cathodic-anodic wave of a reversible reaction the value of $E_{d.e.}$ when $i = 0$ (after correction for the residual current) should coincide with the oxidation-reduction potential of the system, as measured with a platinum or other noble metal indicator electrode by the usual potentiometric technique.

It should be emphasized that the foregoing equations will only be valid when the electrode reaction is reversible, *i. e.*, when the current at every point on the wave is entirely diffusion controlled. When the electrode reaction is relatively slow, and hence not reversible in the present sense, polarization effects other than concentration polarization come into play. In such cases more or less overvoltage is required to initiate and maintain the reaction; the shape of the composite anodic-cathodic wave becomes as shown by the broken curve *4* in Fig. XI-4.   A wave of this type is observed with the titanous–titanic system in the absence of complex-forming ions.[15]

5. CASE 4. STEPWISE REDUCTION OF SIMPLE METAL IONS

When the free energies of the various oxidation states of a metal ion are sufficiently different from each other, reduction from higher to lower oxidation states can take place in stages at the dropping electrode to give a polarogram consisting of two or more separate waves.   A polarogram of this type is obtained in the reduction of chromic ions[16, 17] in which case the first wave corresponds to the reduction of chromic to chromous ion and the second to the complete reduction of chromic ion to the metallic state. Double waves are also obtained in the reduction of aquo ferric ion, and certain of the rare earth ions[18] as well as in the reduction of various complex metal ions.

Actually, however, most metal ions that produce double waves are not present as simple ions, but as complexes, in aqueous solutions.   For this reason, we shall not present a detailed interpretation of the double waves of simple metal ions.   The analysis of the double waves due to stepwise reduction of complex metal ions is discussed in detail in the following chapter.

6. DROPPING AMALGAM ELECTRODES

Amalgams of certain metals when used as dropping electrodes produce well-developed anodic waves resulting from the oxidation of the metal in the amalgam to produce the metal ion in solution

$$M(Hg) = Hg + M^{n+} + ne \tag{41}$$

Since this reaction is just the reverse of the reduction of a metal ion the anodic half-wave potential of the amalgam coincides with the cathodic half-wave potential of the metal ion in those cases where the reduction and oxidation both proceed reversibly.[19-21]   When the reaction is irreversible in one or both directions the anodic half-wave potential is more positive

---

[15] R. Strubl, *Collection Czechoslov. Chem. Communs.*, **10**, 475 (1938).

[16] M. Demassieux and J. Heyrovsky, *J. chim. phys.*, **26**, 219 (1929).

[17] J. Prajzler, *Collection Czechoslov. Chem. Communs.*, **3**, 406 (1931).

[18] W. Noddak and A. Bruckl, *Angew. Chem.*, **50**, 362 (1937).

[19] M. von Stackelberg and H. von Freyhold, *Z. Elektrochem.*, **46**, 120 (1940).

[20] J. Heyrovsky and M. Kalousek, *Collection Czechoslov. Chem. Communs.*, **11**, 464 (1939).

[21] J. J. Lingane, *J. Am. Chem. Soc.* **61**, 976 (1939).

than the cathodic half-wave potential. The equation of the reversible anodic wave is identical with eq. 38. When the solution originally contains some of the metal ion a composite cathodic-anodic wave results, and the equation of this composite wave in reversible cases is identical with eq. 36.

The anodic diffusion current is directly proportional to the concentration of the metal in the amalgam because it is controlled by the rate of diffusion of the metal from the interior of the amalgam drop to the outer surface. The ratio of the anodic and cathodic diffusion currents is given by eq. 40.

Dropping amalgam polarograms are especially useful for providing conclusive proof of the degree of reversibility of electrode reactions involving either simple or complex metal ions. Information thus obtained is more reliable than deductions based on observed wave slopes which latter are subject to a number of uncertainties. Cadmium, lead, and zinc amalgams show reversible behavior in a potassium chloride supporting electrolyte, and the same is true of lead amalgam in sodium hydroxide solutions. On the other hand, zinc amalgam in sodium hydroxide solutions containing zincate ion produces separated anodic and cathodic waves showing that the reaction

$$ZnO^{--} + 2e + 2H_2O + Hg \rightleftarrows Zn(Hg) + 4OH^-$$

does not proceed with thermodynamic reversibility at the dropping electrode.

In principle, dropping amalgam electrodes have potential value for determining small amounts of a more base metal (such as zinc) in the presence of large amounts of a more noble metal (such as lead or copper). A very small amount of zinc ion cannot be determined in the presence of a large amount of lead ion from the cathodic waves because the large lead wave precedes and completely masks the small zinc wave. If, however, an alloy containing a large proportion of lead and only a small amount of zinc were dissolved in mercury, and the resulting amalgam employed in the dropping electrode in a supporting electrolyte such as 1 M potassium chloride, the small *anodic* zinc wave would be easily measurable at a potential more negative than that at which the large anodic lead wave occurs. However, such a procedure presents so many experimental complexities that its feasibility in practical analysis is questionable.

A thorough study of the behavior of dropping amalgam electrodes has recently been reported by Furman and Cooper.[22] These authors describe a convenient method of preparing the amalgams electrolytically.

---

[22] N. H. Furman and W. C. Cooper, *J. Am. Chem. Soc.*, **72**, 5667 (1950).

CHAPTER XII

Polarographic Waves of Complex Metal Ions

1. INTRODUCTION

The polarographic method can be applied advantageously to the study of complex metal ions by virtue of the fact that the half-wave potentials of metal ions are shifted (usually to a more negative value) by complex formation. By measuring this shift as a function of the concentration of the complexing agent both the formula and dissociation constant of the complex can be determined.

Quantitative information can only be obtained, of course, when the reduction or oxidation of the metal ion complex takes place reversibly at the dropping electrode. Therefore, it is essential to establish the reversibility of the electrode reaction in any given case before attempting to draw quantitative conclusions from the experimental data. For this reason the following discussion is devoted largely to the derivation, and illustration by typical experimental examples, of relations that can be used for testing the reversibility at the dropping electrode of the various types of reactions involving complex metal ions.

The fundamental principles on which these relations are based were first recognized by Heyrovsky and Ilkovic.[1] The following discussion is based chiefly on papers by von Stackelberg and Freyhold[2] and Lingane.[3]

2. REDUCTION TO THE METALLIC STATE

The reduction to the metallic state (amalgam) of a complex ion of a metal that is soluble in mercury may be represented by

$$MX_p^{(n-pb)} + ne + \text{Hg} \rightleftharpoons M(\text{Hg}) + pX^{-b} \tag{1}$$

where $M(\text{Hg})$ represents the amalgam formed on the surface of the dropping electrode, and X^{-b} is the complexing agent. It is convenient, although

---

[1] J. Heyrovsky and D. Ilkovic, *Collection Czechoslov. Chem. Communs.*, **7,** 198 (1935).

[2] M. von Stackelberg and H. von Freyhold, *Z. Elektrochem.*, **46,** 120 (1940).

[3] J. J. Lingane, *Chem. Revs.*, **29,** 1 (1941).

not strictly necessary, to regard this net reaction as the sum of the two partial reactions

$$MX_p^{(n-pb)+} \rightleftharpoons M^{n+} + pX^{-b} \tag{2}$$

and

$$M^{n+} + ne + \text{Hg} \rightleftharpoons M(\text{Hg}) \tag{3}$$

where M^{n+} symbolizes the "simple" or hydrated ions of the metal. The assumption of these two partial reactions is merely an artifice and it is not intended to indicate an actual kinetic mechanism. The following derivations are independent of the kinetics of the electrode reaction, provided that all the intermediate steps are very rapid compared to diffusion rates.

If the foregoing reactions are rapid and reversible at the dropping electrode, then the potential of the latter at any point on the wave should be given by

$$E_{\text{d.e.}} = E_a^0 - \frac{RT}{nF_y} \ln \frac{C_a^0 f_a}{a_{\text{Hg}} C_M^0 f_M} \tag{4}$$

or

$$E_{\text{d.e.}} = \epsilon - \frac{RT}{nF_y} \ln \frac{C_a^0 f_a}{C_M^0 f_M} \tag{5}$$

where the constant ϵ is equal to $E_a^0 + (RT/nF_y) \ln a_{\text{Hg}}$, C_a^0 is the concentration of the amalgam formed on the surface of the dropping electrode, C_M^0 is the concentration of the simple metal ions *at the electrode surface*, f_a and f_M are the corresponding activity coefficients, and a_{Hg} is the activity of the mercury on the surface of the dropping electrode.

When the dissociation of the complex ion is sufficiently rapid so that equilibrium with respect to reaction 2 is practically maintained at the electrode surface, then C_M^0 can be replaced by

$$C_M^0 = K_c \frac{C_{MX}^0 f_{MX}}{(C_X^0)^p f_X^p f_M} \tag{6}$$

where K_c is the dissociation constant of the metal ion complex, C_{MX}^0 and C_X^0 are, respectively, the concentrations *at the electrode surface* of the complex metal ion and the complexing agent X^{-b}, and the f's are activity coefficients. Therefore eq. 5 becomes

$$E_{\text{d.e.}} = \epsilon + \frac{RT}{nF_y} \ln \frac{K_c f_{MX}}{f_a f_X^p} - \frac{RT}{nF_y} \ln \frac{C_a^0 (C_X^0)^p}{C_{MX}^0} \tag{7}$$

We also have the following relations:[3]

$$i = k_c(C_{MX} - C^0_{MX}) \tag{8}$$

$$i_d = k_c C_{MX} \tag{9}$$

$$C^0_{MX} = C_{MX} - \frac{i}{k_c} = \frac{i_d - i}{k_c} \tag{10}$$

$$C^0_a = k'i = \frac{i}{k_a} \tag{11}$$

In these equations k_c and k_a are proportional to the square roots of the diffusion coefficients of the complex metal ions and the metal in the amalgams, respectively.

Since the complexing agent X^{-b} is a product of the electrode reaction its concentration at the electrode surface increases with increasing current. We have

$$C^0_X = C_X + p \frac{i}{k_X} \tag{12}$$

where k_X is proportional to the square root of the diffusion coefficient of X^{-b} and C_X is the concentration of X^{-b} in the body of the solution. However, for the sake of simplicity, and since this is usually the case, we will assume that the solution originally contains an excess of X^{-b} at a concentration that is relatively large compared to the concentration of the complex metal ion. When this condition is fulfilled the quantity $p(i/k_X)$ in eq. 12 will be negligibly small and C^0_X can be regarded as virtually a constant and equal to C_X.

When the foregoing relations are substituted into eq. 7, we obtain for the equation of the wave at 25° C., with an excess of the complex-forming substance present in the solution,

$$E_{d.e.} = E_{1/2} - \frac{0.0591}{n} \log \frac{i}{i_d - i} \tag{13}$$

The half-wave potential, $E_{1/2}$, is given by

$$E_{1/2} = \epsilon + \frac{0.0591}{n} \log \frac{K_c f_{MX} k_a}{f_a k_c} - p \frac{0.0591}{n} \log C_X f_X \tag{14}$$

Eq. 13 is valuable for testing the reversibility of the reduction, as will be shown later by several experimental examples.

It will be noted that the concentration of the metal ion complex does not enter into the foregoing expression for its half-wave potential, and hence

$E_{1/2}$ should be constant and independent of the concentration of the complex metal ion. This has been verified experimentally.

From eq. 14 the half-wave potential of a complex metal ion should shift with changing activity of the complex-forming substance according to

$$\frac{\Delta E_{1/2}}{\Delta \log C_X f_X} = -p \frac{0.0591}{n} \tag{15}$$

This relation is important because it enables us to determine the coordination number p of the complex metal ion, and thus its formula. For this purpose it is usually sufficiently accurate to employ the concentration of X^{-b} in place of its activity.

From eq. 14 we see that the half-wave potential depends on the logarithm of the dissociation constant of the complex metal ion, and it is more negative the smaller the value of K_c, *i. e.*, the more stable the complex ion. Although K_c can be evaluated from the observed value of the half-wave potential itself, it is usually more accurate to determine it from the *difference* between the $E_{1/2}$ value of the complex metal ion and that of the corresponding simple metal ion. It has already been shown in Chapter XI that the half-wave potential of a simple metal ion is expressible by

$$(E_{1/2})_s = \epsilon - \frac{0.0591}{n} \log \frac{f_a k_s}{f_s k_a} \tag{16}$$

Hence from eqs. 14 and 16 it follows that the shift of the half-wave potential by complex formation should obey the relation

$$(E_{1/2})_c - (E_{1/2})_s = \frac{0.0591}{n} \log \frac{K_c f_c k_s}{f_s k_c} - p \frac{0.0591}{n} \log C_X f_X \tag{17}$$

in which the subscripts c and s refer to the complex and simple metal ions, respectively. For *approximate* purposes eq. 17 can be simplified to

$$(E_{1/2})_c - (E_{1/2})_s \cong \frac{0.0591}{n} \log K_c - p \frac{0.0591}{n} \log C_X \tag{18}$$

When a more exact result is desired the ratio k_s/k_c can be determined experimentally from the ratio of the observed diffusion currents of the simple and complex metal ions at the same concentration and with all other conditions constant.

Instead of employing K_c explicitly, the quantity $0.0591/n \log K_c$ may be replaced by $E_c^0 - E_s^0$, where E_c^0 and E_s^0 are, respectively, the standard potentials of the reactions

$$MX_p^{(n-pb)+} + ne \rightleftharpoons M(s) + pX^{-b} \tag{19}$$

and

$$M^{n+} + ne \rightleftharpoons M(s) \qquad (20)$$

Equation 18 then becomes

$$(E_{1/2})_c - (E_{1/2})_s = E_c^0 - E_s^0 - p \frac{0.0591}{n} \log C_X \qquad (21)$$

Reduction of the Biplumbite Ion. Lingane[3] has shown that the reduction of the biplumbite ion from strongly alkaline medium is reversible at the dropping electrode, and conforms closely to the foregoing relations.

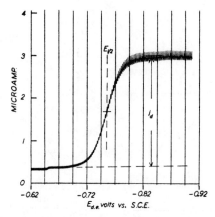

Fig. XII-1. Polarogram of 5×10^{-4} M lead nitrate in 1.09 N sodium hydroxide at 25° C.

This is demonstrated by the typical polarogram of 5×10^{-4} M lead nitrate in 1.09 N sodium hydroxide shown in Fig. XII-1, and by the corresponding plot of $\log i/(i_d - i)$ versus $E_{d.e.}$ in Fig. XII-2. As predicted by eq. 13 the points of the log plot form a good straight line, whose slope of 0.029 v. is in excellent agreement with the theoretical value, 0.0296 v., for $n = 2$.

Lingane measured the half-wave potential of lead in alkaline medium as a function of the hydroxyl ion concentration, and his results are shown graphically in Fig. XII-3. The observed $E_{1/2}$ values are a linear function of $\log C_{OH^-}$ as predicted by eqs. 14 and 15. The slope of the experimental line is -0.083 v., in satisfactory agreement with the theoretical value, which is $-3/2 \times 0.0591$, or -0.089 v., for $p = 3$ and $n = 2$. The small deviation of the experimental points from the theoretical slope for $p = 3$ can be attributed to the simplifying assumption that the concentration of the hydroxyl ion was equal to its activity.   It is evident from these data that the ionic state of the lead at hydroxyl ion concentrations from· 0.01 to 1 N corresponds to the biplubmite ion $HPbO_2^-$, which is reduced reversibly at the d.e. according to

$$HPbO_2^- + 2e + H_2O + Hg \rightleftharpoons Pb(Hg) + 3OH^-$$

The half-wave potential of Pb^{++} in 0.1 N potassium nitrate is -0.388 v. *vs.* the S.C.E., and the half-wave potential of $HPbO_2^-$ in 0.1 N sodium

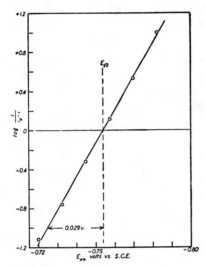

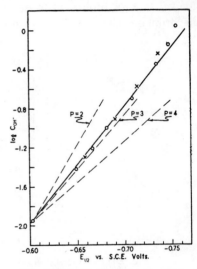

Fig. XII-2. Test of equation of the wave of biplumbite ion; experimental points from Fig. XII-1.

Fig. XII-3. Half-wave potential of lead in alkaline medium as a function of the hydroxide ion concentration.

hydroxide (either with or without potassium nitrate present) is -0.681 v. *vs.* the S.C.E.   Thus the observed difference in the half-wave potentials under these conditions is -0.29 v.   The theoretical difference between the half-wave potentials of $HPbO_2^-$ and Pb^{++} can be calculated from the following data given by Latimer:[4]

$$Pb^{++} + 2e \rightleftharpoons Pb \qquad\qquad\qquad E_s^0 = -0.126 \text{ v. (N.H.E.)}$$

$$HPbO_2^- + 2e + H_2O \rightleftharpoons Pb + 3OH^- \qquad E_c^0 = -0.54 \text{ v. (N.H.E.)}$$

[4] W. M. Latimer, *Oxidation States of the Elements and Their Potentials in Aqueous Solutions*, New York, 1938.

From these data and eq. 21 we have

$$(E_{1/2})_{\mathrm{HPbO_2^-}} - (E_{1/2})_{\mathrm{Pb}^{++}} = -0.41 - \tfrac{3}{2} \times 0.0591 \log C_{\mathrm{OH}^-} \quad (22)$$

This equation predicts that the difference between the half-wave potentials should be -0.32 v., when $C_{\mathrm{OH}^-} = 0.1$ M. The agreement of the observed value (-0.29 v.) with this theoretical value is quite satisfactory. The fact that the observed difference of the half-wave potentials is slightly smaller than the theoretical difference appears to be due chiefly to the fact that the measured half-wave potential of $\mathrm{HPbO_2^-}$ includes an appreciable liquid-junction potential between the strongly alkaline cell solution and the saturated potassium chloride solution in the calomel reference electrode. Although the exact value of this liquid-junction potential is unknown, its *direction* is such that it decreases the measured half-wave potential of $\mathrm{HPbO_2^-}$.

The ratio k_s/k_c, determined experimentally from the diffusion currents of equal concentrations of Pb^{++} and $\mathrm{HPbO_2^-}$, respectively, was found to be 1.05, and hence so close to 1 that it was neglected in the foregoing calculations.

3. REDUCTION OR OXIDATION FROM ONE SOLUBLE OXIDATION STATE TO ANOTHER

Various cases are known in which metal ion complexes are reduced to a lower oxidation state, or oxidized to a higher oxidation state, at the dropping electrode. We will consider a general case in which the net electrode reaction may be represented by

$$MX_p^{(n-pb)+} + ae \rightleftharpoons MX_q^{(n-a-qb)+} + (p-q)X^{-b} \quad (23)$$

The various kinds of waves that result from this type of reaction are the same as those represented schematically in Fig. XI-4.

A general equation of the waves due to this type of reaction may be derived on the basis of the following assumptions: (1) the electrode reaction is reversible; (2) sufficient supporting electrolyte is present so that the current is entirely diffusion controlled; and (3) a sufficient excess of the complexing agent is present in the solution to insure that its concentration at the electrode surface will remain virtually constant and independent of the current. The potential of the dropping electrode at any point on either a cathodic, anodic, or composite wave is then expressible by (assuming concentrations equal to activities)

$$E_{\mathrm{d.e.}} = E^0 - \frac{0.0591}{n} \log \frac{C_{\mathrm{red.}}^0}{C_{\mathrm{ox.}}^0} - \frac{p-q}{a} 0.0591 \log C_X \quad (24)$$

In this equation E^0 is the ordinary standard potential of reaction 23, C^0_{red} and $C^0_{\text{ox.}}$ are, respectively, the concentrations *at the electrode surface* of the complex ions in the lower and higher oxidation states, and C_X is the concentration of X^{-b}.

The following relations also apply

$$(i_d)_c = k_{\text{ox.}} C_{\text{ox.}} \tag{25}$$

$$-(i_d)_a = k_{\text{red.}} C_{\text{red.}} \tag{26}$$

$$C^0_{\text{red.}} = C_{\text{red.}} + \frac{i}{k_{\text{red.}}} = \frac{-(i_d)_a + i}{k_{\text{red.}}} \tag{27}$$

and

$$C^0_{\text{ox.}} = C_{\text{ox.}} - \frac{i}{k_{\text{ox.}}} = \frac{(i_d)_c - i}{k_{\text{ox.}}} \tag{28}$$

In these equations i is to be given its proper sign of $(+)$ for the cathodic part of a wave and $(-)$ for the anodic part.

When the foregoing relations are substituted into eq. 24 the following general equation is obtained, which is applicable to either a cathodic, anodic, or composite wave

$$E_{\text{d.e.}} = E_{1/2} - \frac{0.0591}{a} \log \frac{i - (i_d)_a}{(i_d)_c - i} \tag{29}$$

and the half-wave potential is given by

$$E_{1/2} = E^0 - \frac{0.0591}{a} \log \frac{k_{\text{cx.}}}{k_{\text{red.}}} - \left(\frac{p - q}{a}\right) 0.0591 \log C_X \tag{30}$$

Since the curve of eq. 29 is symmetrical about its midpoint, the half-wave potential should be constant and independent of both the absolute and relative concentrations of the oxidized and reduced forms. The relative values of p and q can be obtained from the shift of $E_{1/2}$ as the concentration of the complexing agent is varied. If p happens to be equal to q then it is evident from eq. 29 that the half-wave potential should be constant and independent of the concentration of the complexing agent.

It should also be noted that the ratio $k_{\text{ox.}}/k_{\text{red.}}$, which is equal to $(D_{\text{ox.}}/D_{\text{red.}})^{1/2}$, can be evaluated experimentally from the ratio of the cathodic and anodic diffusion currents obtained with a solution containing equal concentrations of the oxidized and reduced forms. In most cases this ratio is sufficiently close to 1 so that it can be neglected. When this is true the half-wave potential observed when $C_x = 1\ M$ should practically coincide with the standard oxidation-reduction potential of the system.

Ferric and Ferrous Oxalate Complexes. The reduction and oxidation of the complex ions formed between ferric and ferrous ions and oxalate ion furnishes a good example of the practical application of the foregoing relations:

$$\text{Fe}(\text{C}_2\text{O}_4)_3^{---} + e \rightleftharpoons \text{Fe}(\text{C}_2\text{O}_4)_q^{(2-2q)+} + (3 - q)\text{C}_2\text{O}_4^{--} \qquad (31)$$

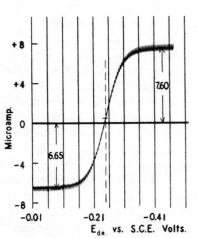

Fig. XII-4. Composite cathodic-anodic wave of a mixture of approximately 0.001 M each of ferric and ferrous iron in 1 M potassium oxalate at 25° C.

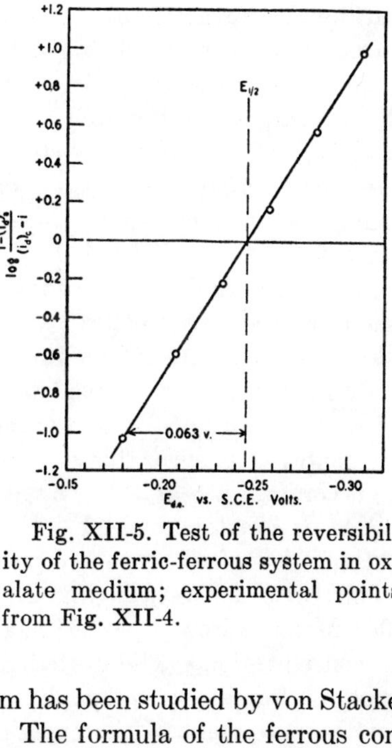

Fig. XII-5. Test of the reversibility of the ferric-ferrous system in oxalate medium; experimental points from Fig. XII-4.

The polarographic behavior of this system has been studied by von Stackelberg and von Freyhold[5] and Lingane.[6] The formula of the ferrous complex is written in the general form because it depends on the concentration of excess oxalate.

The reversibility of this reaction at the d.e. is demonstrated by the polarogram in Fig. XII-4 and the log plot in Fig. XII-5. This polarogram was obtained with a mixture of about 0.001 M ferric iron and 0.001 M ferrous iron in 1 M potassium oxalate, and it has the expected shape of a composite cathodic-anodic wave of a reversible reaction. The part of the curve above the galvanometer zero line is due to the reduction of the

[5] M. von Stackelberg and H. von Freyhold, *Z. Elektrochem.*, **46**, 120 (1940).

[6] J. J. Lingane, *Chem. Revs.*, **29**, 1 (1941).

trioxalato ferric ion, and the lower part to the oxidation of the oxalato ferrous ion. In order to test the reversibility of the reaction, various corresponding values of $E_{d.e.}$ and the quantity $[i - (i_d)_a]/[(i_d)_c - i]$ were carefully measured from the polarogram in Fig. XII-4 and are shown plotted in Fig. XII-5. In agreement with eq. 29 the experimental points fall on a straight line, whose slope of 0.063 v. is in good agreement with the theoretical value, 0.059 v., for $a = 1$.

It will be evident from eq. 30 since $k_{ox.}$ is approximately equal to $k_{red.}$ that the $E_{1/2}$ of reaction 31 should be practically equal to its ordinary standard potential when $C_{C_2O_4^{--}} = 1\ M$. From Figs. XII-4 and XII-5 the observed half-wave potential in $1\ M$ oxalate is -0.245 v. vs. the S.C.E. This agrees reasonably well with the value -0.23 v. (S.C.E.) for the standard potential of this system that Shaper[7] observed by the classical potentiometric method. The polarographic value appears to be more reliable than Shaper's value, since he erroneously assumed that the formula of the ferrous complex was $Fe(C_2O_4)_2^{--}$, independent of the oxalate ion concentration, and this is only correct when the concentration of excess oxalate is relatively small.

Von Stackelberg and von Freyhold stated that the half-wave potential in the reduction of the trioxalato ferric ion was constant and independent of the concentration of oxalate between 0.01 and $1\ M$. However, Lingane[6] was unable to confirm this statement and he demonstrated that although $E_{1/2}$ is constant at -0.242 ± 3 v. (S.C.E.) when the concentration of excess oxalate is greater than about 0.15 M, with smaller concentrations of oxalate it is shifted to a more positive value as $C_{C_2O_4^{--}}$ decreases.

This effect is shown in Fig. XII-6 in which the half-wave potential of 0.001 M ferric iron is plotted against the logarithm of the excess oxalate ion concentration. The dotted lines are the theoretical slopes predicted by eq. 30 for $p - q = 1$ and $p = q$. In view of the large scale of this plot the agreement of the experimental points with the theoretical lines is reasonably satisfactory.

It is evident that $p - q = 1$ when the concentration of excess oxalate is smaller than about 0.15 M (with 0.001 to 0.002 M ferric iron), and at higher oxalate ion concentrations q becomes equal to p. Since there is no doubt that the formula of the ferric complex is $Fe(C_2O_4)_3^{---}$, it follows that the formula of the ferrous complex is $Fe(C_2O_4)_2^{--}$ when $C_{C_2O_4^{--}}$ is less than 0.15 M, and the concentration of ferric iron is 0.001 M. The trioxalato ferrous ion, $Fe(C_2O_4)_3^{----}$, is only formed with a larger excess of oxalate ion.

[7] C. Shaper, Z. physik. Chem., **72,** 315 (1910).

Influence of the Dissociation Constants of the Oxidized and Reduced Complex Metal Ions on the Half-Wave Potential. The difference between the half-wave potentials in the partial reduction of a simple metal ion and in the reduction of a complex ion of the same metal can be derived by considering the two corresponding reactions

$$M^{n+} + a\,e \rightleftharpoons M^{(n-a)+} \tag{32}$$

and

$$MX_p^{(n-pb)+} + ae \rightleftharpoons MX_q^{(n-a-qb)+} + (p-q)X^{-b} \tag{33}$$

Since the number of electrons involved is the same for both reactions, the

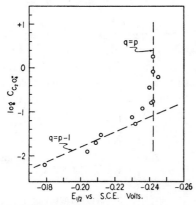

Fig. XII-6. Half-wave potential of trioxalato ferric ion as a function of the oxalate concentration.

difference between their standard potentials is equal to the standard e.m.f. of the reaction

$$MX_p^{(n-pb)+} + M^{(n-a)+} = MX_q^{(n-a-qb)+} + M^{n+} + (p-q)X^{-b} \tag{34}$$

We have

$$E_{34}^0 = E_c^0 - E_s^0 \tag{35}$$

where E_c^0 and E_s^0 are the standard potentials in the reduction of the complex and simple metal ions. In turn, E_{34}^0 is equal to $RT/aF_y \ln K_{34}$, where K_{34} is the equilibrium constant of reaction 34. However, it is evident that

$$K_{34} = \frac{[MX_q^{(n-a-qb)+}](M^{n+})(X^{-b})^{p-q}}{[MX_p^{(n-pb)+}][M^{(n-a)+}]} = \frac{K_{\text{O.C.}}}{K_{\text{R.C.}}} \tag{36}$$

where $K_{O.C.}$ and $K_{R.C.}$ are, respectively, the dissociation constants of the complex ions in the higher and lower oxidation states. It follows, therefore, that

$$E_c^0 - E_s^0 = \frac{RT}{aF_y} \ln K_{34} = \frac{RT}{aF_y} \ln \frac{K_{O.C.}}{K_{R.C.}} \qquad (37)$$

It has already been shown that the half-wave potential in the reduction of a *simple* metal ion to a lower oxidation state is related to the ordinary standard potential of the reaction, E_s^0, by

$$(E_{1/2})_s = E_s^0 - \frac{0.0591}{2a} \log \frac{D_{O.S.}}{D_{R.S.}} \qquad (38)$$

where $D_{O.S.}$ and $D_{R.S.}$ are the diffusion coefficients of the oxidized and reduced forms of the simple metal ion, respectively, and concentrations have been assumed equal to activities. Since $D_{O.S.}$ and $D_{R.S.}$ will usually not differ by more than a factor of 1.5, the last term in this equation has only minor significance, and $(E_{1/2})_s$ is practically equal to E_s^0. For the same reason we may neglect the second term in eq. 30, and write as a good approximation

$$(E_{1/2})_c = E_c^0 - \left(\frac{p-q}{a}\right) 0.0591 \log C_X \qquad (39)$$

From these relations, and eq. 37, it follows that

$$(E_{1/2})_c - (E_{1/2})_s = E_c^0 - E_s^0 - \left(\frac{p-q}{a}\right) 0.0591 \log C_X \qquad (40)$$

or

$$(E_{1/2})_c - (E_{1/2})_s = \frac{0.0591}{a} \log \frac{K_{O.C.}}{K_{R.C.}} - \left(\frac{p-q}{a}\right) 0.0591 \log C_X \quad (41)$$

The shift of the half-wave potential thus depends on the *ratio* of the dissociation constants of the oxidized and reduced complex ions, and also, of course, on the concentration of the complexing agent. If, as is usually the case, the oxidized complex ion is considerably more stable than the corresponding reduced form, then $K_{O.C.}$ is smaller than $K_{R.C.}$, and $(E_{1/2})_c$ is more negative than $(E_{1/2})_s$, when $C_X = 1\ M$. If in a particular case $K_{O.C.}$ and $K_{R.C.}$ would happen to be equal, then $(E_{1/2})_c$ would be more *positive* than $(E_{1/2})_s$ when C_X was less than 1 molar; the two half-wave potentials would be equal when $C_X = 1\ M$; and $(E_{1/2})_c$ would become more *negative* than $(E_{1/2})_s$ only when C_X was greater than $1\ M$. In general when

$$(C_X)^{p-q} \gtreqless \frac{K_{O.C.}}{K_{R.C.}}, \qquad \text{then} \qquad (E_{1/2})_c - (E_{1/2})_s \lesseqgtr 0$$

Lingane employed these relations to evaluate the dissociation constants of the trioxalato ferric ion and the di- and trioxalato ferrous ions. For the reduction of the simple ferric ion we have

$$Fe^{+++} + e \rightleftharpoons Fe^{++}, \qquad E_s^0 \cong (E_{1/2})_s = +0.525 \text{ v. (S.C.E.)}$$

This value is so much more positive than the potential at which anodic dissolution of mercury takes place from the d.e. that it is impossible to measure the half-wave potential of ferric ion directly.[8] For the reduction of the trioxalato ferric ion $(E_{1/2})_c = -0.242$ v. (S.C.E.), and $p = q$, when the oxalate concentration is greater than about $0.15\ M$. Hence from eq. 41 we have

$$0.0591 \log \frac{K_{Fe(C_2O_4)_3^{---}}}{K_{Fe(C_2O_4)_3^{----}}} = -0.242 - 0.525 = -0.767 \text{ v.}$$

and therefore

$$\frac{K_{Fe(C_2O_4)_3^{---}}}{K_{Fe(C_2O_4)_3^{----}}} = 1 \times 10^{-13} \tag{42}$$

From data obtained by Shaper (*loc. cit*) on the solubility of ferrous oxalate in 0.25 to $1.4\ M$ potassium oxalate solutions, the dissociation constant of the trioxalato ferrous ion is 6.1×10^{-7}. Combining this value with eq. 42, the dissociation constant of the trioxalato ferric ion is calculated to be 6×10^{-20}.

The $Cu(NH_3)_4^{++} \rightarrow Cu(NH_3)_2^+$ system furnishes another test of eq. 41. The half-wave potential of the reaction

$$Cu(NH_3)_4^{++} + e \rightleftharpoons Cu(NH_3)_2^+ + 2NH_3 \tag{43}$$

is -0.214 v. (S.C.E.) in a supporting electrolyte composed of $0.2\ N$ ammonium perchlorate and $1\ N$ ammonia.[6] It is impossible to measure experimentally the half-wave potential of the reaction $Cu^{++} \rightarrow Cu^+$ because its value is more negative than that of the reaction $Cu^{++} \rightarrow Cu(Hg)$, and hence in non-complex-forming supporting electrolytes simple cupric

---

[8] I. M. Kolthoff and C. Miller, *J. Am. Chem. Soc.*, **62**, 2171 (1940).

ion produces only a single wave corresponding to the latter reaction. However, if the reduction of the simple Cu^{++} ion is reversible, the hypothetical $E_{1/2}$ value of the reaction $Cu^{++} \rightarrow Cu^{+}$ will be practically equal to its standard potential. From data compiled by Latimer[9] we have

$$Cu^{++} + e \rightleftharpoons Cu^{+} \qquad\qquad E_s^0 \cong (E_{1/2})_s = -0.079 \text{ v. (S.C.E.)}$$

$$Cu(NH_3)_4{}^{++} \rightleftharpoons Cu^{++} + 4NH_3 \qquad K_{O.C.} = 4.6 \times 10^{-14}$$

$$Cu(NH_3)_2{}^{+} \rightleftharpoons Cu^{+} + 2NH_3 \qquad K_{R.C.} = 1.4 \times 10^{-11}$$

When these data are substituted into eq. 41 we obtain

$$(E_{1/2})_c = -0.079 + 0.0591 \log \frac{4.6 \times 10^{-14}}{1.4 \times 10^{-11}} = -0.226 \text{ v. (S.C.E.)}$$

as the theoretical half-wave potential of reaction 43 when $C_{NH_3} = 1\ M$. This value agrees sufficiently well with the observed value, -0.214 v., to demonstrate the general validity of eq. 41. It should also be noted that in 1 M ammonia only about three-fourths of the cupric copper is present as the tetrammino cupric ion, and the remainder is present as the pentammino cupric ion $Cu(NH_3)_5{}^{++}$, which was neglected in the foregoing calculations.

4. STEPWISE REDUCTION OF COMPLEX METAL IONS

When the free energies of the various possible oxidation states of a complex metal ion are sufficiently different, reduction from a higher to a lower oxidation state can proceed in stages at the d.e. to produce a polarogram consisting of two or more separate waves. We will consider a general case in which the polarogram consists of two waves, as shown schematically in Fig. XII-7, which correspond to the two consecutive reactions

$$MX_p^{(n-pb)+} + ae \rightleftharpoons MX_q^{(n-a-qb)+} + (p-q)X^{-b} \tag{44}$$

and

$$MX_q^{(n-a-qb)+} + (n-a)e + Hg \rightleftharpoons M(Hg) + qX^{-b} \tag{45}$$

If these reactions are reversible at the dropping electrode, the potential of the latter at points on the first wave will be governed by reaction 44, and it will obey the relation

$$E_{d.e.} = E_1^0 - \frac{RT}{aF_y} \ln \frac{C_{red.}^0 C_X^{(p-q)}}{C_{ox.}^0} \tag{46}$$

---

[9] W. M. Latimer, *Oxidation States of the Elements and Their Potentials in Aqueous Solutions*, New York. 1938.

where E_1^0 is the standard potential of reaction 44. It will be evident that the first wave corresponds in every respect to the case discussed in the preceding section. Hence the equation of the first wave will be eq. 29 (with $(i_d)_a$ equal to zero), and the half-wave potential of the first wave ($E'_{1/2}$ in Fig. XII-7) will be given by eq. 30.

At points on the second wave the potential of the dropping electrode is governed by reaction 45, and is given by

$$E_{\text{d.e.}} = E_2^0 - \frac{RT}{(n-a)F_y} \ln \frac{C_a^0 C_x^q}{C_{\text{red.}}^0} \tag{47}$$

where E_2^0 is the standard potential of reaction 45.

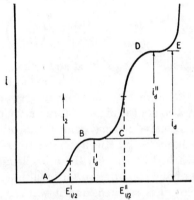

Fig. XII-7. Schematic polarogram of a stepwise reduction.

Although the potential of the d.e. is governed by different reactions on the first and second waves, the *current* at any point on *either* wave is controlled by the rate of diffusion of the oxidized complex ions. If we neglect the slight effect on the diffusion current of the decrease in drop time with increasing negative potential, then it follows from the Ilkovic equation that the following relations will hold for the first and second diffusion currents *taken separately*:

$$i_d' = k'a D_{\text{ox.}}^{1/2} = k_1 C_{\text{ox.}} \tag{48}$$

and

$$i_d'' = k'(n-a) D_{\text{ox.}}^{1/2} C_{\text{ox.}} = k_2 C_{\text{ox.}} \tag{49}$$

where in both cases $D_{\text{ox.}}$ is the diffusion coefficient of the oxidized form and $C_{\text{ox.}}$ is its concentration in the body of the solution. The ratio of two separate diffusion currents is equal to $a/(n - a)$. The *total* diffusion current at DE in Fig. XII-7 is given by

$$i_d = i'_d + i''_d = k'nD_{ox.}^{1/2}C_{ox.} = kC_{ox.} \qquad (50)$$

At points on the first wave (A to B, Fig. XII-7) the concentration of the reduced complex ions at the surface of the dropping electrode is given by

$$(C_{red.}^0)_{A \to B} = \frac{i}{k_{red.}} \qquad (51)$$

When the first diffusion current is reached (B to C in Fig. XII-7)$_{red}^0$ C. attains a maximal value, and from eqs. 48 and 51 this maximal value is expressible by

$$(C_{red.})_{B \to C} = \frac{i_d}{k_{red.}} = \frac{k_1 C_{ox.}}{k_{red.}} = \left(\frac{D_{ox.}}{D_{red.}}\right)^{1/2} C_{ox.} \qquad (52)$$

If the diffusion coefficients of the oxidized and reduced forms happen to be equal, then the maximal concentration of the reduced form present at the electrode surface when the first diffusion current is reached will be equal simply to the concentration of the oxidized form in the body of the solution.

As the potential is increased beyond point C the value of $C_{red.}^0$ decreases again, and it finally becomes practically equal to zero when the second diffusion current is reached at D. On the other hand, the concentration of the oxidized form at the electrode surface will have decreased to practically zero when point B is reached, and it will remain negligibly small at all values of the potential beyond B. If we assume that $C_{red.}^0$ decreases in direct proportion to the increase in current (in excess of i'_d) at points on the second wave, we have

$$(C_{red.}^0)_{C \to D} = \frac{i'_d}{K_{red.}} - bi_2 \qquad (53)$$

where i_2 is the total current minus i'_d (see Fig. XII-7). Since $C_{red.}^0$ becomes practically zero at point D, it is evident that the constant b is given by

$$b = \frac{i'_d}{k_{red.}i''_d} = \frac{a}{k_{red.}(n - a)} \qquad (54)$$

and hence eq. 53 becomes

$$(C_{red.}^0)_{C \to D} = \frac{i'_d}{k_{red.}i''_d} (i''_d - i_2) = \frac{a}{k_{red.}(n - a)} (i''_d - i_2) \qquad (55)$$

When these relations are substituted into eq. 47, we obtain for the equation of the second wave, when an excess of X^{-b} is present,

$$E_{\text{d.e.}} = E''_{1/2} - \frac{0.0591}{(n-a)} \log \frac{i_2}{i''_d - i_2} \qquad (56)$$

where $E''_{1/2}$ is given by

$$E''_{1/2} = E^0_2 - \frac{0.0591}{(n-a)} \log \frac{k_{\text{red.}}(n-a)}{k_a a} - q \frac{0.0591}{(n-a)} \log C_X \qquad (57)$$

Copper-Ammonia Complexes. The double waves obtained in the reduction of various cupric complexes serve as good examples to test the foregoing relations—particularly the double wave in ammoniacal medium.

In the absence of complexing agents, simple cupric ions (actually tetraquo cupric ions, $Cu(H_2O)_4^{++}$) are reduced directly to the metallic state at the d.e. and the polarogram shows only a single wave. The reason for this is evident from the standard potentials of the following reactions:

$$Cu^+ + e + Hg \rightleftharpoons Cu(Hg) \qquad E^0 = +0.108 \text{ v. (N.C.E.)} \qquad (58)$$

$$Cu^{++} + 2e + Hg \rightleftharpoons Cu(Hg) \qquad E^0 = -0.003 \text{ v. (N.C.E.)} \qquad (59)$$

$$Cu^{++} + e \rightleftharpoons Cu^+ \qquad E^0 = -0.115 \text{ v. (N.C.E.)} \qquad (60)$$

The potentials of reactions 58 and 59 were calculated from the standard potentials of the corresponding reactions involving the solid metal, and the known solubility of copper in mercury, by means of relations that have been discussed in Chapter XI. Since the potential of the $Cu^+ \rightarrow Cu(Hg)$ system is more positive than that of the $Cu^{++} \rightarrow Cu(Hg)$ system, cuprous ions are incapable of stable existence at the potential at which cupric ions are reduced, and hence the polarogram of a solution of simple cupric ions shows only the single wave corresponding to $Cu^{++} \rightarrow Cu(Hg)$.

However, if some substance which forms stable complex ions with cupric and cuprous ions, or with cuprous ions alone, is added to a cupric salt solution, then the standard potential and the half-wave potential of the $Cu^+ \rightarrow Cu(Hg)$ system will usually be shifted in the negative direction to a greater extent than that of the $Cu^{++} \rightarrow Cu^+$ system, and the polarogram shows a double wave. This is due to the fact that the shift of the $Cu^{++} \rightarrow Cu^+$ half-wave potential is proportional to $\log (K_{\text{O.C.}}/K_{\text{R.C.}})$ (see eq. 41), whereas the shift of the half-wave potential of the $Cu^+ \rightarrow Cu(Hg)$ system is proportional to $\log K_{\text{R.C.}}$ (see eq. 18) which ordinarily is a much larger negative quantity than $\log K_{\text{O.C.}}/K_{\text{R.C.}}$. The effect of this unequal shift is evident if the foregoing standard potentials of the simple cupric and cuprous ions are compared with the values for the corresponding ammonia complexes, which are[5, 6]

$$Cu(NH_3)_2^+ + e + Hg \rightleftharpoons Cu(Hg) + 2NH_3 \qquad E^0 = -0.522 \text{ v. (N.C.E.)} \quad (61)$$

$$Cu(NH_3)_4^{++} + 2e + Hg \rightleftharpoons Cu(Hg) + 4NH_3 \qquad E^0 = -0.397 \text{ v. (N.C.E.)} \quad (62)$$

$$Cu(NH_3)_4^{++} + e \rightleftharpoons Cu(NH_3)_2^+ + 2NH_3 \qquad E^0 = -0.262 \text{ v. (N.C.E.)} \quad (63)$$

The order of these potentials is just the reverse of those for the corresponding simple ions.

In 1 M ammonia solution the potential required to reduce the $Cu(NH_3)_2^+$ ion is so much more negative than that at which the $Cu(NH_3)_4^{++}$ ion is reduced to $Cu(NH_3)_2^+$ that the polarogram consists of two separate waves of equal height as shown in Fig. XII-8. The first wave corresponds to $Cu(NH_3)_4^{++} \rightarrow Cu(NH_3)_2^+$ and the second to $Cu(NH_3)_2^+ \rightarrow Cu(Hg)$. Similar double waves are obtained with the thiocyanate,[10] pyridine,[6] and chloride complexes[5] of copper.

The reversibility of both stages of the reduction of the $Cu(NH_3)_4^{++}$ ion is easily demonstrable by comparing the difference in potential between two given points on each of the two waves in Fig. XII-8 with the theoretical values predicted by the equations of the waves. The values of $E_{d.e.}$ at $i = (1/4)i_d$ and $i = (3/4)i_d$ are convenient reference points. Whenever the equation of the wave of any type of reaction has the familiar symmetrical form

$$E_{d.e.} = E_{1/2} - \frac{0.0591}{n} \log \frac{i}{i_d - i} \qquad (64)$$

then

$$E_{3/4} - E_{1/4} = -\frac{0.0591}{n} \log \frac{3}{1/3} = -\frac{0.056}{n} \qquad (65)$$

This relation was originally suggested by Tomeš[11] as a criterion of reversibility.

In the reduction of the $Cu(NH_3)_4^{++}$ ion each wave is due to a one-electron change, and hence for each wave $E_{3/4} - E_{1/4}$ should be equal to 0.056 v. From the polarogram in Fig. XII-8 the observed values of $E_{3/4} - E_{1/4}$ are 0.064 v. for the first wave and 0.058 v. for the second, in good agreement with the theoretical value.

---

[10] J. J. Lingane and H. Kerlinger, *Ind. Eng. Chem., Anal. Ed.*, **13**, 77 (1941).

[11] J. Tomeš, *Collection Czechoslov. Chem. Communs.*, **9**, 12, 81, 150 (1937).

Von Stackelberg and von Freyhold investigated the influence of the ammonia concentration on the half-wave potentials of the ammonia-cupric

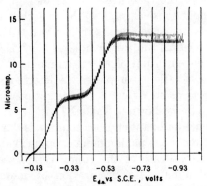

Fig. XII-8. Polarogram of a solution consisting of 0.002 M $Cu(NH_3)_4^{++}$, 0.2 N ammonium perchlorate, and 1 N ammonia, with 0.01 per cent gelatin as a maximum suppressor.

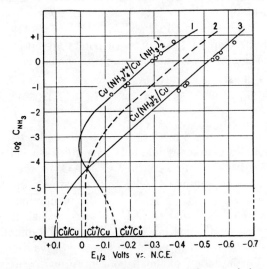

Fig. XII-9. Half-wave potentials of tetrammino cupric ion and diammino cuprous ion as a function of the ammonia concentration in 2 N KNO$_3$ (von Stackelberg and von Freyhold). The lines are the theoretical curves and the circles are experimental points.

complex. Their experimental results are shown in Fig. XII-9, in which the circles are experimental points. The curves in this graph are the theoretical curves calculated by von Stackelberg and von Freyhold. The agreement of the experimental points with the theoretical curves is quite satisfactory.

In the calculation of the theoretical curves in Fig. XII-9 von Stackelberg and von Freyhold took account of the fact that cupric ion forms a series of different ammonia complexes from $Cu(NH_3)^{++}$ to $Cu(NH_3)_5{}^{++}$, and that cuprous ion forms the two complexes $Cu(NH_3)^+$ and $Cu(NH_3)_2{}^+$ depending on the concentration of excess ammonia. From the dissociation constants of these various complexes, as determined by J. Bjerrum,[12] their relative proportions in different concentration of excess ammonia can be calculated. This is shown in Table XII-1.[13]

It is seen that the predominant cuprous complex is the diammino cuprous ion, and the proportion of the monammino cuprous ion is negligible for the present purpose. In the case of the cupric complexes, the tetrammino ion $Cu(NH_3)_4{}^{++}$ predominates at concentrations of ammonia between about 0.05 and 1 M. When the concentration of excess ammonia is decreased below 0.05 M the lower order complexes are formed in increasing amount, and at 10^{-4} M ammonia the monammino cupric ion, $Cu(NH_3)^{++}$, predominates. These facts are responsible for the *positive* shift of the half-wave potential of the $Cu^{++} \rightarrow Cu^+$ system at very small concentrations of ammonia, shown by curve 1 in Fig. XII-9.

From eq. 41 the shift of the half-wave potential of the $Cu^{++} \rightarrow Cu^+$ system by formation of the ammonia complexes should follow the equation

$$(E_{1/2})_c - (E_{1/2})_s = 0.0591 \log \frac{K_{ic}}{K_{ous}} - (p - q)\, 0.0591 \log C_{NH_3} \quad (66)$$

where K_{ic} and K_{ous} are the dissociation constants of the particular cupric and cuprous complexes that predominate at a given concentration of ammonia. The positive shift of $E_{1/2}$ of the $Cu^{++} \rightarrow Cu^+$ system at very small concentrations of excess ammonia is due to two factors. In the first place, when C_{NH_3} is less than about 5×10^{-4} M the predominant cupric complexes are the $Cu(NH_3)_2{}^{++}$ and $Cu(NH_3)^{++}$ ions, and since both of these complexes have larger dissociation constants than the diammino cuprous ion, the quantity $\log K_{ic}/K_{ous}$ in eq. 66 has a positive value when they predominate. Furthermore, at small concentrations of ammonia where the $Cu(NH_3)_2{}^{++}$ and $Cu(NH_3)^{++}$ ions predominate, $(p - q)$ in eq. 66 becomes equal to 0 and -1, respectively. Both of these factors shift $E_{1/2}$

---

[12] J. Bjerrum, *Kgl. Danske Videnskab. Selskab. Math.-fys. Medd.*, **11**, 5 (1931); **11**, 10 (1932); **12**, 15 (1934).

[13] M. von Stackelberg and H. von Freyhold, *Z. Elektrochem.*, **46**, 120 (1940).

in the positive direction.   The inflection point in curve 1 at $C_{\mathrm{NH_3}}$ equal to about $5 \times 10^{-4}\,M$ is due to the fact that the $Cu(NH_3)_2{}^{++}$ ion predominates, and hence $p = q$, at this concentration of ammonia.

The broken curve 2 is the hypothetical curve corresponding to direct

TABLE XII-1

DISSOCIATION CONSTANTS OF THE VARIOUS AMMONIA COMPLEXES OF CUPROUS AND
CUPRIC IONS, AND THEIR RELATIVE PROPORTIONS AS A FUNCTION OF THE EXCESS
AMMONIA CONCENTRATION

The figures given are the relative proportions of the various ionic species calculated from the indicated dissociation constants.   A dash signifies that the proportion of the ion is less than 0.01.

Cuprous complexes	$Cu(NH_3)^+$	$Cu(NH_3)_2{}^+$
K_c	1.2×10^{-6}	1.35×10^{-11}
NH_3, molar		
1	—	1.00
0.01	—	1.00
0.001	0.01	0.99
10^{-4}	0.11	0.89

Cupric complexes	Cu^{++}	$Cu(NH_3)^{++}$	$Cu(NH_3)_2{}^{++}$	$Cu(NH_3)_3{}^{++}$	$Cu(NH_3)_4{}^{++}$	$Cu(NH_3)_5{}^{++}$
K_c	—	4.9×10^{-5}	1.05×10^{-8}	9.5×10^{-12}	4.7×10^{-14}	1.35×10^{-13}
NH_3, molar						
1	—	—	—	—	0.74	0.26
0.01	—	—	0.03	0.32	0.65	—
0.001	—	0.08	0.40	0.44	0.08	—
10^{-4}	0.24	0.50	0.23	0.03	—	—
10^{-5}	0.82	0.17	0.01	—	—	—

reduction of the ammonia-cupric complexes to the metallic state (amalgam).   This curve is unattainable experimentally, because no $Cu(NH_3)_4{}^{++}$ ions exist at the surface of the dropping electrode, and the copper is present entirely as the diammino cuprous ion, at potentials more negative than that at which the first diffusion current is reached.

5. ANALYSIS OF THE WAVE OF AN INCOMPLETELY DISSOCIATED METAL SALT. MERCURIC CYANIDE

Tomes[11] made a careful polarographic study of the reduction of the weak electrolyte $Hg(CN)_2$, a case which has much in common with the reduction of complex metal ions. The net electrode reaction which controls the current is

$$Hg(CN)_2 + 2e \rightleftharpoons Hg + 2CN^- \qquad (67)$$

Since the activity of the deposited mercury is constant, the potential of the dropping electrode will be given by

$$E_{d.e.} = E^0 - \frac{0.0591}{2} \log \frac{(C^0_{CN^-})^2}{C^0_{Hg(CN)_2}} \qquad (68)$$

where E^0 is the standard potential of reaction 67.

Tomes studied the reduction of $Hg(CN)_2$ in buffered solutions *that did not contain excess cyanide*, and under this condition the concentration of CN^- at the electrode surface is a function of the current. Since hydrocyanic acid is very weak ($K_a = 7.2 \times 10^{-10}$) the CN^- ions liberated at the electrode surface are more or less completely hydrolyzed to HCN, depending on the pH of the solution. At any given pH value we have

$$C^0_{CN^-} = K_a \frac{C^0_{HCN}}{C^0_{H^+}} = 7.2 \times 10^{-10} \frac{C^0_{HCN}}{C^0_{H^+}} \qquad (69)$$

If we represent the sum of the concentrations of CN^- and HCN at the electrode surface by C^*, then

$$C^* = C^0_{HCN} + C^0_{CN^-} = \frac{i}{k_i} \qquad (70)$$

and combining this relation with eq. 69 we obtain

$$C^0_{CN^-} = \frac{K_a i}{(K_a + C^0_{H^+})k_1} \qquad (71)$$

It will also be evident that

$$C^0_{Hg(CN)_2} = \frac{i_d - i}{k_2} \qquad (72)$$

When these relations are substituted into eq. 68 we obtain for the equation of the wave when the solution does not contain excess cyanide

$$E_{\text{d.e}} = \epsilon' - 0.0591 \log \frac{K_a}{K_a + C^0_{\text{H}^+}} - 0.0296 \log \frac{i^2}{i_d - i} \qquad (73)$$

where the constant ϵ' is equal to $E^0 - 0.0296 \log k_1/k_2$.

Equation 73 predicts that the wave of Hg(CN)_2 should have the following characteristics: (1) In a well-buffered solution a plot of $E_{\text{d.e.}}$ vs. $\log i^2/(i_d - i)$ should produce a straight line with a slope of 0.0296 v. at 25° C. (2) Because of the i^2 term, the wave is unsymmetrical about its midpoint and the half-wave potential should shift by 0.0296 v. to a more negative value for a ten-fold increase in the concentration of Hg(CN)_2. (3) Since K_a is about 10^{-9}, it becomes negligibly small compared to $C^0_{\text{H}^+}$ when the pH is smaller than about 8. Hence, at pH values less than about 8, the half-wave potential should shift by 0.059 to a more positive value for each unit decrease in the pH of the buffer, provided that the concentration of Hg(CN)_2 is kept constant. On the other hand, when the pH is greater than about 10, $C^0_{\text{H}^+}$ becomes negligibly small compared to K_a, and hence, at a constant concentration of Hg(CN)_2, the half-wave potential should become constant and independent of the pH when the latter is greater than 10.

The experimental data obtained by Tomes are in good agreement with these predictions at pH values less than 10. In more alkaline solutions Tomes observed small deviations from the theoretical relations, which he logically ascribed to the formation of complex Hg(CN)_4^{--} ions at the electrode surface, due to the relatively large proportion of free CN^- ions present at a pH greater than 10. The formation of this complex was neglected in the foregoing derivations, but it will be evident that it could be taken into account from a consideration of the equilibrium $\text{Hg(CN)}_2 + 2\text{CN}^- = \text{Hg(CN)}_4^{--}$.

6. POLAROGRAPHIC WAVES DUE TO IRREVERSIBLE REDUCTION OF COMPLEX METAL IONS

The foregoing derivations were based on the assumption that the dissociation and reduction of complex metal ions are rapid reversible processes. Although, as already shown, this assumption is valid in many cases it is not always true; the rate of formation and dissociation of certain complex metal ions is often quite slow. In the reduction or oxidation of such complexes at the dropping electrode, other polarization effects in addition to concentration polarization come into play. In such cases the equation of the wave will involve, among other factors, the rate constant of the slow step in the electrode reaction. A satisfactory quantitative interpretation of such irreversible waves has not yet been obtained.

The magnitude and direction of the shift of the half-wave potential with temperature is often a useful criterion of the reversibility of an electrode reaction, and it can be used to supplement the tests for reversibility described above. When an electrode reaction is irreversible, $E_{1/2}$ is usually shifted to a more positive value with increasing temperature (easier reduction), and the magnitude of the temperature coefficient is several times larger than that of a reversible reaction. This effect has been observed by Brdicka[14] in the irreversible reduction of the $Co(H_2O)_6^{++}$ ion, and by Lingane and Kerlinger[15] in the reduction of the $Ni(H_2O)_6^{++}$ ion. The excessively large temperature coefficient is related to the activation energy of the irreversible step in the electrode reaction.

---

[14] R. Brdicka, *Collection Czechoslov. Chem. Communs.*, **2,** 489, 545 (1930); **3,** 396 (1931).

[15] Unpublished experiments.

CHAPTER XIII

Waves Due to Hydrogen Discharge.   Catalytic Hydrogen Waves

1. RELATION BETWEEN POTENTIAL, CURRENT, AND HYDROGEN ION CONCENTRATION IN THE DISCHARGE OF HYDROGEN AT THE DROPPING ELECTRODE

The potential at which hydrogen gas is liberated in the electrolysis of aqueous solutions is much more negative than the reversible hydrogen-hydrogen ion potential. The difference between the potential at which hydrogen is actually evolved and the reversible hydrogen-hydrogen ion potential is called the overvoltage of hydrogen. This overvoltage depends on the kind of metal used as electrode, the physical condition of the electrode, the magnitude of the current, the hydrogen ion concentration of the solution, the presence of other ions in the solution, and the temperature.

The relation between the potential, the current, and the hydrogen ion concentration is given by the empirical equation of Tafel:[1]

$$E = a \ln (\text{H}^+) - b \ln i + k \qquad (1)$$

Since we are concerned with electrolysis at the dropping electrode, only the relations at this electrode will be discussed. Herasymenko[2] and Herasymenko and Slendyk[3] found that with the dropping electrode the value of a in eq. 1 is exactly equal to $2RT/F_y$, while the value of b was approximately equal to $3RT/2F_y$. However, the value of b varied with the magnitude of the current. When i was very small b approached a value of RT/F_y, while at currents close to the diffusion current b approached the value $2RT/F_y$. Approximately, then, the discharge of hydrogen ions can be represented by the empirical equation:

$$E = \frac{2RT}{F_y} \ln (\text{H}^+)_0 - \frac{3RT}{2F_y} \ln i + A \qquad (2)$$

---

[1] J. Tafel, Z. physik. Chem., **34**, 107 (1900); **50**, 641 (1905).

[2] P. Herasymenko, Rec. trav. chim., **44**, 499 (1925).

[3] P. Herasymenko and J. Slendyk, Z. physik. Chem., **A49**, 123 (1930).

in which the factor $3RT/2F_y$ is not entirely constant, but varies with the magnitude of the current, and $(H^+)_0$ denotes the hydrogen ion concentration at the surface of the electrode.

The above authors also found that the overvoltage is shifted to more negative values with increasing concentrations of neutral salts in the solution.[4] They showed that the increase of the overvoltage was greater, the greater the charge of the cation of the neutral salt, but in all cases the discharge potential approached a limiting constant value with increasing concentration of the neutral salt. The discussion given below refers to cases where enough neutral salt is present to reach the limiting value.

Various theories have been proposed in the literature to interpret quantitatively the relations between the potential on the one hand and the hydrogen ion concentration and the current on the other. It is beyond the scope of this book to discuss all of these theories[5] and we will limit ourselves to a presentation of the views of Heyrovsky[6] who succeeded in giving a satisfactory interpretation of the phenomena observed in hydrogen discharge at the dropping electrode. According to Heyrovsky the discharge of hydrogen ions to atomic hydrogen is perfectly reversible:

$$H^+ + e \rightleftharpoons H$$

$$\text{(or, better, } H_3O^+ + e \rightleftharpoons H + H_2O)$$

The electrode potential is given by the expression

$$E = \frac{RT}{F_y} \ln \frac{(H^+)_0 k}{(H)_0} \tag{3}$$

If atomic hydrogen were the electrolysis product it would be inferred from eq. 3 that

$$E = \frac{RT}{F_y} \ln (H^+)_0 - \frac{RT}{F_y} \ln i + k'$$

an expression which is quite different from eq. 2.

The rate of electrolysis, which is proportional to the current, is determined by the speed with which molecular hydrogen is formed. If the latter were simply formed by union of two hydrogen atoms $(H + H \rightleftharpoons H_2)$, we would find that $i = k(H_2) = k''(H)^2$, and

$$E = \frac{RT}{F_y} \ln (H^+)_0 - \frac{RT}{2F_y} \ln i + k'''$$

---

[4] See also S. Jofa, *Acta Physicochim. U. R. S. S.*, **10**, 317 (1939).

[5] See, *e. g.*, S. Glasstone and A. Hickling, *Electrolytic Oxidation and Reduction*, New York, 1936.

[6] J. Heyrovsky, *Collection Czechoslov. Chem. Communs.*, **9**, 273 (1937).

Again, this equation does not account for the experimental results (eq. 2). In order to explain this, Heyrovsky assumes that the molecular hydrogen is not formed by direct combination of two hydrogen atoms, but that a hydrogen atom formed by electrolysis combines with a hydrogen ion:

$$H + H^+ \rightleftharpoons H_2^+ \tag{4}$$

The H_2^+ ions in contact with the electrode are assumed to be rapidly discharged to molecular hydrogen,

$$H_2^+ + e \rightleftharpoons H_2$$

If this is true the current will be proportional to the amount of H_2^+ formed. The speed of formation of the latter is governed by eq. 4; hence

$$i = k''''(H)_0(H^+)_0 \tag{5}$$

or

$$(H_0) = \frac{i}{(H^+)_0 k''''} \tag{6}$$

Introducing this into eq. 3 yields

$$E = \frac{RT}{F_y} \ln \frac{(H^+)_0^2}{i} k'''' + \frac{2RT}{F_y} \ln (H^+)_0 - \frac{RT}{F_y} \ln i + A \tag{7}$$

which may be compared with the empirical eq. 2.

It was stated above that, at small values of the current, the factor b in the Tafel equation is about equal to RT/F_y as in eq. 7. To explain the variation of the factor b with the current density, Heyrovsky assumes that the reaction between H and H^+ (eq. 4) occurs by interaction of atomic hydrogen at the surface of the mercury and hydrogen ions in the solution, and that the H_2^+ ions at the surface are discharged. The speed of the reaction between H and H^+ thus depends on the concentration of hydrogen ion near the electrode. This may explain why indifferent electrolytes increase the overvoltage, as their cations replace some of the hydrogen ions near the electrode. Heyrovsky further assumes that the hydrogen molecules formed by electrolysis are adsorbed for some time at the surface of the mercury. These adsorbed molecules diminish the area at which the H_2^+ ions can make contact. With the aid of the Langmuir adsorption isotherm he then concludes that the number of spaces available for the H_2^+ ions at the surface is given by $z/(1 + \omega i)$, in which z is the total number of free spaces and ω the adsorption coefficient of the hydrogen molecules. Instead of eq. 5 we then find that

$$i = k''(H)_0(H^+)_0 \frac{z}{1 + \omega i} \qquad (8)$$

and

$$E = \frac{2RT}{F_y} \ln (H^+)_0^2 - \frac{RT}{F_y} \ln i(1 + \omega i) + A \qquad (9)$$

When i is very small, $i(1 + \omega i)$ is practically equal to i, and the factor b in eq. 1 is equal to RT/F_y. Equation 9 accounts for the fact that the factor b increases with increasing current. Although the final equation derived by Heyrovsky fits the experimental facts it is very doubtful that the proposed mechanism is correct. In this respect reference is made to the important contributions by Frumkin and co-workers.[7]

2. DEUTERIUM

Heyrovsky and Müller[8] and Novak[9] studied the discharge of hydrogen and deuterium at the dropping electrode from mixtures of light and heavy water. Novak found that the half-wave potential of deuterium from DCl in D_2O at 20° C. was 0.087 v. more negative than that of hydrogen from the same concentration of HCl in H_2O. The factor b in Tafel's equation (eq. 1) was found to be somewhat greater in heavy water (0.113) than in light water (0.102). The hydrogen overvoltage in light and heavy water and in their mixture, and the separation coefficient of hydrogen and deuterium at the dropping electrode, have been exhaustively discussed by Heyrovsky.[6]

3. CATALYTIC HYDROGEN WAVES

Herasymenko and Slendyk[10] found that salts containing a cation which deposits at more negative potentials than hydrogen can increase the hydrogen overpotential markedly. Even traces of potassium exert a marked effect, as is evident from experiments carried out by Ilkovic.[11] Slendyk[12]

---

[7] See especially S. Jofa, A. Kolychev and L. Shiftman, *Acta Physicochim. U. R. S. S.*, **12**, 231 (1940).

[8] J. Heyrovsky and O. H. Müller, *Collection Czechoslov. Chem. Communs.*, **7**, 281 (1935).

[9] J. Novak, *Collection Czechoslov. Chem. Communs.*, **9**, 207 (1937).

[10] P. Herasymenko and I. Slendyk, *Z. physik. Chem.*, **A149**, 123 (1930); **161**, 223 (1932). See also S. Jofa and co-workers, *Acta Physicochim. U. R. S. S.*, **10**, 317 (1939).

[11] D. Ilkovic, *Collection Czechoslov. Chem. Communs.*, **4**, 480 (1932).

[12] I. Slendyk, *Collection Czechoslov. Chem. Communs.*, **4**, 335 (1932).

found that dilute amalgams of gold, silver, copper, lead, and cadmium do not affect the hydrogen overpotential. However, platinum and some other metals of the platinum group (not specified by Slendyk) have a great effect. In studying this effect of the platinum metals an outside reference electrode must be used because these metals are precipitated from their salts on the surface of mercury.

Slendyk found that the hydrogen wave in 0.1 N hydrochloric acid started at -1.225 v. *vs.* the N.C.E. but if the solution was 5×10^{-6} M in platinum a small wave was found at -1.00 v. The height of this catalytic wave was much greater (about 20 times) than corresponded to the simple reduction of the platinum in the solution, but was found to be roughly

TABLE XIII-1

CATALYTIC HYDROGEN WAVE IN DIFFERENT CONCENTRATIONS OF HYDROCHLORIC
ACID CONTAINING VARIOUS AMOUNTS OF PLATINUM CHLORIDE

| | Concentration of hydrochloric acid, molar | | | | | |
	0.5	0.1	0.05	0.01	0.005	0.001
PtCl₄, molar	Catalytic current (arbitrary units)					
5×10^{-6}	15	10	4	2	1.5	—
1×10^{-5}	25	25	7	3	3	—
2×10^{-5}	45	32	12	5	4	2
4×10^{-5}	81	52	19	8	—	3

proportional to the platinum concentration. The effect is illustrated in Table XIII-1.

The magnitude of the catalytic current decreases in the presence of neutral salts, the decrease becoming greater with increasing charge of the cations. Thus, in 0.5 N hydrochloric acid which was 1×10^{-5} M in PtCl₄ the catalytic current was 25, in the presence of 0.1 N potassium chloride 20, with 0.01 N barium chloride 23, and with 0.1 N barium chloride 13.

Slendyk made analytical application of the catalytic waves for the determination of traces of platinum in palladium (the latter does not produce a catalytic wave), and in neutral salts. Such determinations are very approximate only, because there is no strict proportionality between the catalytic current and the concentration of platinum, and, moreover, salts affect the magnitude of the catalytic waves. In order to get the most pronounced effect it is best to use 2 N hydrochloric acid as a supporting electrolyte when the platinum concentration is smaller than 10^{-6} M (limit about 10^{-7} M). When the concentration of platinum is greater than 10^{-6} M, a maximum occurs which complicates quantitative measurement.

With higher platinum concentrations it is best to use 0.1 to 0.5 N hydrochloric or sulfuric acid.   The effect of ruthenium is claimed to be 30 times greater than that of platinum.

Heyrovsky[13] found an interesting catalytic wave with perrhenate.   When solutions of the latter in an acetate buffer (pH = 4.7) were treated with hydrogen sulfide, and the excess of the latter was removed by boiling, and the solution was filtered, the filtrate showed a catalytic wave at about −1.2 v. *vs.* the N.C.E.   The height of this wave was found to be about 10 times greater than that of the original perrhenate solution before treatment with hydrogen sulfide.   It was even possible to detect in this way a 10^{-6} M solution of rhenium.   The height of the catalytic wave was found to be proportional to the concentration of the perrhenate.   By employing this catalytic wave it was claimed to be possible to determine traces of rhenium in manganese salts.   It has not been established yet whether this catalytic wave is specific for rhenium.

Several organic compounds also produce catalytic hydrogen waves. Pech[14] found that quinine and quinidine in ammonium chloride solutions gave identical catalytic waves, the heights of which were proportional to the concentration of the alkaloids.   The catalytic wave of quinine was even detectable at a concentration of 10^{-7} M.   Qualitatively, cinchonine and cinchonidine behaved similarly to the two other quinine alkaloids; all of these alkaloids are quinoline derivatives.   Alkaloids derived from isoquinoline, such as codeine, morphine, narcotine, and hydrastin, in 0.1 N hydrochloric acid gave slight catalytic waves that were much smaller than that of quinine.

Strychnine is not reduced at the dropping electrode, but according to Reimers[15] it yields, even in extremely small concentrations (10^{-6} M), a catalytic wave (probably evolution of hydrogen) in 0.1 N ammonium chloride.   This catalytic wave appears at −1.7 v. just before the ammonium ion wave.   Quinine, as we have seen, also yields a similar catalytic wave.   The waves of both alkaloids are greatly affected by the pH of the solution used, and the catalytic effect disappears at a pH greater than 13 for strychnine and 11 for quinine.   Over a pH range between 9 and 12 the catalytic wave of strychnine is about 25 times greater than that of quinine.

In order to determine strychnine in the presence of quinine Reimers uses 0.1 N sodium sulfite solution as a "buffer."   This sulfite solution has the desirable pH and also removes the oxygen from the solution.   By employ-

---

[13] J. Heyrovsky, *Nature*, **135,** 870 (1935).

[14] J. Pech, *Collection Czechoslov. Chem. Communs.*, **6,** 126, 190 (1934).

[15] F. Reimers, *Collection Czechoslov. Chem. Communs.*, **11,** 377 (1939).

ing calibration curves he could detect 1 part of strychnine in the presence of 100 parts of quinine. The maximum of quinine occurs in the sulfite solution at -1.8 v., and that of strychnine at -1.9 v. On the basis of his results Reimers developed a method for the approximate determination of traces of strychnine in the presence of relatively large amounts of quinine. The procedure is empirical and it is necessary to run calibration curves in the mixtures under comparable conditions. The accuracy of the method is only of the order of 15 to 20 per cent.

Of great biological significance are the catalytic waves obtained with traces of cysteine in ammonia-ammonium chloride buffers containing a cobaltous salt, and those with proteins which contain a sulfydryl group in the same medium with $+2$ and $+3$ cobalt.[16] These waves are discussed in greater detail in Chapter XLVI. It should be noted that some amino acids, e. g., phenyl β-alanine, are able to suppress the catalytic cysteine wave.[17]

4. HALF-WAVE POTENTIALS AND CHARACTERISTICS OF CURRENT-VOLTAGE CURVES IN THE DEPOSITION OF HYDROGEN FROM SOLUTIONS OF STRONG AND WEAK ACIDS

It has been mentioned that Herasymenko[2] and Herasymenko and Slendyk[3] found that in the hydrogen ion discharge at the dropping electrode the relation between the potential and the current is satisfactorily expressed by the equation

$$E = \frac{2RT}{F_v} \ln (H^+)_0 - \frac{3RT}{2F_v} \ln i + A \qquad (2)$$

With the aid of this equation the change of the half-wave potential with concentration in the electrolysis of a strong or weak acid can be calculated with a reasonable degree of accuracy.

Strong Acids (in Excess of Indifferent Electrolyte). As in the previous cases $(H^+)_0$ is a function of the current

$$i = k_H\{(H^+) - (H^+)_0\} \qquad (10)$$

In this equation (H^+) represents the concentration of hydrogen ions in the bulk of the solution and $(H^+)_0$ that at the surface of the electrode. Since

$$i_d = k_H(H^+) \qquad (11)$$

---

[16] R. Brdicka, *Collection Czechoslov. Chem. Communs.*, **5**, 112, 148, 238 (1933); *Biochem. J.*, **272**, 104 (1934); *Mikrochemie*, **15**, 167 (1939).

[17] J. Sladek and M. Lipschütz, *Collection Czechoslov. Chem. Communs.*, **6**, 487 (1934).

we find that

$$(H^+)_0 = \frac{i_d - i}{k_H} \tag{12}$$

Introducing this relation into eq. 2 we have

$$E = \frac{2RT}{F_\nu} \ln \frac{i_d - i}{k_H} - \frac{3RT}{2F_\nu} \ln i + A$$

$$= \frac{2RT}{F_\nu} \ln \frac{i_d - i}{i^{3/4}} + A' \tag{13}$$

$$= 0.1182 \log \frac{i_d - i}{i^{3/4}} + A' \ (25° \ C.)$$

At the half-wave point where $i = i_d/2$

$$E_{1/2} = \frac{2RT}{F_\nu} \ln \frac{i_d}{2 \times 0.5^{3/4} i_d^{3/4}} + A'$$

$$= \frac{2RT}{F_\nu} \ln i_d^{1/4} + A'' \tag{14}$$

$$= \frac{RT}{2F_\nu} \ln i_d + A''$$

Therefore, at 25° C. $\Delta E_{1/2}/\Delta \log i_d$ should be equal to $RT/2F_\nu = 0.0296$ v. In the electrolysis of dilute solutions of hydrochloric acid in 1 N lithium or calcium chloride Tomes[18] actually found a change in the half-wave potential of 0.028 v. which is in good agreement with the calculated value.

It is seen that the half-wave potential should change to more positive values with increasing hydrogen ion concentration in the solution. On the other hand, the analysis of the wave according to eq. 13 yields results which are not in exact agreement with Slendyk's experimental data. If we call the potential $E_{1/4}$ when $i = (1/4)i_d$, and $E_{3/4}$ when $i = (3/4)i_d$ it is found from eq. 13 that

$$E_{1/4} - E_{3/4} = 0.100 \text{ v.}$$

$$(E_{1/4} - E_{1/2}) - (E_{1/2} - E_{3/4}) = 0.048 - 0.052 = -0.004 \text{ v.}$$

whereas Slendyk found experimentally 0.09 v. and +0.005 v., respectively.

---

[18] J. Tomes, *Collection Czechoslov. Chem. Communs.*, **9**, 150 (1937).

The deviation is not great, and is caused by the variation of the factor b in the Tafel equation with the magnitude of the current. Theoretically and experimentally it is found that the c.v. curve is not symmetrical about the half-wave point.

Weak Acids (in Excess of Indifferent Electrolyte). This case is much more involved. In the first place, the diffusion current depends on the degree of dissociation of the weak acid:

$$i_d = k_H(H^+) + k_{HA}(HA) \tag{15}$$

In this equation (H^+) is the concentration of hydrogen ions in the solution, (HA) that of the undissociated acid, k_H is proportional to the square root of the diffusion coefficient of the hydrogen ions, and k_{HA} to that of the undissociated acid. Since $(H^+) + (HA)$ is equal to the analytical concentration, $\Sigma(HA)$, of the acid, we may write

$$i_d = k_A \Sigma(HA) \tag{16}$$

It should be realized that k_A varies with the concentration of the weak acid because the degree of dissociation decreases with increasing concentration. At any point on the wave the current is expressible by

$$i = k_A\{\Sigma(HA) - \Sigma(HA)_0\} \tag{17}$$

In this equation $\Sigma(HA)_0$ denotes the sum of the concentrations of the hydrogen ions, $(H^+)_0$, and of the undissociated acid $(HA)_0$, at the electrode. From the dissociation equilibrium of the acid we have

$$(H^+)_0 = \frac{(HA)_0}{(A^-)_0} K_a \tag{18}$$

in which $(A^-)_0$ is the concentration of the anion of the acid at the electrode surface, and K_a is the ionization constant. From this equation it is found that

$$(H^+)_0 = \frac{K_a \Sigma(HA)_0}{(A^-)_0 + K_a} \tag{19}$$

From eqs. 16 and 17 it is seen that

$$\Sigma(HA)_0 = \frac{i_d - i}{k_A} \tag{20}$$

The concentration of the anion $(A^-)_0$ increases during the electrolysis, the amount diffusing from the electrode to the bulk of the solution being proportional to the current:

$$i = k_A\text{-}\{A^-)_0 - (A^-)\} \tag{21}$$

or

$$(A^-)_0 = \frac{i}{k_{A^-}} + (A^-) \tag{22}$$

In this equation k_{A^-} is proportional to the square root of the diffusion coefficient of the anions.   Introduction of eqs. 20 and 22 into eq. 10 yields

$$(H^+)_0 = \frac{K_a\left[\dfrac{i_d - i}{k_A}\right]}{\dfrac{i}{k_{A^-}} + (A^-) + K_a} = \frac{(i_d - i)k_{A^-}K_a}{k_A\{i + k_{A^-}(A^-) + k_{A^-}K_a\}} \tag{23}$$

Therefore

$$E = \frac{2RT}{F_y} \ln\left[\frac{(i_d - i)}{i^{3/4}\{i + k_{A^-}(A^-) + k_{A^-}K_a\}} \frac{k_{A^-}}{k_A} K_a\right] + A' \tag{24}$$

At present no data are available to check eq. 24 experimentally.

The above expression can be simplified if we employ the approximation that $(HA)_0 = \Sigma(HA)_0$, and that $k_{A^-}(A^-)$ is negligibly small with regard to i.   This approximation will yield satisfactory results when the degree of dissociation is less than 5 to 10 per cent.   In this case we can consider k_A and k_{A^-} to be of the same order of magnitude and find

$$(H^+)_0 \cong \frac{\Sigma(HA)_0}{(A^-)_0} K_a \cong \frac{(i_d - i)k_{A^-}}{ik_A} K_a \cong \frac{(i_d - i)}{i} K_a \tag{25}$$

$$E \cong \frac{2RT}{F_y} \ln \frac{(i_d - i)}{i} \frac{3RT}{2F_y} \ln i + A$$

and

$$E_{1/2} \cong -\frac{3RT}{2F_y} \ln \frac{i_d}{2} + A \cong -0.089 \log \frac{i_d}{2} + A \tag{26}$$

From this equation it follows that the half-wave potential of a weak acid should shift to more negative potentials with increasing acid concentration while that of strong acids shifts to less negative potentials.   This conclu-

sion is substantiated by Tomes' results.   Moreover, it follows from eq. 26
that

$$\frac{\Delta E_{1/2}}{\Delta \log (HA)} \cong -0.089 \text{ v.} \tag{27}$$

Actually, Tomes (*loc. cit.*) found that this relation was obeyed in solutions
of acetic acid in 1 N lithium chloride, when the acid concentration was
greater than $3 \times 10^{-3} N$.   At this concentration 8 per cent of the acid is
dissociated, and it is not surprising that eq. 27 does not hold for smaller
concentrations.

Weak Acid in Presence of Excess of Its Own Anions.   When the solution
contains a weak acid with a large excess of its own salt, the acid may be
considered as being completely present in the undissociated form $[(HA) =$
$\Sigma(HA)]$.   Moreover, when the concentration of the salt is large compared
to the concentration of the acid we may write $(A^-)_0 = (A^-)$.   Hence we
find

$$(\text{H}^+)_0 = \frac{\Sigma(HA)_0}{(A^-)} K_a = \frac{i_d - i}{k_A} \frac{K_a}{(A^-)} \tag{28}$$

Under these circumstances k_A is proportional to the square root of the
diffusion coefficient of the uncharged acid molecules.   The potential of
the dropping electrode should be given by

$$E = \frac{2RT}{F_y} \ln \frac{i_d - i}{i^{3/4}} + A' \tag{29}$$

$$E_{1/2} = \frac{RT}{2F_y} \ln i_d + A'' \tag{30}$$

or

$$\frac{\Delta E_{1/2}}{\Delta \log (HA)} = 0.029 \text{ v.}$$

Thus the half-wave potential of a weak acid in the presence of a large
excess of its own salt should shift to less negative potentials with increasing
salt concentration, whereas that of the acid in the absence of its salt shifts
to more negative potentials.   Equations 29 and 30 are identical with eqs.
13 and 14 which hold for solution of strong acids.   As a matter of fact,
Tomes observed in the electrolysis of 2×10^{-3} to $4 \times 10^{-3} N$ solutions of
acetic acid in 0.04 N lithium acetate and 0.5 N lithium chloride a value of
$\Delta E_{1/2}/\Delta \log C_{\text{acid}}$ of 0.027 to 0.028 v., in good agreement with the calculated value 0.029 v.   For the difference $E_{1/4} - E_{3/4}$ he obtained a value
of 0.089 v.

CHAPTER XIV

Polarographic Waves of Organic Substances

1. GENERAL CHARACTERISTICS OF REVERSIBLE WAVES FROM BUFFERED SOLUTIONS

In the reduction or oxidation of organic substances hydrogen ion is usually involved in the electrode reaction. In a general case in which the oxidant and reductant are both uncharged molecules, the electrode reaction may be written

$$R + nH^+ + ne \rightleftharpoons RH_n \tag{1}$$

Ordinarily n is even and frequently 2, although cases are known where $n = 1$, and the reduction product contains an odd electron, e. g., semi-quinones.[1] If the foregoing reaction is reversible at the dropping electrode, the potential of the latter will be given by

$$E_{\text{d.e.}} = E^0 - \frac{0.0591}{n} \log \frac{C^0_{RH_n}}{C^0_R (C^0_{H^+})^n} \tag{2}$$

where E^0 is the ordinary standard potential of the reaction, and concentrations have been assumed equal to activities.

Cathodic, anodic, or combined cathodic-anodic waves may be obtained with a reaction of this type, depending on whether the original solution contains only the oxidant, only the reductant, or a mixture of the two. The general principles involved are identical with the partial reduction or oxidation of metal ions at the dropping electrode, which has been discussed in Chapters XI and XII, and the various types of waves will be like those shown in Fig. 4, p. 207. It is evident, therefore, in the most general case when the original solution contains both the oxidant and reductant, that the following relations will apply:

$$(i_d)_c = k_R C_R \tag{3}$$

$$-(i_d)_a = k_{RH_n} C_{RH_n} \tag{4}$$

$$C^0_R = C_R - \frac{i}{k_R} = \frac{(i_d)_c - i}{k_R} \tag{5}$$

$$C^0_{RH_n} = C_{RH_n} + \frac{i}{k_{RH_n}} = \frac{i - (i_d)_a}{k_{RH_n}} \tag{6}$$

---

[1] L. Michaelis, *Chem. Revs.*, **16**, 243 (1935).

In these equations i is the current at any point on the wave, and $(i_d)_c$ and $(i_d)_a$ are, respectively, the cathodic and anodic diffusion currents. Cathodic current (reduction of R) is given a positive sign, and anodic current (oxidation of RH_n) a negative sign.

It is necessary to take account of the fact that in general $C_{H^+}^0$ is current dependent, since hydrogen ion is a component of the electrode reaction. We shall first consider the equation of the waves obtained with a *well-buffered solution*. If the solution has a sufficient buffer capacity, then $C_{H^+}^0$ will be virtually constant, and equal to C_{H^+} in the bulk of the solution. Under this condition the general equation of the wave will be

$$E_{d.e.} = E_{1/2} - \frac{0.0591}{n} \log \frac{i - (i_d)_a}{(i_d)_c - i} \qquad (7)$$

where the half-wave potential is given by

$$E_{1/2} = E^0 - \frac{0.0591}{n} \log \frac{k_R}{k_{RH_n}} + 0.0591 \log C_{H^+}^0 \qquad (8)$$

or

$$E_{1/2} = E^0 - \frac{0.0591}{n} \log \frac{k_R}{k_{RH_n}} - 0.0591 \text{ pH} \qquad (8a)$$

Equation 7 applies to a cathodic, anodic, or combined cathodic-anodic wave, and eq. 8 predicts that the three waves should have identical half-wave potentials (after correction for any iR drop) provided that the electrode reaction is reversible.

The ratio k_R/k_{RH_n}, which is approximately equal to $(D_R/D_{RH_n})^{1/2}$, can be evaluated experimentally from the ratio of the cathodic and anodic diffusion currents obtained with a solution containing equal concentrations of the oxidant and reductant. This ratio is usually so close to 1 that the second term in eq. 8 is negligibly small. Hence $E_{1/2}$ is practically coincident with the potential that one would measure by the ordinary potentiometric technique in a solution containing equal concentrations of the oxidant and reductant at a given pH. It will also be noted that $E_{1/2}$ is a linear function of the pH, and that it is independent of either the absolute or relative concentrations of the oxidant and reductant in the body of the solution.

Hydroquinone-Quinone System. The reduction of benzoquinone and the oxidation of benzohydroquinone at the dropping electrode have been thoroughly studied by Müller and Baumberger,[2] and Müller.[3] The elec-

---

[2] O. H. Müller and J. P. Baumberger, *Trans. Am. Electrochem. Soc.*, **71**, 169, 181 (1937).

[3] O. H. Müller, *Chem. Revs.*, **24**, 95 (1939); *Cold Spring Harbor Symposia Quant. Biol.*, **7**, 59 (1939); *J. Am. Chem. Soc.*, **62**, 2434 (1940).

trode reaction is

$$Q + 2H^+ + 2e \rightleftharpoons H_2Q$$

where Q and H_2Q represent quinone and hydroquinone, respectively.

A typical set of curves for this reaction is shown in Fig. XIV-1.   Each of these polarograms was obtained in a 0.1 M phosphate buffer of pH = 7.0 at 25° C.   Curve 1 was obtained with 0.001 M quinone, curve 2 with a mixture of 5×10^{-4} M each of quinone and hydroquinone, and curve 3 with 0.001 M hydroquinone.   The shift of the apparent half-wave po-

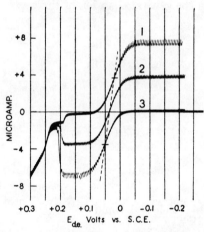

Fig. XIV-1. (1) 0.001 M quinone in 0.1 M phosphate buffer of pH = 7.0 at 25° C.   (2) 5×10^{-4} M quinone plus 5×10^{-4} M hydroquinone in same buffer as (1).   (3) 0.001 M hydroquinone in same buffer as (1) and (2).

tentials, indicated by the inclined broken line, is due to the iR drop in the cell.   When correction is made for this iR drop, the three half-wave potentials become identical, as predicted by eqs. 7 and 8.

The standard potential of the quinone-hydroquinone system is +0.453 v. $vs.$ the S.C.E., and hence from eq. 8 the theoretical half-wave potential for a pH of 7.0 is +0.039 v. $vs.$ the S.C.E.   (The ratio k_R/k_{RH_n} is so close to 1 in this case that the second term in eq. 8 is negligibly small.)   From curve 2 in Fig. XIV-1 the observed half-wave potential is +0.037 v., in very good agreement with the theoretical value.

It will be noted that the anodic diffusion currents in Fig. XIV-1 show a sharp decrease at about +0.2 v., just preceding the rapid increase in the negative current.   This rapid increase in the negative current at +0.23 v. is due to the anodic dissolution of mercury from the dropping electrode.

Apparently a film of mercury phosphate is formed at the electrode which interferes with the normal electrode reactions just before the dissolution wave of mercury.

Müller and Baumberger demonstrated that the half-wave potential of the quinhydrone reaction is a linear function of pH as predicted by eq. 8.

2. USE OF THE DROPPING ELECTRODE FOR THE MEASUREMENT OF OXIDATION POTENTIALS

Müller and Baumberger have shown that the dropping electrode, in conjunction with the quinhydrone system, can be used for pH measurements. For this purpose it is not necessary to obtain the entire wave, but simply to employ the usual null-point ("zero-current") technique. The chief advantage of the dropping electrode for this purpose is that it is less easily polarized then the usual platinum indicator electrode, and hence gives more reliable results in poorly poised[4] solutions.

Kolthoff and Orlemann[5] pointed out that in poorly poised or poorly buffered solutions the "zero-current" potential measured with the dropping electrode is not identical with the oxidation potential of the solution. Quite generally, the true oxidation potential is equal to the potential of the dropping electrode at which the current is equal to the residual current of the medium. In well-poised systems this residual current is hardly of any practical consequence, but it becomes increasingly important in poorly poised or poorly buffered systems. Neglecting the residual current in such systems gives rise to errors in the oxidation potential which may amount to 100 mv. The error becomes especially large when the solution is poorly poised and unbuffered. This case is demonstrated by the diagram in Fig. XIV-2. Curve a represents the residual current of an unbuffered 0.1 N potassium nitrate solution, and curve b is the current–voltage curve of $3.31 \times 10^{-5} M$ quinhydrone in the same salt solution. It is evident that the oxidation potential of the system is not equal to the potential B where the current is zero. Actually, at this point, there is an anodic residual current BC and consequently at point B there is a cathodic current (corresponding to the reduction of quinone) of equal magnitude. The true oxidation potential of the system is found at A where the current–voltage curve intersects the residual current curve. In this particular case the oxidation potential is more than 100 mv. more positive than the value B. This large difference is due to the following facts: (a) Point B just happens to coincide with the half-wave potential of the reduction of quinone to

---

[4] "Poising" in oxidation-reduction reactions is analogous to buffering in an acid-base reaction.

[5] I. M. Kolthoff and E. F. Orlemann, *J. Am. Chem. Soc.*, **63**, 644 (1941).

hydroquinone; in this reduction hydroxyl ions are produced, causing the pH at B to be much greater than at A.   (*b*) At point A the ratio of quinone to hydroquinone is 1 to 1, while at point B it is smaller than 1 to 3, because of the fact that part of the hydroquinone is transformed into its ions by the hydroxyl ions. The same considerations hold when the dropping electrode is used as indicator electrode in the measurement of the pH of an unbuffered or a poorly buffered solution in the presence of a large excess of quinhydrone.

Kolthoff and Orlemann[5] showed that large errors may result with such solutions if the residual current is neglected.   These authors found correct

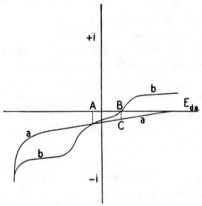

Fig. XIV-2. Polarogram of 3.31 $\times$ 10^{-5} M quinhydrone in unbuffered 0.1 N potassium nitrate (curve *b*), and residual current curve (curve *a*) in the same medium.

values in unbuffered solutions when the potential was read at the point of intersection of the current–voltage curve with the residual current curve. Summarizing, the oxidation potential of poorly poised systems can be measured with the dropping electrode, but the measurement involves the determination of part of the c.v. curve of the system under consideration and also the residual current. The oxidation potential is found at the point of intersection of the two curves. Such a procedure is not very simple but it yields more accurate results than the classical measurement of the oxidation potential with a platinum electrode in poorly poised or poorly buffered solutions containing quinhydrone.

3. THE HYDROGEN ION CONCENTRATION AT THE ELECTRODE IN UNBUFFERED SOLUTIONS

We will first consider the anodic wave of hydroquinone in an unbuffered solution, say in dilute potassium nitrate. During the oxidation hydrogen ions are formed:

$$C_6H_4(OH)_2 \rightleftharpoons C_6H_4O_2 + 2H^+ + 2e$$

Kolthoff and Orlemann[5] gave the following derivation for the calculation of the interfacial concentration of hydrogen ion and the relation between $E_{1/2}$ and the interfacial pH.

The average rate at which hydroquinone is being removed from the electrode surface is proportional to $\bar{\imath}$, where $\bar{\imath}$ is the average current during the life of a drop. The average rate at which hydroquinone is being supplied to the electrode surface (Ilkovic, MacGillavry, and Rideal, see Chap. II) is given by $kD_{Hy}^{1/2}([\overline{Hy}] - [\overline{Hy}]^0)$, where k is constant depending upon the characteristics of the capillary, D_{Hy} is the diffusion coefficient of the hydroquinone, $[Hy]$ is the concentration of hydroquinone in the bulk of the solution, and $[\overline{Hy}]^0$ is the average concentration of hydroquinone at the electrode surface. Since these rates must be equal we have the relation:

$$\bar{\imath} = kD_{Hy}^{1/2}([Hy] - [\overline{Hy}]^0) \tag{9}$$

We also find that the average rate at which quinone is being supplied to the electrode is proportional to $\bar{\imath}$ and the average rate at which it is being removed is given by $kD_Q^{1/2}([\overline{Q}]^0 - [Q])$ where these symbols have meanings analogous to those given above for the hydroquinone case. Again, equating these rates we find:

$$\bar{\imath} = kD_Q^{1/2}([\overline{Q}]^0 - [Q]) \tag{10}$$

In a similar way we find for the hydrogen ions

$$\bar{\imath} = \tfrac{1}{2}kD_{H^+}^{1/2}([\overline{H}]^0 - [H^+]) \tag{11}$$

(The $\tfrac{1}{2}$ appears because of the reaction $C_6H_4O_2 \rightleftharpoons C_6H_4O_2 + 2H^+ + 2e$.) The Ilkovic equation (see Chap. II) gives us the relation

$$i_d = kD_{Hy}^{1/2}[Hy] \tag{12}$$

From these equations we readily find the following relations:

$$[\overline{Hy}]^0 = [Hy]\left(1 - \frac{\bar{\imath}}{kD_{Hy}^{1/2}[Hy]}\right) = [Hy]\frac{i_d - \bar{\imath}}{i_d} \tag{13}$$

$$[\bar{Q}]^0 = \frac{D_{Hy}^{1/2}}{D_Q^{1/2}}([Hy] - [\overline{Hy}]^0) + [Q] \tag{14}$$

$$[\bar{H}^+]^0 = \frac{D_{Hy}^{1/2}}{D_{H^+}^{1/2}}2([Hy] - [\overline{Hy}]^0) + [H^+] \tag{15}$$

For an unbuffered hydroquinone solution at the half-wave potential we therefore have:

$$[\overline{Hy}]^0 = \tfrac{1}{2}[Hy] \tag{16}$$

$$[\overline{Q}]^0 = \left(\frac{D_{Hy}^{1/2}}{D_Q^{1/2}}\right)\{\tfrac{1}{2}[Hy]\} \tag{17}$$

$$[\overline{H^+}]^0 = \frac{D_{Hy}^{1/2}}{D_{H^+}^{1/2}}[Hy] \tag{18}$$

Referring the potential of the dropping electrode to the saturated calomel electrode we also have the following relation at $E_{1/2}$:

$$\overline{pH}^0 = \frac{0.4532 - E_{1/2}}{0.0591} + \tfrac{1}{2}\log\frac{[\overline{Q}]^0}{[Hy]^0} \tag{19}$$

Using the Ilkovic equation for the relation between i_d and the diffusion coefficient (see Chap. II), Kolthoff and Orlemann calculated from the measured diffusion currents at 25° C. that $D_{Hy} = (7.4 \pm 0.2) \times 10^{-6}$ cm.^{2} sec.$^{-1}$, and $D_Q = (8.6 \pm 0.2) \times 10^{-6}$ cm.^{2} sec.$^{-1}$. The diffusion coefficient of the hydrogen ion, from its electrical mobility at infinite dilution, is 9.34×10^{-5} cm.^{2} sec.$^{-1}$ at 25° (see Chap. III). Introducing these values into eq. 19 yields the following relation between the average pH at the electrode interface during the life of a drop and the half-wave potential:

$$\overline{pH}^0 = -0.02 + \frac{0.4532 \times E_{1/2}}{0.0591} \ (25°) \tag{20}$$

We also find from the known diffusion coefficients that eq. 18 can be written as follows:

$$\overline{pH}^0 = 0.56 - \log[Hy] \tag{21}$$

Kolthoff and Orlemann determined the half-wave potential of a 0.001 M hydroquinone solution which was 0.1 M in potassium nitrate, and found a value of $+0.238$ v. According to eq. 20 this corresponds to a $\overline{pH}^0$ value of 3.6 (± 0.1), while the calculated value from eq. 21 is 3.56.

The calculation of the average hydroxyl ion concentration at the surface of the drop in the reduction of quinone from a neutral unbuffered solution is more involved. The electrode reaction is

$$C_6H_4O_2 + 2H_2O + 2e \rightleftharpoons C_6H_4(OH)_2 + 2OH^-$$

If there were no interaction between hydroxyl ions and hydroquinone $\overline{pOH}^0$ could be calculated in the same way that $\overline{pH}^0$ was calculated in the oxidation of hydroquinone. However, since hydroquinone behaves as a weak dibasic acid, part of the hydroxyl ions are transformed into uni- and divalent hydroquinone ions and the calculation becomes very complicated.

4. REVERSIBLE ELECTROREDUCTION WITH FORMATION OF SEMIQUINONES

In the reduction of a relatively large number of substances L. Michaelis and co-workers observed the intermediate formation of a substance—called a semiquinone—corresponding to the addition of one electron to the oxidized form R. This was found with substances which contained oxygen or nitrogen at the end with a system of double bonds. With the oxygen-containing substances the stability of the semiquinone is favored in alkaline medium, and with the nitrogen-containing substances, in acid medium.

At a constant pH (buffer solution) the two-step reduction can be represented by the equations:

$$R + e \rightleftharpoons R^-$$

$$R^- + e \rightleftharpoons R^{--}$$

The intermediate form R^- is the semiquinone, denoted below as S. The semiquinone is in reversible equilibrium with R and R^{--} which is represented by the dismutation reaction

$$2R^- \rightleftharpoons R + R^{--} \tag{22}$$

The semiquinone has properties of a free radical and can dimerize in solution

$$2S \rightleftharpoons S_2 \rightleftharpoons R + R^{--} \tag{23}$$
$$\quad\quad \text{dimerization} \quad\quad \text{dismutation}$$

Michaelis and co-workers[6] derived equations describing the change of the oxidation potential of R upon stepwise reduction, or of R^{--} upon stepwise oxidation, by the addition of a chemical reagent. These are the equations of the potentiometric titration curves. The fundamental equation is the classical one:

$$E = E^0 + \frac{RT}{2F_\nu} \ln \frac{[Ox]}{[Red]} \tag{24}$$

---

[6] L. Michaelis, *J. Biol. Chem.*, **96**, 703 (1932); *Chem. Revs.*, **16**, 243 (1935); *Trans. Electrochem. Soc.*, **71**, 107 (1937). L. Michaelis and M. P. Schubert, *Chem. Revs.*, **22**, 437 (1938).

in which [Ox] is the total concentration of the oxidized form [R] and [Red] the total concentration of the reduced form.

Müller[7] pointed out in a fundamental paper that an analysis of the current–voltage curve of the polarographic wave or waves of R permits the calculation of the oxidation potential of the system and of the various equilibria involved. The rapid performance of the determination of a polarogram is considered by Müller as a great advantage over the more involved potentiometric method. On the other hand, Müller admits that the potentiometric method is more accurate than the polarographic one. He recommends the polarographic method especially for preliminary studies. In studies on the polarographic reduction of riboflavin Brdicka[8] independently had interpreted his polarograms on the basis of Michaelis' classical work. The same author[9] gave a complete analysis of the current–voltage curves. Both Müller and Brdicka based their derivations on the classical papers of Michaelis.

The following derivations refer to Brdicka's generalized treatment. It is assumed that the various equilibria involved are established practically instantaneously. The occurrence of an adsorption wave is not considered. The following equilibria must be considered.

$$\frac{[Ox][Red]}{[S^2]} = k \text{ (dismutation constant)} \tag{25}$$

$$\frac{[S^2]}{[Ox][Red]} = k \text{ (semiquinone formation constant)} \tag{26}$$

$$\frac{[D]}{[S^2]} = \gamma \text{ (dimer formation constant)} \tag{27}$$

$$\frac{[D]}{[Ox][Red]} = q \text{ (dimerization constant)} \tag{28}$$

D denotes the dimer. It is seen that $q = k\gamma$.

(a) Semiquinone Formation without Dimerization

According to the Ilkovic equation:

$$i = 2g([Red^0] - [Red]) + g([S^0] - [S]) \tag{29a}$$

in which g is a proportionality constant (it is assumed that D_{red} and D_S

[7] O. H. Müller, *Ann. N. Y. Acad. Sci.*, **40**, 91 (1940).

[8] R. Brdicka and E. Knobloch, *Z. Elektrochem.*, **47**, 721 (1941). R. Brdicka, *ibid.*, **48**, 686 (1942).

[9] R. Brdicka, *Z. Elektrochem.*, **47**, 314 (1941).

are equal). If the solution contains only the oxidized R we can write:

$$i = 2g[\text{Red}^0] + g[\text{S}^0] \tag{29b}$$

If the total concentration of the oxidized form is equal to a we have:

$$i_d = 2ga \tag{30}$$

and
$$[\text{Red}^0] + [\text{S}^0] + [\text{Ox}^0] = a = i_d/2g \tag{31}$$

The potential of the dropping mercury (oxidation potential) is determined by the ratio of the completely oxidized and reduced forms at the interface:

$$\frac{[\text{Ox}^0]}{[\text{Red}^0]} = \exp\left\{\frac{2(E - E_{1/2})F_y}{RT}\right\} = P \tag{32}$$

From (29a), (31), and (32) it is found that:

$$[\text{Ox}^0] = \frac{P(i_d - 2i)}{2(P - i)g} \tag{33a}$$

$$[\text{S}^0] = \frac{i(P + 1) - i_d}{(P - 1)g} \tag{33b}$$

$$[\text{Red}^0] = \frac{i_d - 2i}{2(P - 1)g} \tag{33c}$$

The relation between current i and potential E is found by introducing the various equilibrium concentrations:

$$k = \frac{[\text{S}^0]^2}{[\text{Ox}^0][\text{Red}^0]} = \frac{4}{P}\left(\frac{i(P + 1) - i_d}{i_d - 2i}\right)^2 \tag{34}$$

$$i = \frac{i_d}{2}\frac{\sqrt{kP} + 2}{P + \sqrt{kP} + 1} \tag{35a}$$

$$E - E_{1/2} = -\frac{RT}{2F_y}\ln\frac{i}{i_d - i} - \frac{RT}{2F_y}\ln$$

$$\frac{\sqrt{(2i - i_d)^2(k - 4) + 4i_d^2} + (2i - i_d)\sqrt{k}}{\sqrt{(2i - i_d)^2(k - 4) + 4i_d^2} - (2i - i_d)\sqrt{k}} \tag{35b}$$

If there is no semiquinone formation ($k = 0$) eq. 35 becomes identical with eq. 7.

When $k = 4$ eq. 35 becomes

$$E - E_{1/2} = -\frac{RT}{F_y} \ln \frac{i}{i_d - i} \tag{36}$$

corresponding to a reduction in which n is equal to 1.

In case k is greater than 4 its value can be found from the slope of the tangent of the current–voltage curve at $E = E_{1/2}$:

$$\delta = \left(\frac{di}{dE}\right)_{i=1/2 i_d} = -\frac{F_y}{RT} \frac{i_d}{2 + \sqrt{k}} = -39.72 \frac{i_d}{2 + \sqrt{k}} \tag{37}$$

$$k = \left(2 + \frac{F_y i_d}{RT\delta}\right)^2 = \left(2 + 39.72 \frac{i_d}{\delta}\right)^2 \tag{38}$$

(b) Semiquinone Dimerizes Completely

Instead of eq. 18 can be written

$$[\text{Red}^0] + 2[\text{D}^0] + [\text{Ox}^0] = a \tag{39}$$

$$i = \frac{i_d}{2}\left(1 + \frac{(P - 1)\{P + 1 - \sqrt{(P + 1)^2 + 8agP}\}}{4agP}\right) \tag{40a}$$

$$E - E_{1/2} \tag{40b}$$
$$= \frac{RT}{2F_y} \ln \frac{ag(i_d - 2i) - i_d + \sqrt{a^2g^2(i_d - 2i)^2 + i_d^2(2ag + 1)}}{-ag(i_d - 2i) - i_d + \sqrt{a^2g^2(i_d - 2i)^2 + i_d^2(2ag + 1)}}$$

For further details the reader is referred to the papers of Michaelis' Brdicka, and Müller.

5. EFFECT ON POLAROGRAPHIC WAVES OF ADSORPTION OF THE OXIDIZED FORM AND/OR THE SUBSTANCE FORMED BY REDUCTION

Appearance of a Prewave

In studies of fundamental importance Brdicka interpreted involved polarographic waves obtained in the reduction of an organic compound whose reduction product is strongly adsorbed on the interface mercury–water and hence at the dropping electrode. In a study of the reduction of riboflavin[10] in acid medium a prewave was always observed before the

---

[10] R. Brdicka, Z. Elektrochem., **48**, 278 (1942). See also O. H. Müller, *Trans. Electrochem. Soc.*, **87**, 441 (1945).

normal reduction wave. Similar phenomena were observed in the reduction of methylene blue.

The polarogram consists of two waves, a small prewave of constant height which is independent of the concentration, followed by a normal reduction wave. The total diffusion current (sum of the prewave and the normal one) is proportional to the concentration of methylene blue in the solution. The second wave decreases with decreasing concentration of methylene blue, until at a very small concentration (of the order of 0.5 $\times$ 10^{-4} M) only the prewave is observed. The half-wave potential of the prewave is a few hundredths of a volt more positive than the true oxidation potential of the system. On the other hand, the half-wave potential of the normal wave corresponds closely, but not exactly, to the oxidation potential of the thermodynamically reversible methylene blue system and it changes with pH in a manner found by Clark[11] in his classical experiments on the oxidation potential of methylene blue.

The occurrence of the prewave at potentials more positive than correspond to the thermodynamically reversible reduction is attributed by Brdicka to an adsorption of the reduced form of methylene blue on the surface of the dropping electrode. As a result of this adsorption the activity of the reduced form is considerably less than when it is in true solution. The difference in half-wave potential between the prewave and the normal one corresponds to the energy involved in the adsorption of the reduced form. The difference between the two half-wave potentials decreases with increasing temperature, until at 90° C. only the normal wave is found. This is explained by a decrease in the energy of adsorption with increasing temperature.

The current–voltage curves can be interpreted quantitatively when the adsorption of the leuco dye is considered. The Langmuir adsorption isotherm can be written in the following form:

$$\alpha = \frac{z\omega c}{1 + \omega c}$$

in which α is the amount adsorbed in moles per cm.^{2} of surface, ω the adsorption coefficient, z the maximum number of adsorbed molecules per cm.^{2}, and c the molar concentration of the adsorptive in the solution.

In deriving the equation of the polarographic waves Brdicka assumes that adsorption equilibrium is attained instantanteously. Actually in the interpretation of the experimental curves a correction for the rate of establishment of equilibrium must be applied.

---

[11] W. M. Clark, B. Cohen, and H. D. Gibbs, *Public Health Reports*, **40**, 1155 (1925).

The oxidation potential E of a reversible system can be written as follows:

$$\frac{[\text{Red}]^0}{[\text{Ox}]^0} = e^{-2F(E-E_0)/RT} \qquad (41)$$

Instead of $[\text{Ox}^0]$ we can write the Ilkovic relation:

$$[\text{Ox}^0] = \frac{(i_d - i)}{k} = \quad \text{or} \quad \frac{(i_d - i)}{2g} \qquad (42)$$

in which g is the proportionality factor between the total diffusion current i_d and the molar concentration of the reduced substance.

In considering i as a function of the concentration of reductant at the interface $[\text{Red}^0]$, both the amount of $[\text{Red}]$ diffusing away and the amount which remains attached to the electrode by adsorption must be taken into account:

$$i = 2g[\text{Red}^0] + 2F_y \frac{z \; \Delta q\omega[\text{Red}^0]}{1 + \omega[\text{Red}^0]} \qquad (43)$$

in which Δq is the average increase of the surface of the electrode per second.

When the surface is completely saturated the second term of eq. 43 becomes $2F_y z \, \Delta q$. This term determines the magnitude of the prewave i_a if the value of $2g[\text{Red}^0]$, which is very small, is neglected. The limiting current of the prewave is called the adsorption current i_a. Combining (41), (42), and (43) it is found that:

$$E - E_0 = \frac{RT}{2F_y} \ln \frac{\omega(i - i_a) - 2g}{2\omega(i_d - i)} + \frac{\sqrt{[2g - \omega(i - i_a)]^2 + 8g\omega i}}{2\omega(i_d - i)} \qquad (44)$$

By filling out values for g, i_d, i_a, and ω the experimental c.v. curves can be calculated. Brdicka calculated for the leuco form of methylene blue at 25° C. the following values: $z = 1.62 \times 10^{-10}$ mole cm.$^{-2}$ $= 10^{14}$ molecule cm.$^{-2}$, and $\omega = 10^{-8}$:

$$\omega = v e^{\varphi/RT}$$

in which v is the molecular volume in the adsorbed state when a monomolecular layer is on the surface and φ is the molar adsorption energy. Assuming a cubic form of the adsorbed molecule $v = 0.606 \, \varphi$, a value of 11.2 kcal. mole^{-1} for φ was calculated.

With the aid of eqs. 41 and 42 it is possible to calculate the current at which $[\text{Ox}^0] = [\text{Red}^0]$. The potential at this point corresponds to the standard potential E_0 of the thermodynamically reversible system. Let i_d denote the total diffusion current, i_a the adsorption current, then $i_d' = i_d - i_a$, and

$$i_{E_0} = \frac{i_d'}{2} + i_a$$

The true oxidation potential is not found at a potential corresponding to the total half-wave current, but at the potential of the half-wave current of the second wave plus a constant value i_a.

It is interesting to note that, whereas a normal diffusion current changes with $m^{2/3}t^{1/6}$ (or in proportion to $\sqrt{h}$), the adsorption current i_a is a function of $m^{2/3}t^{-1/3}$, and, therefore, i_a changes in proportion with the height of the mercury h.

In the above the adsorption of the reduced form in favor of the oxidized form has been considered. If the oxidized form is more strongly adsorbed than the reduced form a postwave instead of prewave is found, i. e., an apparently normal wave is observed followed by a small "adsorption" wave. Under those circumstances:

$$i = i_a - 2g[Ox^0] - 2F_v \frac{z \, \Delta q \omega [Ox^0]}{1 + \omega [Ox^0]} \tag{45}$$

Small adsorption waves were formed by Brdicka[12] in the polarographic reduction of colchicine and colchiceine.

Müller[13] made interesting observations on the occurrence of "anomalous" waves in the polarographic reduction of various dyes. In general his results seem to be in agreement with Brdicka's interpretation. In Fig. XIV-3 are reproduced some of Müller's results[14] obtained with rosinduline GG in a phosphate buffer of pH 6.8. Curves a to j correspond to concentrations of 7.65, 5.10, 3.83, 3.06, 2.19, 1.70, 1.13, 0.85, 0.68, and 0.57 $\times$ 10^{-4} M, respectively. At the higher concentrations the prewave and the "normal" wave are clearly seen. The height of the normal wave decreases with decreasing concentration until it disappears at a concentration of 1.1×10^{-4} M. The adsorption wave is also found on the anodic wave of the reduced dye as is evident from Fig. XIV-4, which demonstrates the reversibility of the entire electrode reaction.

---

[12] R. Brdicka, *Casopis Ceskoslov. Lekarnictva*, **58**, 37 (1945).

[13] O. H. Müller, *Trans. Electrochem. Soc.*, **87**, 441 (1945).

[14] O. H. Müller, *The Polarographic Method of Analysis*, Journal of Chemical Education, Easton, Pa., 1951.

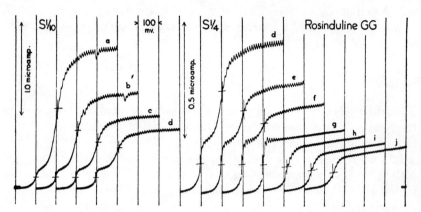

Fig. XIV-3. Polarogram of different concentrations of rosinduline GG in a 0.15 M, pH 6.8, phosphate buffer at 23° C., each curve starting at −0.3 v. (*vs*. S.C.E.). Half-wave potentials are indicated. First four curves were taken with one-tenth, the last 7 curves with one-fourth, of maximum galvanometer sensitivity.[14]

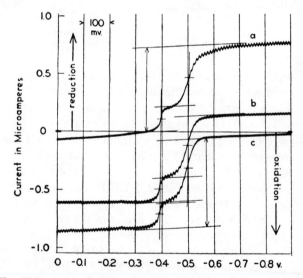

Fig. XIV-4. Polarogram of 3.63×10^{-4} M rosinduline GG in a phosphate buffer of pH 6.8: (*a*) when the dye is present in the scarlet red, totally oxidized form; (*b*) when the dye has been partially reduced with hydrogen gas in the presence of platinized asbestos; and (*c*) when the dye has been fully reduced with hydrogen gas in the presence of platinized asbestos, and the solution is practically colorless.[14]

The half-wave potential of the adsorption wave is independent of the concentration when the latter is large enough to produce a normal wave. At concentrations below that of the appearance of the normal wave the half-wave potential becomes more negative with increasing dilution.

TABLE XIV-1

COMPOUNDS INVESTIGATED BY MÜLLER FOR ANOMALOUS POLAROGRAPHIC WAVES
(ADSORPTION WAVES) AND MAXIMUM SEPARATION OF HALF-WAVE POTENTIALS
OF THE TWO WAVES

Compound	Anomalous wave	pH studied	Max. separation of half-wave potentials of anomalous and regular waves, mv.	At pH
Quinones				
p-Benzoquinone	−	1 to 8	−	
Duroquinone	−	1 to 13	−	
Indophenols	− (?)	6.6		
Indigo disulfonate	+	2 to 8	50	4.0
Phenazines				
Phenazine	+	4.6	75	4.6
α-Oxyphenazine	+	3 to 13	38	4.7
Pyocyanine	+	3.0		
Rosinduline GG	+	1 to 8	120	4.6
Oxazines				
Oxonine	−	3.0		
Oxonine	+	5 to 7	32	5.1
Cresyl violet	+	6.8	74	6.8
Thiazines				
3-Aminothiazine	+	8.0	140	8.0
Thionine	+	4.6	120	4.6
Methylene blue[a, b]	+	3 to 7	133	5.5
Riboflavin[a]	+	2 to 6	100	2.2

[a] See also Brdicka's results (l.c.).
[b] On the reversible polarographic reduction of methylene blue, see also M. von Stackelberg and H. von Freyhold, Z. Elektrochem., **46**, 120 (1940); also **45**, 466 (1939).

Results obtained by Müller[15, 16] with various other substances are summarized in Table XIV-1. Quinones did not show any "abnormal" waves.

Voriskova[17] made a detailed study of the polarographic behavior of pyocyanin which is α-oxymethylphenazine. In 0.5 normal sulfuric acid two waves are observed, the first wave being greater than the second wave.

---

[15] O. H. Müller, Ann. N. Y. Acad. Sci., **40**, 91 (1940).
[16] O. H. Müller, J. Biol. Chem., **145**, 425 (1942); Trans. Electrochem. Soc., **87**, 441 (1945).
[17] M. Voriskova, Collection Czechoslov. Chem. Communs., **12**, 607 (1947).

The difference between the two waves is almost independent of the concentration of the dye. When the total diffusion current becomes smaller than the difference between the two waves only the first wave is observed.

When the concentration is such that two waves are found the second wave is composed of a prewave and a normal wave. The height of the prewave is independent of the concentration of the dye.

With increasing pH the difference in half-wave potential of the two waves decreases until, at a pH of about 6, only one wave is observed. In agreement with the interpretation of Michaelis[18] of the behavior of pyocyanine during the potentiometric titration with a reducing agent Voriskova attributes the two-step reduction in acid medium to semiquinone formation (see Section 4).

The difference in height between the first and the second waves is explained by adsorption of the totally reduced form on the surface of the mercury. The semiquinone which is formed in the first reduction step is in equilibrium with the oxidized and the totally reduced forms. The latter is withdrawn by adsorption. This interpretation accounts for the fact that the difference in height between the two waves is independent of the concentration. When the concentration becomes so small that only one wave is obtained the reduction corresponds to a two-electron transfer, since all of the reduced form now remains adsorbed.

The prewave of the second wave is attributed to an additional adsorption layer of the reduced form. In agreement with the above interpretations it was found that the difference between the first and the second waves and the height of the prewave are proportional to the height of the mercury in the reservoir.

6. EFFECT OF ADSORBED SUBSTANCES ON REVERSIBLE OXIDATION OR REDUCTION WAVES

Wiesner[19] investigated the effect of dissolved *eosin*, and in some instances of tetraiodofluorescein, on the cathodic or anodic waves of benzoquinone, hydroquinone, naphthoquinone, toluhydroquinone, 1,2-naphthoquinone-4-hydrosulfonate, and ascorbic acid. Very small concentrations of the dye do not affect the "reversible" waves. When the eosin concentration has attained a certain value the height of the reversible wave decreases with increasing eosin concentration (see Fig. XIV-5). When dealing with reduction waves the remaining part of the oxidizing substance (quinone)

---

[18] L. Michaelis, *Oxydation-Reduktions Potentiale*. 2d ed., 1932. Springer, Berlin (p. 123, Fig. 19).

[19] K. Wiesner, *Collection Czechoslov. Chem. Communs.*, **2**, 594 (1947).

is reduced at a more negative potential and a second wave is observed. This second wave corresponds to an irreversible reduction. With an electrooxidized substance only a reduction in height of the reversible part of the wave is observed; no second wave is observed before the anodic dissolution wave of mercury.

The reduction in height of the reversible wave does not depend upon the nature of the substance which is oxidized or reduced, but is determined by the concentration of the eosin and the characteristics of the capillary.

Apparently the adsorbed layer of the dye interferes with the normal polarographic reduction or oxidation of a reversible system. When the concentration of the dye is very small the time required for the formation of a compact adsorption layer is so large that no interference is found (see

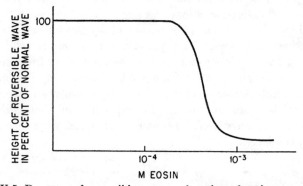

Fig. XIV-5. Decrease of reversible wave as function of eosin concentration.

Fig. XIV-5). With increasing concentration of the dye and also with decreasing drop time the tendency to be adsorbed increases. At a certain concentration the adsorbed layer becomes more compact and is comparable to a two-dimensional crystallization.

If a certain substance shows a prewave due to adsorption of its reduced form, e. g., methylene blue, lactoflavin, etc., and a capillary-active dye is more strongly adsorbed than the reduced form, the dye may replace the reduced form from the surface of the mercury. Under such circumstances the prewave disappears. Thus, Wiesner found that the prewave due to adsorption of the leuco form of indigo trisulfonate disappears upon addition of sufficient eosin. However, he does not mention that the adsorbed dye affects the normal reduction wave of the indigo trisulfonate, although he had found that adsorbed eosin greatly affects the waves corresponding to reversible reductions or oxidations. This effect deserves further study.

In unpublished work (1943) Kolthoff and D. R. May found that the reduction wave of oxygen is displaced to more negative potentials by traces of lauryl disulfide. This was attributed to adsorption of disulfide which interferes with the normal reduction of oxygen. The effect is so great that it can be made the basis of a quantitative determination of the disulfide.

7. THE ELECTRODE REACTION ITSELF IS REVERSIBLE BUT THE NET REACTION IS IRREVERSIBLE

If the electrode reaction is reversible but the reaction product formed by electrolysis is unstable, and is irreversibly transformed to another compound, the net reaction of electrolysis becomes irreversible. Such a case was encountered by Smith, Kolthoff, Wawzonek, and Ruoff[20] in the oxidation of hydroxychromans and hydroxycoumarans at the dropping electrode. In proper buffer solutions in 50 per cent methanol the above compounds gave well-defined anodic waves and diffusion currents.

Chemical or electrochemical oxidation of hydroxychromans and coumarans produces quinones. The quinones are reversibly reduced to the corresponding hydroquinones and not to the original hydroxychromans or coumarans. From an analysis of the anodic waves of these compounds it was concluded that the electrochemical oxidation involves a reversible reaction, but that the oxidation product formed is unstable and is irreversibly transformed to the corresponding quinone. The following reaction mechanism was postulated:

$$ (A) \rightleftharpoons (B) \qquad + 2H^+ + 2e \tag{46} $$

$$ (B) \rightarrow (C) \tag{47} $$

[20] L. I. Smith, I. M. Kolthoff, S. Wawzonek, and P. M. Ruoff, J. Am. Chem. Soc., **63**, 1018 (1941).

In this case the hydroxy compound B is unstable and is irreversibly transformed into the quinone C. The net reaction is therefore given by the equation:

$$A + H_2O \rightarrow C + 2H^+ + 2e$$

On the other hand the potential is determined by the reversible reaction:

$$A + H_2O \rightleftharpoons B + 2H^+ + 2e$$

and hence the potential of the dropping electrode on the anodic wave is given by:

$$E_{\text{d.e.}} = \text{Const.} + \frac{0.0591}{2} \log \frac{C_B^0}{C_A^0} + 0.0591 \log C_{H^+}^0 \qquad (48)$$

Since well-buffered solutions were used, $C_{H^+}^0$ could be taken equal to C_{H^+} in the bulk of the solution and could be considered constant during the electrolysis in a particular medium. It is easily derived that

$$C_A^0 = \frac{i_d - i}{k_A} \qquad (49)$$

The concentration of B at the surface of the electrode (C_B^0) is unknown, since B is transformed to the end product C. The rate at which C is formed is proportional to the concentration of B. Hence, we can write:

$$C_B^0 = \alpha C_C^0 \qquad (50)$$

In turn, C_C^0 is proportional to the current i, and we find

$$i = k' C_C^0 = \frac{k'}{\alpha} C_B^0 \qquad (51)$$

or

$$C_B^0 = \frac{\alpha i}{k'}$$

Since A and C have about the same molecular size k may be taken (approximately) equal to k'. Introducing eqs. 49 and 51 into eq. 48 we obtain for a well-buffered solution:

$$E_{\text{d.e.}} = \text{Const.} + \frac{0.0591}{2} \log \left[\frac{i}{(i_d - i)} \frac{k_A \alpha}{k'} \right] + 0.0591 \log C_{H^+} \qquad (52)$$

or at a given pH:

$$E_{\text{d.e.}} = E_{1/2} + \frac{0.0591}{2} \log \frac{i}{(i_d - i)} \tag{53}$$

Hence, the shape of the wave is identical with that of a reversible reaction which involves the transfer of two electrons. However, the value of $E_{1/2}$ is not the oxidation potential of the system $A + H_2O \rightleftharpoons B + 2H^+ + 2e$, but it also involves the rate constant α for the rearrangement of the hydroxy compound B to the quinone C. The latter reaction is analogous to the well-known rearrangement of pyridinium hydroxides to α-hydroxydihydropyridines.

In agreement with eq. 53 it was found that the half-wave potential of the anodic waves of hydroxychromans and coumarans was constant and independent of the concentration. Upon plotting the value of log $[i/(i_d - i)]$ against E in the case of $2,2,5,7,8$-pentamethyl-6-hydroxychroman (A) a straight line was found with a slope of 0.0326 v., in fairly good agreement with the theoretical slope of 0.0296 v.

We anticipate that the oxidation or reduction of a number of organic compounds at the dropping electrode may belong to the class discussed in this section.

8. CASES IN WHICH THE ELECTRODE REACTION IS IRREVERSIBLE

Some characteristics of polarographic waves obtained in the irreversible reduction of metal ions, of complex ions, and of hydrogen ions have been described in previous chapters. Many cases of irreversible reactions are found when dealing with organic compounds. An exact interpretation of current–voltage curves obtained in irreversible reductions and oxidations at various kinds of electrodes cannot be given at present, although numerous theories have been presented in the literature.[21]

Experimentally, in many cases the following relation between the current and the potential has been found in irreversible reductions:

$$i = kC^0 e^{\alpha E F_y / RT} \tag{54}$$

---

[21] See, e. g., T. Erdey-Gruz and M. Volmer, Z. physik. Chem., **A150,** 203 (1930). M. Volmer, Physik. Z. der Sowjetunion, **4,** 346 (1933). M. Volmer and H. Wick, Z. physik. Chem., **A172,** 429 (1935). F. P. Bowden, Trans. Faraday Soc., **24,** 473 (1928); Proc. Roy. Soc. London, **A126,** 107 (1929). For an excellent review see K. Wirtz, Z. Elektrochem., **44,** 303 (1936). Cf. also the following: J. A. V. Butler, Electrocapillarity, New York, 1940. R. W. Gurney, Proc. Roy. Soc. London, **A134,** 137 (1931). G. Kimball, J. Chem. Phys., **8,** 199 (1940). P. van Rysselberghe, J. Am. Chem. Soc., **68,** 2047 (1946).

in which C^0 is the concentration of the electroreducible substance at the electrode surface.   In experiments with the dropping electrode:

$$C^0 = k'(i_d - i) \tag{55}$$

and

$$i = k''(i_d - i)e^{\alpha E F_y/RT} \tag{56}$$

or

$$\ln \frac{i}{(i_d - i)} = \text{Const.} + \frac{\alpha E F_y}{RT} \tag{57}$$

$$E = E_{1/2} + \frac{RT}{\alpha F_y} \ln \frac{i}{(i_d - i)} \tag{58}$$

In such cases the half-wave potential is found to be constant and independent of the concentration.   The plot of $\log i/(i_d - i)$ vs. E yields a straight line and the value of α can be found from the slope.   Very often a value of α is found which is less than one.   It is emphasized here that one cannot conclude that the electrode reaction is reversible merely from the fact that the half-wave potential (at constant pH) does not vary with the concentration, or that the plot of E vs. $\log i/(i_d - i)$ yields a straight line, even if α is found to be equal to or greater than one.

CHAPTER XV

Waves Dependent on Reaction Rates. Catalytic Waves

1. REACTION RATE AT THE DROPPING ELECTRODE DETERMINES HEIGHT OF WAVE PARTLY OR COMPLETELY

First we consider the case in which a substance occurs in two forms O_A and O_B , both of which are reducible at the dropping electrode but at different potentials (O_A being reduced at a more positive potential than O_B), and in which there is a reversible equilibrium between the two forms:

$$O_A \rightleftharpoons O_B \tag{1}$$

$$\frac{[O_A]}{[O_B]} = K \tag{2}$$

If equilibrium is established very rapidly, only one wave is observed corresponding to reduction of O_A . If we denote the total concentration of O by O_t , then

$$O_A = O_t \left(\frac{K}{K+1}\right) \tag{3}$$

and

$$E = E_a^0 + \frac{RT}{nF_y} \ln \left(\frac{K}{K+1}\right) \frac{[O_t]^0}{[R]^0} = E^{0\prime} + \frac{RT}{nF_y} \ln \frac{[O_t]^0}{[R]^0} \tag{4}$$

in which R is the reduced form, and E_a^0 the standard potential of the reaction $O_A + ne = R$. The indicated concentrations are those *at the electrode surfaces*. The other extreme case is that the rate of establishment of equilibrium 1 is so small that it can be disregarded during the life of each mercury drop. Under such circumstances two waves are found whose heights correspond to the concentrations of O_A and O_B in the body of the solution.

The situation becomes much more involved if the rate of establishment of equilibrium in reaction 1 has to be considered. Reduction reactions in which wave heights are affected by reaction rates have been discussed by Brdicka and Wiesner.[1]

(a) Occurrence of Two Waves. Relation between Waves as Function of pH

Brdicka and Wiesner (1947) gave a complete discussion of the polarographic reduction of an acid whose undissociated form is reduced at a more positive potential than its anion. Keto acids like pyruvic acid and phenylglyoxylic acid contain, in the undissociated form, a perfectly conjugated bond with two doubly bonded oxygen atoms at the end of the molecule. In the mesomeric anion, however, both oxygens of the carboxyl group are equivalent, and the anion is no longer conjugated.

$$R-\underset{\underset{O}{\parallel}}{C}-\underset{\underset{O}{\parallel}}{C}-OH \qquad \left[R-\underset{\underset{O}{\parallel}}{C}-C\underset{\diagdown O}{\diagup O} \right]$$

undissociated acid   anion

With such acids generally only one wave is found in strongly acid medium; over an intermediate pH range two waves occur, the more positive one corresponding to the reduction of the undissociated acid and the more negative one to that of the anion. At a higher pH only the anion wave is observed. Calling the diffusion current corresponding to the reduction of the undissociated acid i_+ , and that of the anion i_- , it was found that:

$$pH = \text{Const.} + \log (i_-/i_+) \qquad (5)$$

It should be emphasized that this equation can only be approximately correct. Equation 5 is of the same form as the familiar equation for a dissociation equilibrium:

$$pH = pK_a + \log ([A^-]/[HA]) \qquad (6)$$

If the rate of establishment of equilibrium between HA and A^- at the dropping electrode is negligibly small, the first diffusion current (i_d) corresponds to the concentration of HA in the bulk of the solution and $(i_d)_{A^-}$ to that of A^-:

$$[i_d]_{HA} = a[HA] \qquad (7)$$

$$[i_d]_{A^-} = a[A^-] \qquad (8)$$

---

[1] R. Brdicka, *Chem. Listy*, **39**, 35 (1945); **40**, 232 (1946). R. Brdicka and K. Wiesner, *Vestnik Kral. Ces. Spol. Nauk*, **18**, 16 (1943); *Naturwissenschaften*, **31**, 247, 391 (1943). K. Wiesner, *Z. Elektrochem.*, **49**, 164 (1943). R. Brdicka and K. Wiesner, *Chem. Listy*, **40**, 66 (1946); *Collection Czechoslov. Chem. Communs.*, **12** (1947).

in which $a = 605 \times 10^{3} \, nD^{1/2}m^{2/3}t^{1/6}$, while it is assumed that $D_{HA} \approx D_{A^-}$.
If, however, the rate of the reaction

$$A^- + H^+ \rightleftharpoons HA \tag{9}$$

is appreciable, more HA will be formed by the association reaction during
the lifetime of a drop. Consequently, i_+ will be greater than $(i_d)_{HA}$.
If the rate of association were extremely large only one wave would be
found.

With intermediate rates of association:

$$i_+ = (i_d)_{HA} + i_k \tag{10}$$

$$i_- = (i_d)_{A^-} - i_k \tag{11}$$

where i_k is proportional to the velocity constant of reaction 9. Diagrammatically the relations are represented in Fig. XV-1.

The instantaneous increase of undissociated molecules at the interface is
given by:

$$d(HA)/dt = k[A^-]^0[H^+]^0 \tag{12}$$

In the following it is assumed that the medium is well buffered, so that
$[H^+]^0 = [H^+]$, where $[H^+]$ is the hydrogen ion concentration in the bulk
of the solution. The limiting current i_k , due to reduction of HA formed
by association at the interface, is given by:

$$i_k = nF_v10^3 \, q\mu k[H^+][A^-]^0 \tag{13}$$

in which q is the average area of the mercury drop and μ the thickness of
the surface layer in which the association occurs. The volume μq is expressed in cm.^{3}, the concentrations of HA and A^- in moles per liter, and
the current i_k in microamperes; therefore the factor 10^3 is introduced.

The current i_k must be proportional to the rate of diffusion of A^- from the
bulk of the solution to the electrode, hence:

$$i_k = a([A^-] - [A^-]^0) \tag{14}$$

Since, according to eq. 8:

$$(i_d)_{A^-} = a[A^-]$$

we get:

$$i_k = [i_d]_{A^-} - a[A^-]^0 \tag{14a}$$

and

$$i_k = \frac{\mu k[\text{H}^+](i_d)_{\text{A}^-}}{\mu k[\text{H}^+] + [(a \times 10^{-3})/nF_\nu q]} \tag{15}$$

$$\mu k = \frac{i_k}{[\text{H}^+][(i_d)_{\text{A}^-} - i_k]} \cdot \frac{a \times 10^{-3}}{nF_\nu q} \tag{16}$$

If $k[\text{H}^+]$ is very large eq. 15 becomes:

$$i_k = (i_d)_{\text{A}^-}$$

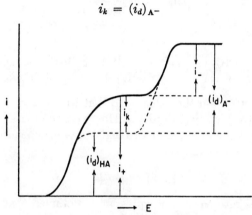

Fig. XV-1. Polarogram of an acid whose undissociated form is reduced at a more positive potential than its anion A^-. The diffusion currents $(i_d)_{\text{HA}}$ and $(i_d)_{\text{A}^-}$ correspond to the concentrations of HA and A^- in the body of the solution. i_+ and i_- are the observed limiting currents.

and only one wave is obtained. In the other extreme, when $k[\text{H}^+]$ is negligibly small $i_k = 0$, and $i_+ = (i_d)_{\text{HA}}$, and $i_- = (i_d)_{\text{A}^-}$.

$$[\text{A}^-] = c - [\text{HA}] \tag{17}$$

where c is the analytical concentration of the acid, we obtain from the expression for the ionization constant:

$$[\text{A}^-] = \frac{K_c}{K + [\text{H}^+]} \tag{18}$$

and

$$(i_d)_{\text{A}^-} = a[\text{A}^-] = ac \frac{K}{K + [\text{H}^+]} \tag{19}$$

Substituting this value of $(i_d)_{A^-}$ in eq. 15:

$$i_k = \frac{\mu k[H^+]acK}{(K + [H^+])\{\mu k[H^+] + [(a \times 10^{-3})/nF_v q]\}} \tag{20}$$

Since $i_+ = (i_d)_{HA} + i_k$,

and

$$(i_d)_{HA} = ac\frac{[H^+]}{K + [H^+]} \tag{21}$$

we have:

$$i_+ = \frac{ac[H^+]}{K + [H^+]} \cdot \left\{\frac{\mu k(K + [H^+]) + [(a \times 10^{-3})/nF_v q]}{\mu k[H^+] + [(a \times 10^{-3})/nF_v q]}\right\} \tag{22}$$

It is of interest to find the value of $[H^+]$ at which $i_+ = i_-$. The pH at which $[HA] = [A^-]$ is equal to pK_a. However, the pH at which $i_+ = i_-$ can be shifted by several pH units to a higher value, depending on the value of k and pK_a. When $i_+ = i_-$:

$$i_+ = ac/2 \tag{23}$$

Introducing this into eq. 22 an expression is obtained that gives the relation between μk and experimentally determinable data:

$$\mu k = \frac{K - [H^+]}{(K + [H^+])[H^+]} \cdot \frac{a \times 10^{-3}}{nF_v q} \tag{24}$$

The factor $(a \times 10^{-3})/nF_v q$ depends on the constants of the capillary and on the diffusion coefficient of the substance which is reduced. In general its value is of the order of 10^{-3}. In the experimental work carried out by Brdicka and Wiesner its value was 2.3×10^{-3}.

Consider a case in which $pK_a = 7$, and in which $i_+ = i_-$ at a pH of 8. According to eq. 24, $\mu k = 1.9 \times 10^5$. Estimating the thickness of the interface to be 10^{-7} cm., the velocity constant k becomes 1.9×10^{12}. If $i_+ = i_-$ at a pH of 9 instead of 8, $\mu k = 2.3 \times 10^6$. For every further shift of pH by one unit the velocity constant must increase ten times. For a much stronger acid with pK_a of 3, μk must have the value of only 19 if $i_+ = i_-$ at pH = 4. Hence, in this case the constant must be 10^4 times smaller than in the case of the acid with $pK_a = 7$ in order to cause a shift of one unit in pH. If μk were 2.3×10^5, i. e., about the same value which yielded a pH shift of one unit in the case $pK_a = 7$, the shift for an acid with $pK_a = 3$

would be 5 units. Hence, instead of finding $i_+ = i_-$ at pH $= 3$, at which [HA] $=$ [A$^-$], we find $i_+ = i_-$ at a pH of 8. The reason for these differences with different pK_a values is explained by the fact that the rate of association (eq. 12) is proportional to the hydrogen ion concentration.

Table XV-1 gives the shift in pH units from the pK_a value for acids of varying pK_a .

In a limiting case, in which $(i_d)_{HA}$ is negligibly small, i_+ becomes equal to i_k and i_- equal to $ac - i_k$. Under such conditions it can be shown that eq. 5 must be valid.

Koutecky and Brdicka[2] point out that in the above derivation of eq. 20, which determines the kinetic current, simplifications have been made and that the expression is only approximate, although in general it is satisfactory for the interpretation of the experimental results. In a more rigorous treatment one must take account of the fact that the instantaneous concentration of HA at the surface of the electrode is not only determined

TABLE XV-1

pH AT WHICH $i_+ = i_-$, $\mu k = 2 \times 10^5$, AND $(a \times 10^{-3})/nF_vq = 2 \times 10^{-3}$

pK_a	2	3	4	5	6	7	8	9	10
pH	8	8	8	8	8	8.07	8.4	9.07	10
pH $-$ pK_a	6	5	4	3	2	1.07	0.4	0.07	0

by the rate of diffusion of HA from the bulk of the solution to the surface of the electrode and by the rate of association $k_1[H^+][A^-]^0$, in which k_1 is the association constant of the acid, but also by the rate of dissociation of HA. Considering only the concentration of HA formed kinetically, we have:

$$[d(HA)/dt]_{kin.} = k_1[H^+][A^-]^0 - k_2[HA]^0$$

in which k_2 is the rate constant for the dissociation of the acid, k_2/k_1 being equal to the ionization constant K of the acid.

In addition the rate of formation of HA is not only determined by the hydrogen ion concentration, but also by the concentration of other Brønsted-Lowry acids which are present at the surface of the electrode. The anions A$^-$ can react directly with a Brønsted acid, which is always a constituent of the buffer used, for example:

$$A^- + H_2PO_4^- \rightarrow HA + HPO_4^{--}$$

[2] J. Koutecky and R. Brdicka, Collection Czechoslov. Chem. Communs., 12, 337 (1947).

Koutecky and Brdicka developed a set of equations that take the various reactions into account, and by means of very involved mathematics developed an equation which describes the value of the limiting current as a function of the rate of formation of HA by diffusion as well as by reaction rates at the surface of the electrode. In the interpretation of experimental results the fundamental expression can be reduced with reasonable assumptions to the simpler one discussed in this section. For an exact intrepretation the reader is referred to the paper of Koutecky and Brdicka.

It should be emphasized here that the value of μ, the so-called thickness of the layer in which the association occurs, is not a true constant, but that it depends on the properties of the acid under consideration and on the pH of the solution under investigation. Wiesner[3] had already derived statistically that

$$\mu = \sqrt{D/2k_1K}$$

in which D is the diffusion coefficient of the acid, k_1 its association constant, and K its ionization constant. In their more exact treatment Koutecky and Brdicka arrive at the expression:

$$\mu = \sqrt{D/k_1K}$$

when K is much greater than $[H^+]$.

The exact value of μ—and even its order of magnitude—is still quite doubtful. Therefore, any calculation of a rate constant from kinetic currents must be accepted with great reserve. From work carried out by E. Parry at the University of Minnesota it seems that rate constants calculated from i_k are of the order of 10^4 too large.

(b) Dependence of Various Currents on Height of Mercury in the Reservoir

Normal diffusion currents in accordance with the Ilkovic equation are approximately proportional to the square root of the height of the mercury in the reservoir. On the other hand, under certain conditions, *limiting currents which are determined by a rate constant are found to be independent of the height of the mercury in the reservoir.* The reason is that pure kinetic currents depend on the value of q (eqs. 15 and 20). In extreme cases i_k becomes proportional to q or to $m^{2/3}t^{2/3}$ and is, therefore, independent of the height of the mercury. This is the case when $(i_d)_{HA}$ is negligibly small, or when $i_+ \cong i_k$ and when $(a \times 10^{-3})/nF_yq \gg \mu k[H^+]$.

Equation 15 can then be written:

$$i_k = \frac{\mu k[H^+]acnF_yq}{(a \times 10^{-3})(K + [H^+])} = \frac{10^{+3}\mu k[H^+]cnF_yq}{K + [H^+]} \qquad (15a)$$

[3] K. Wiesner, *Chem. Listy*, **41**, 6 (1947).

This is an extreme case. When $(a \cdot 10^{-3})/nF_y q \ll \mu k[\mathrm{H^+}]$, then $i_k = (i_d)_{\mathrm{A^-}}$ $= i_d$ and i becomes dependent upon the height of the mercury in the reservoir.

The factor a which varies with the square root of the height of the mercury in the reservoir has cancelled out in eq. 15a and i_k becomes independent of the height of the mercury.

The above considerations are of great practical consequence. In a polarographic study of pyruvic acid Müller and Baumberger[4] report only one wave at a pH equal to or smaller than 4.1. With increasing pH two waves appear.

The height of the first wave decreases and that of the second one increases with increasing pH, the sum of the two being constant and proportional to the analytical concentration of pyruvic acid. At a pH greater than 8 only one wave is found. Müller and Baumberger attributed the first wave to a reduction of the keto form, and the second wave to that of the enol form, of pyruvic acid. However, Brdicka[5] showed conclusively that the first wave is due to a reduction of undissociated pyruvic acid and the second wave to that of the pyruvate ion. The pH at which $i_+ = i_-$ is found at a pH which is about 4 units greater than the pK_a value. Polarographically a keto-enol equilibrium does not play a part in the case of pyruvic acid. This equilibrium is established very slowly as shown by Arndt.[6] It was shown by Brdicka that phenylglyoxylic acid showed two-step reductions analogous to the case of pyruvic acid, enolization in this case being out of the question. The esters of both acids, in which the carboxylic group is blocked, show only a single wave between pH 5 and 8, substantiating the conclusion that the two-step reduction of the acids is due to undissociated molecules and anions, respectively.

Another example of the occurrence of kinetic waves was found by Kolthoff and Liberti[7] in the reduction of phenylnitrosohydroxylamine. In acid medium one wave is found corresponding to a reduction which involves 6 electrons. At a pH of 10 or greater, again one wave is observed whose height corresponds to a reduction involving 4 electrons. In the pH range between 7 and 9 two waves are found. The first wave corresponds to that of the free acid HA which is formed at the electrode by the reaction $\mathrm{A^-} + \mathrm{H^+} \rightarrow \mathrm{HA}$, and the second wave to the reduction of the anion. When the first wave is small its height becomes independent of the height

[4] O. H. Müller and J. P. Baumberger, *J. Am. Chem. Soc.*, **61**, 590 (1939).

[5] R. Brdicka, *Chem. Listy*, **40**, 232 (1946).

[6] F. Arndt, M. Ozansoy, and H. Ustünyar, *Rev. faculté sci. univ. Istanbul*, **4**, 83 (1939).

[7] I. M. Kolthoff and A. Liberti, *J. Am. Chem. Soc.*, **70**, 1885 (1948).

of the mercury in the reservoir. This is typical for kinetic currents under special conditions as discussed above.

2. OCCURRENCE OF ONE WAVE WHOSE HEIGHT IS DETERMINED BY A RATE CONSTANT. WAVES OF REDUCING SUGARS AND OF FORMALDEHYDE

A typical example of the occurrence of a "kinetic" wave is described by Wiesner.[8] Cantor and Peniston[9] made a polarographic investigation of various reducing sugars and found only one wave whose height, in general, is much smaller than that of a substance, at the same concentration, which gives a normal wave. Cantor and Peniston concluded that the height of the wave corresponds to the equilibrium concentration of the reducible form of the sugar in the bulk of the solution. However, Wiesner showed conclusively that the height of the wave is much greater than corresponds to the equilibrium concentration of the reducible form. Actually, the trace of reducible form present in the solution would give a wave of indetectable height under the experimental conditions. During the reduction of the reducible form, equilibrium is disturbed at the dropping electrode, and new reducible form is formed. The height of the wave is then determined by the rate constant of the reaction:

$$\text{sugar (nonreducible)} \rightarrow \text{sugar (reducible)}$$

Denoting the *apparent* diffusion current by i_k we can write, as in eq. 13:

$$i_k = nF_y \times 10^{-3} \times q\mu k c^0 \tag{25}$$

in which c^0 is the concentration of the nonreducible form of the sugar at the interface. Since the concentration of the reducible form in the bulk of the solution is negligibly small, the concentration of the nonreducible form in the bulk of the solution may be put equal to the analytical sugar concentration c. Since:

$$i_k = a(c - c^0)$$

We derive:

$$\mu k = \frac{i_k}{i_{hd} - i_k} \times \frac{a \times 10^{-3}}{nF_v q} \tag{26}$$

in which i_{hd} is the hypothetical diffusion current ($i_{hd} = kc$) which would be observed if all of the sugar were reduced; in other words, if the rate constant k were extremely great.

[8] K. Wiesner, *Collection Czechoslov. Chem. Communs.*, **12**, 64 (1947).

[9] L. M. Canton and Q. M. Peniston, *J. Am. Chem. Soc.*, **62**, 2113 (1940).

It is readily seen that i_k will be independent of the height of the mercury in the reservoir when i_k is very small compared to i_{hd}. Thus $(i_{hd} - i_k) \cong i_{hd} = ac$, and the a cancels out in eq. 26. When i_k is not negligibly small with regard to i_{hd}, i_k becomes dependent upon the height of the mercury in the reservoir, but less so than according to the Ilkovic relation.

Wiesner carried out experiments with glucose, galactose, and xylose in a phosphate buffer and in dilute lithium hydroxide solutions and showed that i_k was independent of the height of the mercury in the reservoir. In these cases i_k is negligibly small with regard to i_{hd}. Under these circumstances i_k changes during the growth of the drop with q or $t^{2/3}$ and not with $t^{1/6}$ as a true diffusion current does. Oscillographically, Wiesner showed that i_k is actually proportional to q or to $t^{2/3}$.

When i_k is not negligibly small with regard to i_{hd}, as is the case with fructose, Wiesner demonstrated that i_k changes with the height of mercury in the reservoir, but less so than a diffusion current does. This indicates that i_k is partly diffusion and partly rate controlled. Under these circumstances it is possible to calculate i_{hd} in the following way. Since the concentration of the reducible form of fructose is negligibly small the observed apparent diffusion current is again equal to i_k.

We now compare i_k with the value of i_d of an "indicator" substance. Let x be the ratio of the hypothetical diffusion current to the indicator diffusion current.

$$\frac{i_k}{i_{hd} - i_k} = \frac{i_k}{x i_d - i_k} \tag{27}$$

From eqs. 26 and 27 and the relation $i_d = ac'$ we find:

$$\frac{i_k i_d}{x i_d - i_k} = \mu k \frac{n F_y q a c'}{a \times 10^{-3}} = \mu k \frac{n F_y q c'}{10^{-3}} \tag{28}$$

Hence $i_k i_d / [x i_d i_k]$ is constant and independent of the height of mercury in the reservoir.

Let i_{k_1} and i_{d_1} denote the currents at a height of mercury h_1, and i_{k_2} and i_{d_2} those at a height h_2 then:

$$\frac{i_{k_1} i_{d_1}}{x i_{d_1} - i_{k_1}} = \frac{i_{k_2} i_{d_2}}{x i_{d_2} - i_{k_2}}$$

$$x = \frac{i_{k_1} i_{d_1} i_{k_2} - i_{k_2} i_{d_2} i_{k_1}}{i_{k_1} i_{d_1} i_{d_2} - i_{k_2} i_{d_2} i_{d_1}} \tag{29}$$

By using zinc sulfate as an "indicator" substance and varying the height of mercury between 17 and 46 cm., Wiesner found a practically constant value of k in eq. 28. The value of i_{hd} calculated from x in the relation $i_{hd} = xi_d$ was in satisfactory agreement with the value calculated from the Ilkovic equation.

Formaldehyde. This aldehyde yields limiting currents which vary with the pH of the solution and which increase much more with the temperature than diffusion currents do. Vesely and Brdicka,[10] and simultaneously Bieber and Trümpler,[11] explained the polarographic behavior of aqueous solutions of formaldehyde in a qualitative and quantitative manner. In the following reference is made to the paper of the Czechoslovakian authors. Spectrophotometrically[12] it has been shown that in aqueous medium formaldehyde is present mainly in the hydrated form, methylene glycol:

$$
\begin{array}{cc}
H & OH \\
 & \diagdown \ / \\
 & C \\
 & \diagup \ \diagdown \\
H & OH
\end{array}
$$

the concentration of the aldehyde form being less than 0.1 per cent of that of the hydrated form. Bieber and Trümpler, on the basis of their own spectrophotometric measurements, conclude that the ratio of the aldehyde to the hydrated form is even less than 10^{-4}. The two forms are in reversible equilibrium:

$$
\begin{array}{cccc}
H \quad OH & & H & \\
\diagdown \ / & & \diagdown & \\
C & \rightleftharpoons & C{=}O & + \ H_2O \\
\diagup \ \diagdown & & \diagup & \\
H \quad OH & & H &
\end{array}
$$

and it is assumed that only the aldehyde form is polarographically reducible. Since the concentration of the aldehyde form is so extremely small the limiting currents are controlled by the rate of dehydration of the hydrated form. It appears that this reaction is subject to acid-base catalysis in the Brønsted sense. Therefore, in buffer solutions the limiting current is dependent not only upon the pH, but also upon the kind and concentrations of the acidic and basic constituents of the buffer. This is actually found; the authors (K. and L.) expect that the same is true for the kinetic

---

[10] K. Vesely and R. Brdicka, *Collection Czechoslov. Chem. Communs.*, **12,** 313 (1947).
[11] R. Bieber and G. Trümpler, *Helv. Chim. Acta*, **30, 706** (1947).
[12] S. A. Schow, *J. chim. phys.*, **26, 69** (1929).

currents observed with the reducing sugars. Thus, the polarograph provides a means of determining the rate constant in a typical case of acid-base catalysis. Upon studying the effect of pH—especially in strongly alkaline medium—the weak acidic character of formaldehyde must be taken into account. According to von Euler and Lövgren[13] pK_a is 14.0 at 0°, and 12.48 at 50° C. Levy[14] reports a value of pK_a of 12.87 at 30° C. and Wadano[15] of 12.79 at 23°. Thus, in about 0.04 N sodium hydroxide formaldehyde is present to the extent of 50 per cent in the undissociated hydrated form and 50 per cent in the form of the anions:

at 25° C. At such a very high pH the rate of association of the anions with hydrogen ions to form the hydrated form becomes negligibly small under polarographic conditions. Therefore, the effective concentration of the hydrated form of formaldehyde becomes smaller than the total concentration of the hydrated form at high alkalinities.

In the quantitative interpretation of the observed currents Vesely and Brdicka again use the expressions for the kinetic current:

$$i_k = 2F_v 10^3 q\mu k_2 f_{aq}^0 \tag{13}$$

and

$$i_k = a(f_{aq} - f_{aq}^0) \tag{14}$$

in which k_2 is the constant of dehydration of the hydrated form f_{aq} to the reducible aldehyde form f:

$$df^0/dt = k_2 f_{aq}^0$$

Assuming that Wiesner's expression, discussed in the previous section, holds, the following value for μ is introduced:

$$\mu = \sqrt{Dk_h/2k_2}$$

in which K_h is the equilibrium constant

$$K_h = f/f_{aq} = k_2/k_1$$

[13] H. von Euler and T. Lövgren, Z. anorg. Chem., **147**, 123 (1925).
[14] M. Levy, J. Biol. Chem., **105**, 157 (1934).
[15] M. Wadano, Ber., **67**, 191 (1934).

By introducing into eq. 13 the relation between a and the factors which determine it (Ilkovic equation), and also the relation between q and the characteristics of the capillary, the following equation is obtained:

$$i_k = \frac{0.573\sqrt{t_1 k_2 K_h}}{1 + 0.573\sqrt{t_1 k_2 K_h}} \; (i_d)_{f_{aq}} \qquad (13a)$$

in which $(i_d)_{f_{aq}}$ is the hypothetical diffusion current calculated on the basis of complete reduction of all the formaldehyde:

$$(i_d)_{f_{aq}} = a f_{aq}$$

By assuming that the diffusion coefficient of formaldehyde is equal to that of methanol ($D = 1.62 \times 10^{-5}$ cm.^{2} sec.$^{-1}$ at 20° C.) and that 2 electrons are involved in the reduction, the value of $(i_d)_{f_{aq}}$ is easily calculated. In strongly alkaline medium the dissociation of formaldehyde as an acid must be considered:

$$(i_d)_{f_{aq}} = (i_d)_{f_c} \frac{[H^+]}{K_a + [H^+]} \qquad (13b)$$

in which f_c is the total concentration of formaldehyde and K_a its ionization constant. The rate constant k_2 is equal to the sum of all the rate constants which determine the acid-base catalyzed dehydration of the hydrated form of formaldehydes:

$$k_2 = k_{H^+}[H^+] + k_{OH^-}[OH^-] + k_{HA}[HA] + k_{A^-}[A^-] + k_{H_2O}[H_2O]$$

in which [HA] is the concentration of the acid constituent of the buffer and [A$^-$] that of the alkaline constituent. In relatively strongly alkaline medium $k_{OH^-}[OH^-]$ is much greater than the sum of all the other terms, and we can write:

$$k_2 = k_{OH^-}[OH^-] = k_{OH^-}(K_w/[H^+])$$

Substituting in eqs. 13a and 13b we get:

$$i_k = \frac{b}{[H^+]^{1/2} + b} \cdot (i_d)_{f_{aq}} \qquad (13c)$$

$$i_k = \frac{b[H^+]^{1/2}}{[H^+] + K_a + b[H^+]^{1/2} + bK_a[H^+]^{-1/2}} (i_d)_{f_c} \qquad (13d)$$

in which:

$$b = 0.573 \sqrt{t_1 k_{OH^-} K_w K_h}$$

Vesely and Brdicka determined the limiting current in dilute sodium hydroxide solutions and calculated from the experimental results a value of $K_h k_{OH^-}$ of 1.18 at 20° C. The solid line in Fig. XV-2 gives the height of the waves of the formaldehyde at a pH greater than 8, while the broken curve represents the calculated values. It is seen that at a pH greater than 11 the calculated and experimental curves coincide. Therefore, the agreement between theory and experiment is excellent. The experimental values at a pH less than 11 were obtained in Sørensen borate buffers. Since the hydroxyl ion concentration in these buffers is low, the catalysis is

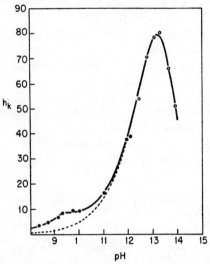

Fig. XV-2. Variation of the limiting currents in the reduction of $3.75 \times 10^{-3}\, M$ formaldehyde with pH. Up to pH = 11.2 Sørensen borate buffer, and from pH = 12.05, solutions of sodium hydroxide were used. Dotted line calculated on basis of OH^- catalysis only.

mainly determined by the concentration of the borate ions, the contribution by the boric acid being negligibly small. Indeed, it was shown that at constant pH the limiting current increased with the borate ion concentration of the buffer. The absolute values of k_{OH^-}, $k_{H_2BO_3^-}$, and k_{H_2O} can be calculated from the results if K_h is known. Taking Bieber and Trümpler's value of 10^{-4} for K_h, Vesely and Brdicka calculated that $k_{OH^-} = 1.2 \times 10^4$, $k_{H_2BO_3^-} = 38$, and $k_{H_2O} = 1.8 \times 10^{-3}$.

3. CATALYTIC CURENTS WHICH DEPEND ON REACTION RATES AT THE ELECTRODE. CATALYZED HYDROGEN PEROXIDE WAVES

The reduction of oxygen proceeds in two steps, the first wave corresponding to a reduction to hydrogen peroxide and the second to a reduction of the peroxide to hydroxyl ions. Several substances, like hemoglobin or hematin,[16] heme,[17] and salicylaldehyde-ethylene diimine ferric chloride,[17] shift part of the second (hydrogen peroxide) wave to more positive potentials. The polarogram of oxygen now consists of three waves: the first one remains unchanged, a second wave occurs at more positive potentials than that of hydrogen peroxide, and a third wave is that of the peroxide. The sum of the heights of the second and third waves is equal to that of the first wave. The substances which give rise to the above effect therefore exert a catalytic effect at the electrode interface which results in the appearance of a "prewave" of hydrogen peroxide.

A detailed study of the effect of ferriheme and ferroheme on the catalytic hydrogen peroxide wave has been made by Brdicka and Wiesner.[18] The ferriheme-ferroheme is a reversible oxidation-reduction system at the platinum electrode,[19] and the reduction wave of ferriheme at the dropping electrode corresponds to a reversible reaction (Brdicka and Wiesner). The catalytic wave can be attributed to either one of the following reactions. The ferroheme Fe_h^{++} formed upon reduction of ferriheme Fe_h^{+++} is oxidized by hydrogen peroxide at the surface of the electrode. Thus, the height of the ferriheme wave is increased. The rate-determining step of the oxidation is the reaction:

$$Fe_h^{++} + H_2O_2 \rightarrow Fe_h^{+++} + OH^- + OH \qquad (30)$$

and the rate is:

$$d(Fe_h^{+++})/dt = k(Fe_h^{++})(H_2O_2) \qquad (31)$$

A second interpretation of the catalytic wave, which according to Brdicka and Wiesner is more probable, is that the ferroheme forms a complex with hydrogen peroxide. The peroxide is activated in this complex and is reduced immediately after it is formed; in other words, it is reduced at potentials corresponding to the ferriheme-ferroheme wave:

$$Fe_h^{++} + H_2O_2 \rightarrow Fe_h^{++} \cdot (H_2O_2) \qquad (32)$$

The rate of this reaction is given by:

$$d[Fe_h^{++} \cdot (H_2O_2)]/dt = k[Fe_h^{++}][H_2O_2] \qquad (33)$$

From a quantitative polarographic viewpoint it is immaterial whether

[16] R. Brdicka and C. Tropp, *Biochem. Z.*, **289**, 301 (1937).

[17] R. Brdicka and K. Wiesner, *Natur.*, **31**, 247 (1943).

[18] R. Brdicka and K. Wiesner, *Collection Czechoslov. Chem. Communs.*, **12**, 39 (1947).

[19] E. S. G. Barron, *J. Biol. Chem.*, **121**, 285 (1937).

reaction (30) or (32) is responsible for the catalytic effect. In both cases the rate is determined by the product $[Fe_h^{++}][H_2O_2]$ (eqs. 31 and 33).

The oxidation potential E of the ferriheme-ferroheme system is given by:

$$E = E^0 - \frac{RT}{F_y} \ln \frac{[Fe_h^{++}]^0}{[Fe_h^{+++}]^0} \tag{34}$$

and the corresponding equation of the polarographic wave is:

$$E = E_{1/2} - \frac{RT}{F_y} \ln \frac{i}{i_d - i} \sqrt{\frac{D_{Fe_h^{++}}}{D_{Fe_h^{+++}}}} \tag{35}$$

In the following $D_{Fe_h^{++}}$ is assumed equal to $D_{Fe_h^{+++}}$.

When the concentration of ferriheme is very small its diffusion current is negligibly small with regard to the height of the catalytic current i_k. The magnitude of i_k is then given by:

$$i_k = 2F_y \times 10^3 q\mu k [Fe_h^{++}]^0 [H_2O_2]^0 \tag{36}$$

If the total concentration of the heme system is b, then:

$$[Fe_h^{++}]^0 + [Fe_h^{+++}]^0 = b$$

The rate of disappearance of the hydrogen peroxide must be equal to the rate of its supply. If the molar concentration of oxygen in the solution is c, we have:

$$i_k = ac - a[H_2O_2]^0 = i_d - a[H_2O_2]^0 \tag{37}$$

in which i_d is the first diffusion current of oxygen and a is the Ilkovic constant in the expression for the diffusion current. From eqs. 36 and 37 we have:

$$[H_2O_2]^0 = \frac{i_d}{2F_y \times 10^3 q\mu k [Fe_h^{++}]^0 + a} \tag{38}$$

and

$$i_k = \frac{2F_y q\mu k [Fe_h^{++}] i_d}{10^{-3} \times a + 2F_y q\mu k [Fe_h^{++}]^0} \tag{39}$$

The limiting value $(i_k)_l$, or the apparent diffusion current, is then given by:

$$(i_k)_l = \frac{2F_y q\mu k b i_d}{10^{-3} \times a + 2F_y q\mu k b} \tag{40}$$

$$\mu k = \frac{(i_k)_l}{b[i_d - (i_k)_l]} \frac{a \times 10^{-3}}{2F_y q} \tag{41}$$

Experimentally, Brdicka and Wiesner found μk practically constant at a given pH and independent of the concentration of the heme system and the height of mercury in the reservoir. When μk is plotted as a function of pH a curve is obtained very similar to the dissociation curve of hydrogen peroxide. This indicates that the velocity constants in eqs. 30 or 33 are determined by the concentration of the undissociated molecules of hydrogen peroxide and not by its anions.

The value of the reaction rate constant k could also be evaluated with the assumption that the thickness μ is 10^{-7} cm. A value of k of the order of 10^{11} was thus derived. There seems to be evidence that this rate constant is of the order of 10^4 times greater than the true rate constant. Apparently the exact value of μ must be quite different from that given.

The dependence of $(i_k)_l$ upon the height of mercury in the reservoir varies between two extremes. When $(i_k)_l$ is very small as compared to i_d its value becomes independent of the height of the mercury. Under these conditions $2F_y q\mu k b \ll 10^{-3} \times a$ and eq. 40 can be written:

$$(i_k)_l \cong \frac{2F_y q\mu k b a c}{10^{-3} \times a} \tag{40a}$$

The constant a, which is dependent upon the height of mercury, cancels out.

The other extreme is when $(i_k)_l$ approaches i_d. Under these conditions $10^{-3} \times a$ becomes negligibly small with regard to $2F_y q\mu k b$ and $(i_k)_l$ varies with the square of the height of the mercury, like an ordinary diffusion current. These conclusions were confirmed experimentally.

The Equation of the Catalyzed Wave

The potential of the ferriheme-ferroheme system is given by eq. 34. The concentration (Fe_h^{++}) is a function of the potential E:

$$(Fe_h^{++})^0 = \frac{b}{1 + e^{(E-E^0)F_y/RT}} \tag{42}$$

Substituting this in eq. 39 and combining with eq. 40 we find:

$$i_k = \frac{(i_k)_l i_d}{i_d + (i_d - (i_k)_l)e^{(E-E^0)F_y/RT}} \tag{43}$$

and

$$E = E^0 - \frac{RT}{F_y} \ln \frac{i_k}{(i_k)_l - i_k} - \frac{RT}{F_y} \ln \frac{(i_d - (i_k)_l)}{i_d} \tag{44}$$

$$E = E^0 - \frac{RT}{F_y} \ln \frac{i_k}{(i_k)_l - i_k} - \frac{RT}{F_y} \ln \frac{a}{a + 2F_y \times 10^{-3}q\mu k b} \tag{45}$$

If $(i_k)_l$ is very small as compared to i_d the third term of the right-hand side of eq. 44 becomes negligibly small and the expression becomes identical with eq. 35. Under these conditions the half-wave potential becomes identical with that of the ferriheme-ferroheme system. When $(i_k)_l$ approaches i_d the half-wave potential shifts to more positive values. For sufficiently large values of b the half-wave potential shifts by 0.059 v. (25° C.) to a more positive value with a ten-fold increase in b.

Brdicka and Wiesner (*loc. cit.* 1947) found two iron complexes, salicylaldehyde-ethylene diimine hydrochloride and a complex from salicylaldehyde, hydrazine, and ferric chloride, which gave catalyzed hydrogen peroxide waves similar to those of ferriheme.

The first reduction wave is also increased by catalase[20].

The System Ferric Iron-Hydrogen Peroxide. This system has been studied in detail by E. P. Parry.[21] The reduction wave of ferric to ferrous iron is found at the dissolution potential of mercury, while hydrogen peroxide is reduced at a much more negative potential. When ferric iron is electrolyzed in the presence of hydrogen peroxide the limiting current is greater than the diffusion current of the ferric iron. The difference between the two is the kinetic current, the value of which is determined by the rate of the (over-all) reaction:

$$2Fe^{++} + H_2O_2 \rightarrow 2Fe^{+++} + 2OH^-$$

In a 0.0002 M ferric iron solution in 0.25 M sulfuric acid which is 0.02 M in hydrogen peroxide the kinetic wave is of the same order of magnitude as the diffusion current of the ferric iron. Thus, as a result of the kinetic current, the hydrogen peroxide concentration at the surface of the electrode would be practically equal to the concentration in the bulk of the solution. At the kinetic current region the concentration of ferrous iron at the surface of the electrode is practically equal to the concentration of ferric iron in the bulk of the solution. Thus, we may write:

$$i_k = C[Fe^{++}]^0[H_2O_2]^0 \cong C[Fe^{+++}][H_2O_2]$$

in which $[Fe^{+++}]$ and $[H_2O_2]$ denote concentrations in the bulk of the solution. Actually it was found that the kinetic current is proportional to the concentration of ferric iron and the peroxide concentration when the latter is less than about 0.015 M. When the peroxide concentration becomes greater the kinetic current increases slightly less than linearly with the peroxide concentration. This deviation from proportionality is attributed

---

[20] R. Brdicka, K. Wiesner, and K. Schäferna, *Naturwissenschaften*, **31**, 390 (1943).
[21] E. P. Parry, Ph.D. Thesis, University of Minnesota, 1950.

to an "induced" decomposition of hydrogen peroxide by the Haber and Weiss or a similar mechanism:

$$H_2O_2 + Fe^{++} \rightarrow Fe^{+++} + OH^- + OH^{\cdot} \qquad (I)$$

$$OH^{\cdot} + H_2O_2 \rightarrow H_2O + HO_2^{\cdot} \qquad (II)$$

$$HO_2^{\cdot} + H_2O_2 \rightarrow O_2 + H_2O + OH^{\cdot} \qquad (III)$$

$$OH^{\cdot} + Fe^{++} \rightarrow OH^- + Fe^{+++} \qquad (IV)$$

The sum of (I) and (IV) represents the over-all reaction. The reaction couple II and III involves a chain mechanism; by this induced decomposition the hydrogen peroxide concentration becomes less at the electrode than it would be on the basis of the kinetic current only. Thus $[H_2O_2]^0$ is no longer equal to the bulk concentration, but is smaller. Apparently, the induced decomposition becomes more appreciable at large peroxide concentrations. That the interpretation is qualitatively correct could be proved by the appearance of an oxygen (see eq. III) reduction wave (at potentials more negative than where i_k starts) and by the effect of acrylonitrile (AN) on the kinetic current. Acrylonitrile reacts with $OH^{\cdot}$ radicals to form a monomer free radical which rapidly adds many more acrylonitrile molecules to form polyacrylonitrile. The reaction of AN with $OH^{\cdot}$ is much faster than reactions II and IV. Thus all the $OH^{\cdot}$ formed in reaction I is caught by the acrylonitrile and no induced decomposition of peroxide occurs (II and III). In agreement with this interpretation the kinetic current was found strictly proportional to the hydrogen peroxide concentration in the presence of AN. Moreover, the kinetic current with AN is exactly one-half of the value observed without AN at peroxide concentrations less than 0.015 M. This decrease of the kinetic current is easily explained quantitatively. In the absence of AN the kinetic current is determined by the over-all reaction between 2 moles of ferrous iron and 1 mole of peroxide, while in the presence of AN the reaction ratio is one (eq. I).

Parry also calculated from the kinetic current the rate constant of reaction I using Brdicka's expression taking μ equal to 10^{-7} cm. He found a value for k of 1.2×10^6 liters per mole second at 30° C. as compared to a value of 61 liters per mole second at 25° and 110 at 35° as determined by the direct chemical method by Baxendale, Evans, and Park.[22] Thus, the polarographic value is 10^4 times that determined chemically. This large discrepancy shows *that the polarographic method cannot be relied upon for*

---

[22] J. H. Baxendale, M. G. Evans, and G. S. Park, *Trans. Faraday Soc.*, **42**, 155 (1946).

the determination of rate constants from kinetic current measurements. It seems that the value of the parameter μ is highly uncertain and apparently much greater than assumed by Brdicka and co-workers.

Catalytic (Kinetic) Currents in the Systems Molybdate, Tungstate, or Vanadate and Hydrogen Peroxide. These systems were investigated systematically by E. P. Parry (*loc. cit.*). Traces of the above constituents in the presence of a large excess of hydrogen peroxide yield relatively large

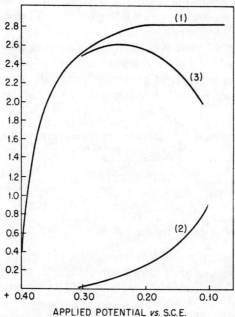

Fig. XV-3. The kinetic wave for peroxymolybdate in 0.25 M H$_2$SO$_4$: (1) 1.09×10^{-6} M MoO$_4^{--}$ and 0.0538 M H$_2$O$_2$; (2) 0.0538 M H$_2$O$_2$ only; and (3) the kinetic current—curve (1) less curve (2). Ordinate, microamp.

catalytic (kinetic) currents at potentials positive *vs.* the S.C.E. As an example the kinetic current of molybdate in dilute sulfuric acid is given in Fig. XV-3.

For molybdate the mechanism can be represented by:

$$\text{MoO}_4^{--} + \text{H}_2\text{O}_2 \rightarrow \text{MoO}_5^{--} + \text{H}_2\text{O} \qquad \text{(V)}$$

$$\text{MoO}_5^{--} + 2\text{H}^+ + 2e \rightarrow \text{MoO}_4^{--} + \text{H}_2\text{O} \qquad \text{(VI)}$$

Molybdate (and tungstate and vanadate) in acid medium are partly polymerized and it is not certain whether it is the simple MoO$_4^{--}$ ion which reacts with peroxide to form the peroxymolybdate ion or another form of molybdenum. From the large values of the kinetic current it can be inferred that reaction V is extremely fast. What has been said for molybdate also holds *mutatis mutandis* for tungstate and vanadate. Table XV-2 compares the heights (at maximum i_k) of the kinetic currents in the same acid medium and at the same concentrations of molybdate, tungstate, and vanadate, respectively.

Parry investigated systematically the effects of the following on the catalytic current: concentration of sulfuric acid and other acids, pH in general, temperature, concentration of molybdate (or W or V) and hydrogen peroxide. For details, see Parry (*loc. cit.*).

From an analytical view it is of special interest that the largest kinetic waves are observed for a given concentration of molybdate or vanadate in a phosphate buffer with pH of about 5. Tungstate gives a much smaller current than the other two. For example, in a 0.1 M phosphate buffer of

TABLE 2

COMPARISON OF i_k WITH 10^{-5} M MOLYBDATE, TUNGSTATE, OR VANADATE IN 0.25 M SULFURIC ACID[a]

	Mo	W	V
E at maximum of i_k (*vs.* S.C.E.)	+0.24	+0.32	+0.33
i_k in microamperes	15.1	4.3	0.25

[a] Hydrogen peroxide concentration 0.04 M.

pH 4.9 and a hydrogen peroxide concentration of 0.007 M a solution which was 8×10^{-7} M in vanadate gave a current of 18.6 microamp.; 1.6×10^{-6} M molybdate of 6.5 microamp., and 8×10^{-6} M tungstate of 1.2 microamp. The kinetic current shows a very pronounced maximum as illustrated in Fig. XV-4. This is not an ordinary polarographic maximum and it is practically not affected by ordinary maximum suppressors. In the phosphate buffer the heights of the vanadate- and molybdate-catalyzed currents measured at the maximum were found to be proportional to the concentration. Analytical application of these catalyzed waves is evident. As little as 0.01 γ of vanadium or molybdenum per 10 ml. can be easily determined. Unfortunately, foreign anions decrease the kinetic current. At concentrations less than 0.03 M perchlorate, nitrate, and sulfate have practically no effect, but at concentrations greater than 0.1 M nitrate, and more so sulfate, decrease the kinetic current markedly. Oxalate and tartrate, which form complexes with molybdate, tungstate, and vanadate, decrease the kinetic current very much; the effect is already large in 0.0002 M solutions of these ions.

4. ANODIC CURRENTS CATALYZED BY ACTIVE HYDROGEN

Wiesner[23] observed that the diffusion current corresponding to anodic waves of the reduced forms of benzoquinone (hydroquinone), or 2,6-dichlorophenol indophenol, indigo monosulfonate, phenosafranine, and a compound of quinone with proline was greatly increased by the presence

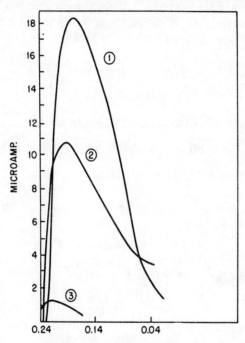

APPLIED POTENTIAL *vs.* S.C.E.

Fig. XV-4. (1) $8 \times 10^{-7}\,M$ VO_3^- and $0.007\,M$ H_2O_2; (2) $1.6 \times 10^{-6}\,M$ MoO_4^{--} and $0.012\,M$ H_2O_2; (3) $8 \times 10^{-6}\,M$ WO_4^{--} and $0.007\,M$ H_2O_2 in $0.1\,M$ phosphate buffer pH = 4.9.

of a suspension of palladium saturated with hydrogen. The hydrogen is in an active form and reduces the anodically formed quinone when it is formed at the dropping electrode. The current i is equal to $i_1 + i_2$, in which i_1 corresponds to the normal current determined by diffusion and i_2 is determined by the rate of oxidation of hydrogen or the rate of reduction of the oxidized form by active hydrogen.

$$i_1 = 605 \times 10^3 n D^{1/2} m^{2/3} t^{1/6}\, (c - c^\circ) \tag{46}$$

[23] K. Wiesner, *Z. Elektrochem.*, **49**, 164 (1943).

The velocity of hydrogen oxidation (dy/dt) is given by:

$$dy = k'qX[H^+]^0[Ox]^0\, dt \qquad (47)$$

in which dy is the amount of oxidized hydrogen in moles in the time dt, k' is the velocity constant, and X the active surface of the palladium per square centimeter of the electrode. Since the experiments are carried out in buffer solutions $[H^+]^0 = [H^+]$, $[H^+]$ being the hydrogen ion concentration in the solution. With a given amount of catalyst (palladium) suspension $k'X[H^+]^0 = k$.

The value of $q = 0.0085m^{2/3}t^{2/3}$, and:

$$dy = 0.0085m^{2/3}t^{2/3}k[Ox]^0\, dt \qquad (47a)$$

Expressing dy in terms of the quantity of electricity Q in coulombs we find:

$$dQ = 0.0085m^{2/3}t^{2/3}kF_y[Ox]^0\, dt \qquad (48)$$

The average value of i_2 then becomes:

$$i_2 = 1/t \int_{t=0}^{t=t} 0.0085m^{2/3}t^{2/3}kF_y[Ox]^0\, dt = \tfrac{3}{5}\, 0.0085m^{2/3}t^{2/3}kF_y[Ox]^0 \qquad (49)$$

It is seen that i_2 is independent of the height of the mercury in the reservoir. Experimentally this was shown to be the case.

The equation of the wave is found as follows:

$$E = E^0 - \frac{RT}{2F_y} \ln \frac{[Red]^0}{[Ox]^0} \qquad (50)$$

$$i = 2\, a(c - [Red]^0) + A[Ox]^0 \qquad (51)$$

in which a is the constant of the Ilkovic equation (46) and A the constant in eq. 49, while c is the concentration of the reduced form in the solution.

The total apparent diffusion current $I = i_1 + i_2$:

$$I = (2a + A)c \qquad (52)$$

and:

$$i = 2a[Ox]^0 + A[Ox]^0 \qquad (53)$$

(effusion of Ox from electrode to solution)

When the various relations are introduced into eq. 50:

$$E = E^0 - \frac{RT}{2F_y} \ln \frac{I - i}{i} \qquad (54)$$

The equation, therefore, is identical with that of the normal anodic wave. However, I depends less upon the height of the mercury in the reservoir than a normal diffusion current does.

5. LIMITING CURRENTS (APPARENT DIFFUSION CURRENTS) OF CATALYZED HYDROGEN WAVES. CATALYST REACTS IN DISSOLVED STATE

Several substances decrease the hydrogen overpotential at the dropping mercury electrode; when present in small quantities they give rise to catalytic hydrogen waves. The catalyst can exert its effect when present in the metallic phase, like traces of platinum metals. This effect is discussed on page 238 and is not considered further here.

Other substances, like traces of proteins,[24] thio acids and their disulfides,[25] quinoline derivatives,[26] and alkaloids,[27] give rise to typical catalytic hydrogen waves by reaction of the dissolved or adsorbed catalyst at the surface of the dropping electrode.

The height of these catalytic waves does not increase linearly with the concentration of the catalyst. With sulfhydryl (—SH) containing substances the catalyst is activated by cobalt ions. Jurka[28] made a systematic investigation of the height of the catalytic protein waves as a function of the concentration of cobalt and protein in a buffer which was 0.1 M in ammonium chloride and 0.1 M in ammonia. Fig. XV-5 shows how the height of the double wave at a given cobalt concentration depends on the protein concentration. The curves resemble typical adsorption isotherms. Brdicka[29] interprets these curves by assuming that the adsorbed protein on the surface of the electrode, which is in adsorption equilibrium with the bulk of the solution, exerts the catalytic effect.

According to the Langmuir adsorption isotherm:

$$N_A = zwc/(1 + wc)$$

in which N_A is the number of adsorbed molecules per unit surface, z is the

[24] J. Heyrovsky and J. Brdicka, *Collection Czechoslov. Chem. Communs.*, **2**, 370 (1930).

[25] J. Brdicka, *Collection Czechoslov. Chem. Communs.*, **5**, 112, 148 (1933); **8**, 366 (1936); *Biochem. Z.*, **272**, 104 (1934); *J. chim. phys.*, **35**, 89 (1938).

[26] P. Herasymenko and I. Slendyk, *Collection Czechoslov. Chem. Communs.*, **6**, 204 (1934).

[27] J. Pech, *Collection Czechoslov. Chem. Communs.*, **6**, 190 (1934). F. Reimers, *ibid.*, **11**, 377 (1939).

[28] E. Jurka, *Collection Czechoslov. Chem. Communs.*, **11**, 243 (1939).

[29] R. Brdicka, *Collection Czechoslov. Chem. Communs.*, **11**, 614 (1939).

number of molecules when the surface is completely covered with adsorbed molecules, c is the concentration of the protein in solution, and w is the adsorption coefficient.

If the height h of the wave is proportional to the number of adsorbed molecules we have:

$$h = h_z wc/(1 + wc) \qquad (55)$$

in which h_z is the limiting value of the catalytic current attained at a constant cobalt concentration with increasing protein concentration.

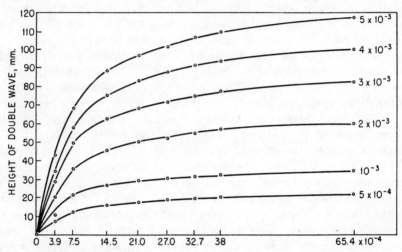

Fig. XV-5. Height of the double protein wave as a function of the protein concentration. Figures on curves, $CoCl_2$ concentration in normality. Abscissa, serum concentration.

Fig. XV-6 shows how the height of the double wave depends upon the cobalt concentration at a given protein concentration. According to Brdicka this dependence is given by:

$$h = k_c[Co^{++}]^{0.74}$$

The following equation combines the effect of protein concentration c and cobalt concentration on the height of the wave:

$$h = \frac{k_{cs}[Co^{++}]^{0.74}wc}{1 + wc} \qquad (56)$$

Referring to Jurka's experiments k_{cs} was found to be equal to 6620 and w to 1450.

Klumpar[30] investigated the effect of concentrations of cobalt and cysteine on the catalytic cysteine wave. He found that the following expression holds equally well for cysteine as for protein waves:

$$h = A \frac{[\text{Co}^{\text{II}}]}{D[\text{Co}^{\text{II}}]^+} \cdot \frac{[\text{Cyst}]}{C\,[\text{Cyst}] + 1}$$

in which h is the height of the wave, and A, C, and D are constants. The values vary with experimental conditions, A being of the order of 10^{10}. Klumpar rejects the view that the catalytic wave is determined by adsorp-

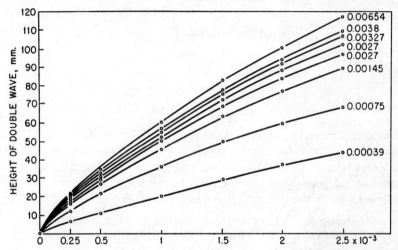

Fig. XV-6. Height of double wave as a function of the cobalt concentration. Abscissa, concentration of CoCl$_2$.

tion of cysteine and cobalt (cobalt cysteinate complex). Another process, which is rather determining, must be responsible for the catalytic wave.

In the absence of cobalt a single catalytic protein wave is observed whose height is given by an equation similar to eq. 55.

Brdicka assumes that the catalytic current i is determined by the expression:

$$i = k[\text{H}][\text{H}^+][\text{RSH}]_a K_{\text{RSH}}$$

$[\text{RSH}]_a$ is the concentration of the adsorbed sulfhydryl compound and K_{RSH} is its ionization constant. It seems that instead of the ionization constant the rate constant of the dissociation should be used, the ionization constant K_{RSH} being equal to $k_{\text{assoc.}}/k_{\text{dissoc.}}$.

[30] K. Klumpar, *Collection Czechoslov. Chem. Communs.*, **13**, 11 (1948).

The concentration of the hydrogen atoms is given by the expression:[31]

$$[H] = k'[H^+]e^{-EF_y/RT} \tag{56}$$

By introducing this into eq. 55 and differentiating, the deposition potential of hydrogen is obtained:

$$\frac{di}{dE} = k''[H^+]^2[RSH]_a K_{RSH}\left(-\frac{F_y}{RT}e^{-E_1F_y/RT}\right) \tag{57}$$

In the absence of the catalyst the deposition potential E_2 is:

$$\frac{di}{dE} = k''[H^+]^2[H_2O]_a K_{H_2O}\left(-\frac{F_y}{RT}e^{-E_2F_y/RT}\right) \tag{58}$$

and:

$$E_1 - E_2 = \frac{RT}{F_y}\ln\frac{[RSH]_a}{[H_2O]_a}\frac{K_{RSH}}{K_{H_2O}} \tag{59}$$

The exact significance of this expression is problematical.

On the basis of derivations by Brdicka and Wiesner given earlier in this chapter it is anticipated that the catalytic currents discussed in this section should be independent of the height of the mercury in the reservoir. This was shown to be the case by Müller and Davis[32] and confirmed by others.

---

[31] J. Heyrovsky, *Collection Czechoslov. Chem. Communs.*, **9**, 273 (1937).
[32] O. H. Müller and J. S. Davis, Jr., *J. Biol. Chem.*, **159**, 667 (1945).

Part Two

INSTRUMENTATION AND TECHNIQUE

CHAPTER XVI

Polarographic Instrumentation

1. MANUAL EQUIPMENT

The *essential* instrumentation for polarographic measurements and amperometric titrations is simple and can be assembled relatively cheaply from components usually available in the chemical laboratory. The requirements of a circuit for measuring polarographic current–voltage curves are: (*a*) a means of applying a variable and known voltage ranging from 0 to 2 or 3 v. to the cell, and (*b*) a method for measuring the resulting small current, which usually is smaller than 100 microamperes (10^{-4} amp.). It is desirable that the applied voltage be known to the order of ± 0.001 v., and the maximum sensitivity of the current-measuring device should be 0.01 microamp. or better.

One of the simplest circuits which meets these requirements is illustrated schematically in Fig. XVI-1. This circuit is especially useful for instructional purposes, and at the same time is capable of higher precision and accuracy than can be obtained with any commercial polarograph.[1]

The voltage applied to the cell circuit is regulated by the rheostat or "potential divider" R_1 (50 or 100 ohm radio-type potentiometer such as General Radio Co. Type 214) which is powered by two 1.5 volt dry cells.

In a recording polarograph the resistance of the bridge, corresponding to R_1 in the manual circuit, must be small compared to the total resistance of the cell circuit in order that the applied voltage will be directly proportional to the position of the sliding contact. This is not necessary with the manual circuit in Fig. XVI-1 because the applied voltage is measured directly with the potentiometer, but it is desirable that R_1 be not larger than about 100 ohms.

The current is measured in terms of the iR drop across the 10,000 ohm precision fixed resistance R_2 (*e. g.*, General Radio Co. Type 500 J) in series with the cell by means of the potentiometer. By reversing the double-pole double-throw switch the voltage applied to the cell is measured with the same potentiometer.

The current–voltage curve is obtained by increasing the applied voltage stepwise from zero and measuring it with the potentiometer. At each

---

[1] J. J. Lingane, *Anal. Chem.*, **21**, 47 (1949).

voltage step the switch is reversed, the voltage drop E across R_2 is measured, and the current is computed from Ohm's Law $i = E/R_2$. If $R_2 = 10,000$ ohms, then each millivolt potential drop across R_2 corresponds to $10^{-3}/10^4$ $= 10^{-7}$ amp. or 0.1 microamp.

To expedite the measurements and avoid unnecessary points, the entire voltage range that is of interest should first be explored using rather large voltage increments, e. g., 0.2 v., and the points should be plotted as the measurements are made. In this way the character of the polarogram

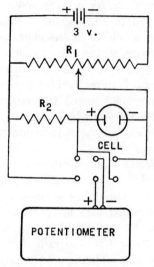

Fig. XVI-1. Simple manual circuit for polarographic
analysis and amperometric titrations.[1]

quickly becomes evident and the appropriate additional points required to precisely define rapidly changing parts of the polarogram may then be taken using smaller voltage increments, e. g., 0.01 v.

The potentiometer used should be precise to ±0.1 mv. and it should have a range from 0 to 3 v. The familiar Leeds and Northrup Student's Type Potentiometer serves excellently. The range of this instrument is only 0–1.6 v. but this can be extended to 0–3.2 v. by standardizing against the Weston standard cell with the potentiometer set at one-half the voltage of the standard cell, i. e., at 0.5090 v. if the standard cell voltage is 1.0180, and then multiplying the observed readings by 2.

Because the current oscillates as a result of the periodic growth and fall of the mercury drops, the galvanometer used as a null-point detector in the potentiometer circuit should have a period that is long compared to the drop time. The optimum galvanometer period is three to four times the drop time. If the natural period is shorter than this the galvanometer should be overdamped by placing across its terminals a resistance that is smaller than the critical damping resistance of the instrument. The appropriate resistance is determined by trial with the particular instrument, and it should be such that the galvanometer oscillations do not extend over more than about 2 cm. on the scale. In adjusting the potentiometer to the null point the balance point is taken when the oscillations extend an equal distance on either side of the galvanometer zero point. The "box-type" galvanometers manufactured by Leeds and Northrup Co. and by Rubicon Co., Philadelphia, are very satisfactory as null-point instruments. Appropriate characteristics are approximately as follows: sensitivity (critically damped) 0.005 to 0.01 microamp. per millimeter, critically damped period 3 to 5 sec., internal resistance 1000 ohms, and critical damping resistance about 7000 ohms. A resistance of 500 to 1000 ohms across its terminals will increase the period of such a galvanometer to the desirable value.

The accuracy of this manual apparatus depends on the accuracy of the potentiometer and standard resistance R_2. Assuming that the potentiometer is precise to ± 0.1 mv., which is commonplace, it is evident that the current measurement will be precise to ± 0.01 microamp. over the range from 0 to 160 microamp. if the potentiometer has the usual range of 0–1.6 v. and $R_2 = 10,000$ ohms. Potentiometers are commonly equipped with an auxiliary "low range" of 0–0.016 v. and with such an instrument currents in the range 0–1.6 microamp. can be measured with a precision of ± 0.0001 microamp. and with an accuracy that depends on the accuracy of R_2 and that of the potentiometer bridge.

Instead of measuring the current in terms of the iR drop across a standard resistance it can be measured directly with a galvanometer having the appropriate characteristics, and, by employing an accurately uniform scaled resistance as the rheostat R_1, the applied voltage can be read directly. These modifications lead to a somewhat more convenient apparatus whose precision is less than the circuit of Fig. XVI-1 but adequate for most purposes. The fundamental circuit requirements are indicated in Fig. XVI-2.

The total voltage across the bridge AB is read on the voltmeter V and adjusted to an integral value by means of the variable resistor R_1. The voltmeter V should have a range of 0–3 v. and a precision of at least ± 0.01 v. The variable resistor R_1 should have a resistance that is two to three times that of the bridge to permit a selection of bridge voltages over a 3- to 4-fold range.

A ten-turn Beckman Helipot potentiometer manufactured by National Technical Laboratories, Pasadena, Calif. available with a guaranteed linearity of ±0.1 per cent is especially suitable as the bridge AB. It can be purchased with a dial scale which is graduated to 1/100 of a turn or 0.1 per cent of the complete range.

The bridge resistance in Fig. XVI-2 must be small (not more than 100 ohms and preferably 50 ohms) to insure a linear relation between the bridge

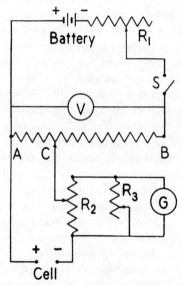

Fig. XVI-2. Simple circuit for obtaining current–voltage curves manually.

reading and the voltage applied to the cell. The desired relation is

$$E_a = (R_{AC}/R_{AB})E_b \tag{1}$$

where E_a is the voltage applied to the cell circuit and E_b is the voltage across the bridge measured by the voltmeter V. Representing the constant bridge current by i_B and the cell current by i_C the voltage applied to the cell circuit is equal to the voltage drop between A and C, and is given by

$$E_a = E_{AC} = (i_B - i_C)R_{AC} \tag{2}$$

That is, the voltage drop between A and C is smaller than it would be if the cell circuit were disconnected by the quantity $i_C R_{AC}$, because part of the constant bridge current is diverted through the cell circuit. The total voltage E_b across the bridge is constant and expressible by

$$E_b = (i_B - i_C)R_{AC} + i_B R_{BC} \tag{3}$$

or since $R_{AC} + R_{BC} = R_{AB}$

$$E_b = i_B R_{AB} - i_C R_{AC} \tag{4}$$

Therefore, from eqs. 2 and 4

$$E_a = \left(\frac{i_B R_{AC} - i_C R_{AC}}{i_B R_{AB} - i_C R_{AC}}\right) E_b \tag{5}$$

Equation 5 approaches the desired eq. 1 only when $i_C R_{AC}$ is so small compared to both $i_B R_{AC}$ and $i_B R_{AB}$ that it can be neglected. This condition will prevail when i_B is made large compared to i_C. Since the maximal value of R_{AC} is R_{AB}, the desired eq. 1 will be obeyed to 0.1 per cent or better provided the bridge current is 1000 times the cell current. Because the maximal cell current seldom exceeds 100 microamp. (10^{-4} amp.) the bridge current should be 0.1 amp., corresponding to a bridge resistance of 20 ohms if E_b is 2 v. Because R_{AC} generally is smaller than R_{AB}, and the cell current ordinarily is much less than 100 microamp., no significant error will result if the bridge resistance is as large as 100 ohms but evidently it should not be larger.

The current is measured by means of a calibrated galvanometer, G, which is provided with an Ayrton shunt, R_2, by means of which the sensitivity can be varied by a known amount (see Fig. XVI-2). The second shunt, R_3, serves the dual purpose of providing the proper damping resistance for the galvanometer and of permitting the maximum sensitivity of the instrument to be adjusted to an integral value (say, exactly 0.01 microamp. per millimeter), which greatly facilitates the conversion of the readings from arbitrary scale divisions to microamperes.

Two precision decade resistance boxes may be used to serve the dual purpose of the Ayrton shunt and the damping resistance, as shown in Fig. XVI-3. The total resistance $R_1 + R_2$ of both boxes is adjusted to provide the desired degree of damping; preferably $R_1 + R_2$ is set to some even value such as 100 or 1000 ohms. The desired sensitivity is then obtained by adjusting the ratio of R_1 to $R_1 + R_2$. In making this adjustment R_2 is decreased by the same amount that R_1 is increased to keep $R_1 + R_2$ constant. Representing the maximum sensitivity of the galvanometer by S^0 (corresponding to $R_2 = 0$) the sensitivity at other values of the ratio

$R_1/(R_1 + R_2)$ is given by

$$S = \left(\frac{R_1}{R_1 + R_2}\right) S^0 \tag{6}$$

where the sensitivity is defined as galvanometer deflection per unit current in the cell circuit, and is usually expressed in the units mm. per microampere. This arrangement provides a much greater variety of sensitivity settings than the usual type of Ayrton shunt.

A moving coil mirror galvanometer read by means of a telescope and scale or lamp and scale is most suitable. The instrument should be one whose deflection is directly proportional to current. The type 3514 taut

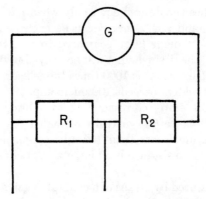

Fig. XVI-3. Galvanometer shunt assembled from two decade resistance boxes.

suspension galvanometer manufactured by Rubicon Co., Philadelphia, is especially suitable. This instrument is mounted in a wooden case which minimizes zero drift due to temperature changes, and the taut suspension construction renders the instrument much less sensitive to vibration than instruments with a freely suspended coil. Typical optimum characteristics are approximately as follows: sensitivity 0.0007 microamp. per millimeter, critically damped period 5 sec., internal resistance 500 ohms, and critical damping resistance 13,000 ohms. The authors use this instrument in the circuit of Fig. XVI-3 with $R_1 + R_2$ adjusted to 1000 ohms. When thus overdamped the period is increased to an optimum value of the order of 15 sec. and the maximum sensitivity is approximately 0.001 microamp. per millimeter when the deflection is read on a scale at a distance of 120 cm. from the galvanometer.

Strictly a curved scale with radius of curvature equal to the distance from the scale to the galvanometer mirror should be used because it is the *angular* deflection which is proportional to the current through the galvanometer coil. Actually a straight scale may be used without significant error provided the distance between it and the galvanometer is relatively large. Let d be the observed linear deflection on a straight scale located at a distance D from the galvanometer, θ the angular deflection (radians) of the galvanometer coil, and i the galvanometer current. Then

$$\theta = ki \tag{7}$$

$$d = D \tan \theta = D \tan (ki) \tag{8}$$

When D is large compared to d, the angular deflection will be small and the value of $\tan \theta$ approaches θ itself. Under this condition eq. 8 approaches the desired relation

$$d = D\theta = Dki = k'i \tag{9}$$

When θ is less than 0.17 radian (less than 10°) $\tan \theta$ will be less than 1 per cent larger than θ itself and the error involved in using eq. 9 will be correspondingly less than 1 per cent. If the scale length is 50 cm. then the minimum value of D for a maximal "tangent error" of 1 per cent is 50/0.17 = 294 cm. or practically 3 meters. With a 20 cm. straight scale D may be as small as 1.2 meters.

In reading the dropping electrode current the *average* of the galvanometer oscillations should be observed rather than the maximum or minimum. To keep the oscillations from being inconveniently large the galvanometer should be damped sufficiently so that its period is three or four times greater than the drop time. (In recording instruments a greater degree of damping than this is undesirable because it results in appreciable recording lag.) Methods of calibrating the galvanometer are described in a following section.

The *total e.m.f.* applied to the cell circuit, E_a, is distributed across both the polarographic cell and the parallel circuit comprised of the galvanometer and its shunts. Since we are interested only in the e.m.f. actually applied to the cell, the *net* resistance of the parallel circuit composed of R_2, R_3, and the galvanometer itself (Fig. XVI-2) should be kept small, so that the potential drop across the galvanometer and shunts will be negligibly small, and E_a will be equal practically to the e.m.f. actually applied to the cell. Ordinarily the net resistance of the galvanometer and shunts will be smaller than 1000 ohms, and when this is true the potential drop across this part of the circuit will be of the order of 1 mv. per microampere, or less. This is negligible for most practical purposes, but when necessary it can be easily corrected for from the known resistances of the galvanometer and the shunts and the measured current. It should be borne in mind that the effective resistance of the galvanometer and shunts depends on the setting of the Ayrton shunt, and it has a maximum value when the setting is in the neighborhood of 0.5.

Professor Breckpot of the University of Louvain designed the ingenious manual polarograph shown schematically in Fig. XVI-4 which is taken from a recent paper by Favre.[2] Rotation of the hand wheel, N, increases the e.m.f. applied to the polarographic cell and simultaneously rotates the mirror, M. The galvanometer light spot, reflected from the mirror up to the large glass plate, E, moves along one axis in direct relation to the applied e.m.f. and along the other according to the current. A sheet of translucent graph paper is placed on the glass plate and as the hand wheel is rotated the path of the light spot is traced with a pencil to obtain the polarogram. Although very simple, this instrument possesses many of the virtues of an automatic polarograph. A very similar *Handschreiber* incorporated in the Leybold polarograph has been described by Hohn.[3]

Figure XVI-5 shows the manually operated "Elecdropode" manufactured by Fisher Scientific Co., Pittsburgh, Pa. This instrument utilizes a circuit very similar to that of Fig. XVI-2. It is completely self-contained and easily portable. Mounting the cell and dropping electrode assembly directly on the instrument cabinet is objectionable because it does not permit temperature control. However, it is a simple matter to dismount the cell assembly and place it in a thermostat.

Manual instruments for polarographic analysis have also been marketed by the firm of Dr. H. Geissler, Nachfolger, Bonn (the "Abresch Polarometer"), and by American Instrument Co., Silver Springs, Md. ("Aminco Polarometric Analyzer").

Figure XVI-6 shows a manual instrument recently developed by E. H. Sargent and Co., Chicago. The voltage applied to the d.e. cell is regulated by a precision, ten-turn potentiometer, powered by dry batteries. The current is indicated by a galvanometer on the 30-cm. scale at the top of the panel which is correctly curved to eliminate tangent error. An Ayrton shunt provides ten different galvanometer sensitivities over a range from 0.006 to 6 microamp. per millimeter. Means are provided for both up- and down-scale current compensation.

The manual instrument manufactured by Cambridge Instrument Co.,

[2] R. Favre, *Anal. Chim. Acta*, **2**, 556 (1948).
[3] H. Hohn, *Chemische Analyse mit dem Polarographen*, Springer, Berlin, 1937.

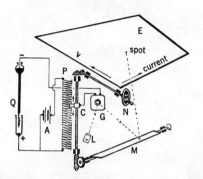

Fig. XVI-4. Principle of Breckpot manually operated polarograph.

Fig. XVI-5. Fisher Elecdropode.

Fig. XVI-6. Sargent manual polarograph.

Fig. XVI-7. Cambridge Instrument Co. Voltamoscope.

Grand Central Terminal, New York, is shown in Fig. XVI-7. The current may either be read directly on the galvanometer or by means of a self-contained potentiometer using the galvanometer as a null-point indicator. Galvanometer damping and countercurrent adjustments are provided. The bridge voltage is standardized against a self-contained standard cell.

Fig. XVI-8. Aminco polarometric analyzer.

Figure XVI-8 shows the manual instrument manufactured by American Instrument Co., Silver Spring, Md.

2. RECORDING POLAROGRAPHS

The Heyrovsky-Shikata Polarograph. In 1925 Heyrovsky and Shikata[4] invented the polarograph, which automatically obtains and photographically records current–voltage curves. A photograph of the first polarograph

[4] J. Heyrovsky and M. Shikata, *Rec. trav. chim.*, **44**, 496 (1925).

constructed by Heyrovsky and Shikata at Charles University in Prague is reproduced in Fig. XVI-9, and an early commercial model of the instrument constructed by the firm of Drs. V. and J. Nejedly, Prague, is shown in Fig. XVI-10.

The principle of the polarograph is illustrated in Fig. XVI-11. In this figure D is the electrolysis cell containing the solution to be analyzed, and B is a potentiometric bridge, consisting of a cylinder of insulating material wound with a rather low resistance wire (*ca.* 15 ohms) in 20 turns, by means of which a variable e.m.f. is applied to the cell. Current for the bridge is supplied from storage battery H; total

Fig. XVI-9. The first polarograph constructed by Heyrovsky and Shikata at Charles University, Prague.

potential drop across the slide wire can be adjusted exactly to any desired value (usually 2 or 4 v.) by a regulating resistance. Total potential drop across the slide wire is indicated by a voltmeter, permanently mounted in the instrument. To obtain a more accurate adjustment of the potential drop across the bridge, an arrangement is provided for switching a Weston standard cell in the circuit in place of the cell, against which the bridge is balanced in the usual way using the recording galvanometer as a null-point instrument. Each turn of the bridge wire then corresponds to a definite, known increment of applied e.m.f. (say, 100 or 200 mv.). The bridge is rotated by a small electric motor, A, whose speed may be varied. A transmission is provided for disconnecting the bridge from the driving motor, and for reversing the direction of rotation. Usually the voltage is applied at a rate of 0.1 to 0.3 v. per minute.

A roll of photographic paper is carried by the cylinder C, enclosed by a light-tight housing, and connected by a system of gears to the bridge so that the two revolve simultaneously. The gear ratio is such that one complete revolution of the bridge corresponds to a lateral movement of about 1 cm. on the photographic paper. G is a galvanometer lamp which projects a very thin beam of light onto the mirror of the galvanometer E, from whence it is reflected to the moving photographic paper. The galvanometer is provided with a shunt, F, for regulating its sensitivity. When current flows through the galvanometer, the light beam traces a thin line on the photographic paper parallel to the axis of the roll. The photographic drum is en-

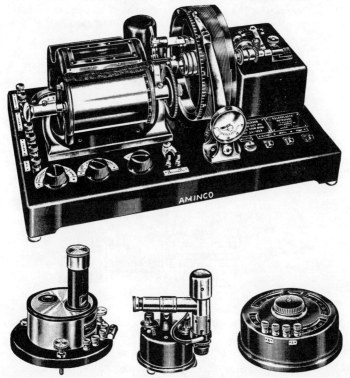

Fig. XVI-10. Heyrovsky-Shikata polarograph manufactured by the firm of Drs. V. and J. Nejedly, Prague (photograph courtesy American Instrument Co.).

closed in a housing provided with a narrow collimating slit through which the light beam from the galvanometer mirror enters. Each time the roll turns through a distance of 1 cm. (100 or 200 mv. of applied e.m.f.) an auxiliary light, automatically flashed on by a switch operated by a small peg on the edge of the potentiometric drum, illuminates the entire slit and a thin line is printed on the paper. These lines mark the increments of applied e.m.f.

With the cell in readiness and the dropping electrode in operation, the bridge is turned back until the moving contact is at zero. The motor is then started, and the movement of the sliding grooved contact along the bridge wire applies a uniformly

increasing e.m.f. to the cell.   As long as the applied e.m.f. is smaller than the decomposition potential of the particular solution in the cell, the current through the
cell circuit is very small (residual current), and the beam of light from the galvanometer mirror remains practically stationary, and the slow rotation of the drum traces
a line along the circumference of the photographic roll.   When the decomposition
potential is reached and exceeded the increase in current through the cell circuit
deflects the galvanometer; the light beam traces the discharge curve (polarographic
wave), and then attains a constant displacement corresponding to the limiting
current.

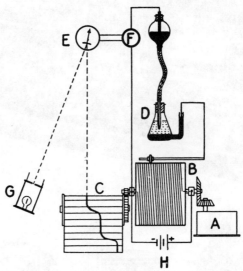

Fig. XVI-11. The principle of the Heyrovsky-Shikata polarograph.

Proper galvanometer or recorder damping is, of course, much more important when polarograms are recorded automatically than when the measurements are made manually.   The influence of the degree of galvanometer damping on recorded polarograms is illustrated by the three
polarograms in Fig. XVI-12.   These were all obtained with the same solution of 1 millimolar lead ion and 1.16 millimolar cadmium ion in 1 M potassium chloride with a Heyrovsky type polarograph.   The drop time of the
electrode on open circuit was 5 sec.   The period of the recording galvanometer, expressed as time required to attain 95 per cent of full deflection,
was adjusted (by varying the shunting resistance) to 83 sec. for curve *1*,
18 sec. for curve *2*, and 3 sec. for curve *3*.   The sensitivity was adjusted—
only approximately and not exactly—to the same value for the three curves.
The e.m.f. was applied at a rate of 0.2 v. per minute.
With an 83-sec. period (curve *1*) the oscillations are reduced to a very

small magnitude but the response is so slow that the diffusion current plateau of lead ion is not fully developed before the reduction of cadmium ion begins, and also the apparent half-wave potentials of both waves are significantly more negative than the true values. A satisfactory polarogram could be recorded with this very long galvanometer period if the

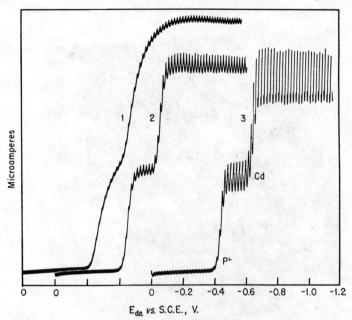

Fig. XVI-12. Influence of degree of galvanometer damping on recorded polarograms. All three curves were recorded with the same solution consisting of about 1 millimolar concentration each of lead and cadmium ions in 1 millimolar potassium chloride containing 0.005 per cent gelatin. The drop time was 5.0 seconds on open circuit. The voltage was applied to the cell at a rate of 0.2 v. per minute. The galvanometer sensitivity was only approximately, and not exactly, the same for the three curves. The galvanometer period (95 per cent deflection) was: (1) 83 sec., (2) 18 sec., and (3) 3 sec.

rate of application of the applied voltage were made much smaller, e. g. 0.05 v. per minute, but the time required for the recording would then be inconveniently long.

Curve 3 obtained with a galvanometer period (3 sec.) that was somewhat smaller than the drop time represents the other extreme. In this case the oscillations are so large that the measurement of their average is inconvenient. Furthermore, with such a small ratio of galvanometer period to drop time the average of the oscillations tends to become smaller than the true average current.

Curve *2* demonstrates that a galvanometer period of 18 sec. is about optimum for a 5 sec. drop time.   The response is rapid enough with the usual rate of application of the applied voltage (0.2 v. per minute) so that the apparent half-wave potential does not differ significantly from the true value observed with manual measurement, and the oscillations are small enough so that there is no difficulty in measuring their average.

Fig. XVI-13. Sargent-Heyrovsky Model XII photographically recording polaro-graph.

The polarograph has several advantages over manual measurement.   In the first place, the curves can be obtained in a fraction of the time required to obtain them manually; a complete curve can be recorded in 10 minutes or less, regardless of the number of waves that it contains.   A continuous curve is obtained, rather than a series of points, and very small waves, or slight peculiarities which might otherwise escape notice, are automatically detected and recorded.   Furthermore, a permanent record is obtained in a single operation, and several curves may be recorded on a single sheet of paper.

The modified Heyrovsky polarograph manufactured by E. H. Sargent and Co., Chicago, is shown in Fig. XVI-13.   This instrument is self-contained, simple to operate, and in general is quite satisfactory. A brochure containing a complete description of the instrument is available from the manufacturer. The voltage scale of the Sargent-Heyrovsky instrument is not as precise as that of the original Heyrovsky-Shikata polarograph because only a single-turn slide wire is used as the polarizing bridge and the voltage across the bridge is read on an ordinary voltmeter. The instrument could be improved by replacing the single-turn slide wire with a Beckman Helipot potentiometer and by providing an internal Weston standard cell against which the bridge voltage could be accurately adjusted. Additional desirable improvements would be the use of a reversible motor to drive the bridge so that polarograms could be recorded with both increasing and decreasing applied voltage in order to correct for the recording lag in measuring half-wave potentials, and the use of a larger camera so that easily available 8 × 10 inch photographic paper could be used instead of the 6 × 10 inch paper now required which must either be obtained on special order or cut from the 8 × 10 inch paper. A further improvement would be the incorporation of a standard resistance used in calibrating the galvanometer (*vide infra*).

The construction of photographically recording polarographs of the Heyrovsky-Shikata type has been described by Furman, Bricker, and Whitesell,[5] Abichandani and Jatkar,[6] and Lingane.[7] Philbrook and Grubb[8] described an improved wiring diagram for the Sargent-Heyrovsky polarograph and a vibration-free mounting for this instrument. Modifications of the circuit of the Sargent-Heyrovsky polarograph have also been described by Baumberger and Bardwell.[9]

The photographically recording polarographs manufactured by the German firms Leybold, Köln, and Hellige, Freiburg i. Br., are described in detail in von Stackelberg's recent monograph.[10]

Visible Recording Polarographs. To eliminate processing a photographic record several types of visible recording polarographs have been developed. The Model XXI instrument manufactured by E. H. Sargent and Co. is shown in Fig. XVI-14. The current is recorded in terms of the iR drop across a known resistance in series with the polarographic cell by means of a Brown Elektronik potentiometer recorder. In our hands this instrument

[5] N. H. Furman, C. E. Bricker, and E. B. Whitesell, *Ind. Eng. Chem., Anal. Ed.*, **14**, 333 (1942).

[6] C. T. Abichandani and S. K. K. Jatkar, *J. Ind. Inst. Sci.*, **A23**, 131 (1941).

[7] J. J. Lingane, *J. Am. Chem. Soc.*, **68**, 2448 (1946).

[8] G. E. Philbrook and H. M. Grubb, *Anal. Chem.*, **19**, 7 (1947).

[9] J. P. Baumberger and K. Bardwell, *Ind. Eng. Chem., Anal. Ed.*, **15**, 639 (1943).

[10] M. von Stackelberg, *Polarographische Arbeitsmethoden*, de Gruyter, Berlin, 1950.

has not performed as satisfactorily as the photographic Model XII of the same manufacturer (Fig. XVI-13).

The Leeds and Northrup "Electrochemograph" shown in Fig. XVI-15 is also a visible recording polarograph. This new instrument has been designed and engineered exceptionally well and its performance characteristics are excellent. After amplification the current is recorded on a "Speedo-

Fig. XVI-14. Sargent Visible Recording Polarograph Model XXI.

max" potentiometer recorder. The current amplification is accomplished without introducing a significant iR drop in the cell circuit, and a variety of current sensitivities may be selected. Provision is made for several degrees of recorder damping with remarkably little distortion of the wave form. A convenient arrangement is provided for accurately adjusting the bridge voltage against a self-contained Weston standard cell, which enables the instrument to provide accurate and reliable values of half-wave potentials. The polarogram may be recorded with either increasing or decreasing applied voltage, and several starting voltages and ranges of bridge voltage may be selected.   The instrument incorporates a precisely regulated rectifier unit for the d.c. bridge supply which eliminates batteries and enables complete operation from a 110 v. a.c. line.

The visible recording polarograph manufactured by Radiometer, Copenhagen, Denmark, is shown in Fig. XVI-15a.   This instrument employs a

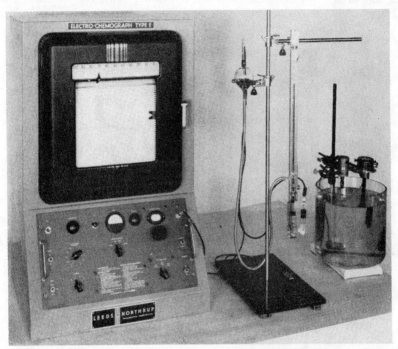

Fig. XVI-15. Leeds and Northrup Electrochemograph and dropping electrode equipment.   In use the H-type cell is immersed in a constant temperature water bath of the type shown on the extreme right.

pen-writing milliammeter as the recording element.   The iR drop generated by the electrolysis current in a precision resistor is converted to an alternating current signal by a vibrating reed.   The a.c. signal is amplified, converted back to direct current by a full-wave cuprous oxide rectifier, and then presented to the recording milliammeter.   Because this method of amplification produces a d.c. output whose polarity is fixed regardless of the polarity of the original iR drop, the recorder deflects in the same direction regardless of the direction of current flow in the cell.   Aside from the method of recording, the instrument utilizes conventional circuitry.

The "Voltamograph" of Cambridge Instrument Co., shown in Fig. XVI-16, is a visible recording polarograph.   The current is recorded by a pen-writing galvanometer in terms of the amplified iR drop across a standard resistance.   The current sensitivity is variable in steps from 0.0025 to 2.5 microamp. per millimeter.   Provision is made for standardizing the bridge voltage against a self-contained standard cell, and three

Fig. XVI-15a. Recording polarograph manufactured by Radiometer, Copenhagen.

ranges of bridge voltage, $+0.2$ to -0.7, $+0.4$ to $+1.4$, and $+0.8$ to $+2.8$, are provided.   The rectilinear chart is only 8 cm. on the current axis and 17 cm. on the voltage axis, which is smaller than desirable for precise measurements.

Müller[11] described the "polarographic scanner" shown in Fig. XVI-17, which can be assembled in about 1 hour using standardized precision mechanical components available from Servomechanisms Inc., Old Country and Glen Cove Roads, Mineola, N. Y.   A reversible synchronous motor is mounted on a pedestal block and coupled through a precision gear train to

[11] R. H. Müller, *Anal. Chem.*, **22**, 76 (1950).

a ten-turn Helipot potentiometer (50 ohms) which serves excellently as the polarographic bridge. A revolution counter coupled to the Helipot indicates the applied voltage directly. The current is recorded in terms of the iR drop across a standard resistor by an auxiliary 0 to 2.5 mv. Brown Electronik potentiometer recorder, and any desired current sensitivity may be obtained by using a precision Beckman Helipot potentiometer as a

Fig. XVI-16. Cambridge Instrument Co. Voltamograph.

variable standard resistor. Pedestals mounted below the table accommodate line- and motor-reversing switches, potentiometers, and rheostats for span adjustment and sensitivity control. In addition to the recording potentiometer, the other auxiliary equipment needed is a voltmeter to read the total bridge voltage (the recording potentiometer could be used for this purpose also) and dry batteries to power the bridge.

Lykken, Pompeo, and Weaver[12] developed a polarograph which retains the inherent simplicity and reliability of a galvanometer as the primary

---

[12] L. Lykken, D. J. Pompeo, and J. R. Weaver, *Ind. Eng. Chem., Anal. Ed.*, **17**, 724 (1945).

current-measuring element and yet provides the convenience of visibly recorded polarograms. A schematic diagram of the instrument is shown in Fig. XVI-18. The ingenious "photopen" recorder employs a double cathode phototube mounted directly on the pen carriage. By means of intermediate electronic relays the phototube signal is made to control the direction of rotation of the motor which drives the recording pen. The

Fig. XVI-17. Polarographic scanner according to Müller.[11]

motor remains at rest as long as the galvanometer light beam is focused between the two cathodes of the phototube, but the slightest movement of the light beam activates one or the other side of the phototube, and the pen rapidly and faithfully follows the movement of the galvanometer. The rest of the circuit follows good conventional practice.

Schulman, Battey, and Jelatis[13] designed a visible recording polarograph with an undamped, high-speed recording system. The current is amplified

    [13] J. H. Schulman, H. B. Battey, and D. G. Jelatis, *Rev. Sci. Instruments*, **18**, 226 (1947).

electronically and recorded on an Esterline-Angus recorder which gives a full-scale deflection in about 0.5 sec. This response time is so small that something approaching the entire current–time curve during the formation of individual drops is obtained. Provision is also made for conventional damped operation. The high-speed recorder permits high rates of voltage

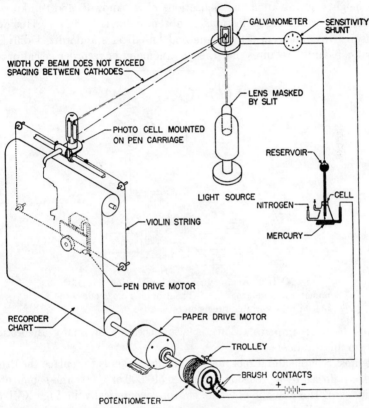

Fig. XVI-18. Schematic diagram of Lykken-Pompeo-Weaver polarograph.[12]

change (up to about 0.8 v. per minute) with very little distortion of the wave form; this characteristic may be advantageous in certain types of polarographic studies. This instrument is available under the name "Polaro-Analyzer" from Rutherford Instrument Co., Alexandria, Va.

Hohn[14] invented a rugged recording polarograph for routine industrial laboratory use. The polarographic current operates a galvanometer which controls the amount of light reaching two photocells connected in opposi-

[14] H. Hohn, *Metall u. Erz*, **40**, 197 (1943).

tion to the grid of a triode.   The recording pen is operated by the output
of the triode.

3.   CALIBRATION OF GALVANOMETER OR RECORDER

Practical polarographic analyses can be performed by merely comparing
wave heights or galvanometer deflections of a "known" and "unknown"
without converting the deflections to absolute current values.   However,
the use of the more convenient method based on standardized diffusion
current constants[15] requires that the galvanometer or recorder be calibrated

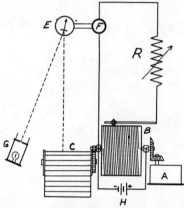

Fig. XVI-19. Arrangement for calibrating the galvanometer of a polarograph. The dropping electrode is replaced by a variable precision resistance, R.

in units of microamperes.   This is also necessary in many theoretical
polarographic studies.

The most reliable and direct method of calibration is to replace the dropping electrode cell by a precision resistance (10,000 or 1000 ohms) connected
in series with the galvanometer as shown schematically in Fig. XVI-19.
An e.m.f. is applied across the resistance and the galvanometer by manual
adjustment of the potentiometric drum of the polarograph, so as to obtain
a convenient deflection of the galvanometer light.   The potential drop
across the terminals of the resistance is then measured with a potentiometer,
and the current through the circuit is calculated from Ohm's Law and compared with the galvanometer deflection.

The following method is also convenient.   A precision resistance box
(0–9999 ohms) is connected to the polarograph in place of the dropping

---

[15] J. J. Lingane, *Ind. Eng. Chem., Anal. Ed.*, **15**, 588 (1943).

electrode cell as shown by R in Fig. XVI-19, and an e.m.f. is applied by manual adjustment of the potentiometric drum B. The potential drop across the drum is previously accurately standardized in the usual manner with the aid of a Weston standard cell. The setting of the resistance box, R, and the setting of the Ayrton shunt, F, are adjusted so that the applied e.m.f. and the deflection of the galvanometer are both sufficiently large for accurate measurement, and the applied e.m.f. is read from the setting of the drum.

Let E be the total potential drop across the standard resistance and the galvanometer, R the value of the standard resistance, and R_g the resistance of the parallel circuit comprised of the galvanometer and the Ayrton shunt. From Ohm's Law the current through the circuit is

$$i = E/(R + R_g) \qquad (10)$$

If R_g is known the current can be computed directly, but R_g varies with the setting of the Ayrton shunt and its value for the particular shunt setting used may not be known. The R_g term can be cancelled and an accurate value of i obtained in the following way. E, R, and the setting of the Ayrton shunt are adjusted to produce a conveniently measurable deflection, and the values of E, R, and the deflection are noted. Then, without changing the setting of the shunt, the value of R is increased about two-fold, which causes the galvanometer deflection to decrease correspondingly. The value of E is then increased *until the galvanometer deflection is restored exactly to its original value*. Since both the current (deflection) and the value of R_g are constant for the two sets of corresponding values of R and E, we have simply

$$E_1 = i(R_1 + R_g)$$

$$E_2 = i(R_2 + R_g)$$

or

$$i = (E_2 - E_1)/(R_2 - R_1) \qquad (11)$$

If f is the setting of the Ayrton shunt, *i. e.*, the fraction of the maximum galvanometer sensitivity, s^0 the maximum sensitivity of the galvanometer (microamp. per millimeter), d the constant deflection in millimeters, and if E is expressed in volts and R in ohms, we have

$$i = s^0 d/f \qquad (12)$$

or from eq. 11:

$$s^0 = \frac{f(E_2 - E_1)}{d(R_2 - R_1)} \times 10^6 \text{ (microamp. per mm.)} \qquad (13)$$

The following data were obtained in a typical calibration:

$$R_1 = 3000 \text{ ohms}, E_1 = 0.455 \text{ v.}$$

$$R_2 = 6000 \text{ ohms}, E_2 = 0.905 \text{ v.}$$

$$d = 71.2 \text{ mm.}, \quad \text{and } f = 0.001$$

from which we find:

$$s^0 = \frac{0.001(0.905 - 0.455)}{71.2(6000 - 3000)} \times 10^6 = 2.11 \times 10^{-3} \text{ microamp. per mm.}$$

Photographic paper undergoes significant dimensional changes during processing, especially drying.[16] Therefore polarographs which employ photographic recording must be calibrated by recording current calibration marks directly on the paper at the time a polarogram is recorded. An error of several per cent can result if one assumes that the calibration obtained on the visual scale corresponds to that on the processed paper. The following technique has been standard practice in the authors' laboratories for many years. Either before or after a polarogram is recorded the camera shutter is opened momentarily with the circuit open to produce a dot which corresponds to the galvanometer zero. A precision resistance, e. g., 10,000 ohms, is then placed in the circuit, the applied e.m.f. adjusted to obtain a satisfactorily large deflection of the galvanometer, and the camera shutter is again opened momentarily to record this deflection as a second dot. At the same time the potential drop across the precision resistance is measured with an auxiliary potentiometer and the current corresponding to the recorded deflection is computed from Ohm's Law. After the paper is processed the distance between the current dots is measured, and the sensitivity of the galvanometer is then computed from this measured deflection and the known current. It is not necessary, of course, that the setting of the Ayrton shunt be the same when the current marks are placed on the paper as when the polarogram is recorded, because the actual sensitivity when the polarogram is recorded can be evaluated from the known ratio of the shunt settings.

No general statement can be made as to how frequently the calibration

16 R. K. Ladisch and C. E. Balmer, *Anal. Chem.*, **21,** 679 (1949).

of the galvanometer or recorder should be checked, because this depends
on the particular instrument and the history of its use and abuse. In
careful work it is our practice to place current calibration marks on every
recorded polarogram.

4. CONDENSER DAMPING OF GALVANOMETER OR RECORDER OSCILLATIONS

The type of galvanometer usually employed in polarographic measurements has a relatively long period (*ca.* 15 sec.) and with such an instrument
the oscillations due to the periodic growth and fall of the mercury drops at
the dropping electrode are much smaller than the true change in current
during the life of a drop. The oscillations usually amount to about 3 to

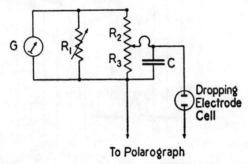

To Polarograph

Fig. XVI-20. Electrolytic condenser, C, connected across galvanometer shunts to decrease galvanometer oscillations.

10 per cent of the average current and are so uniform that ordinarily there
is no difficulty in measuring their average value. In certain cases, however, the oscillations are large enough to be troublesome, and it is desirable
to have a method of decreasing their magnitude, or to eliminate them al-
together. This is particularly desirable in the "compensation" method of
measuring small diffusion currents, discussed in a following section.

Lingane and Kerlinger[17] have shown that an effective although not entirely satisfactory method of increasing the effective period of the galvanometer is to connect an electrolytic condenser of high capacitance across the
galvanometer and its shunts as shown in Fig. XVI-20. With a condenser
of the proper capacitance the galvanometer oscillations are reduced to
only a small fraction of their normal magnitude.

The effect of the condenser is demonstrated by the c.v. curves in Fig.

17 J. J. Lingane and H. Kerlinger, *Ind. Eng. Chem., Anal. Ed.*, **12**, 750 (1940). See also E. Forche, *Polarographische Studien*, Leipzig, 1938.

XVI-21, which were obtained with a Heyrovsky-Shikata type polarograph with an air-free solution of 0.001 M cadmium sulfate in 1 N potassium chloride. Curve *1* was obtained in the ordinary way (drop time 4 sec.), and curve *2* was obtained with a 2000 microfarad electrolytic condenser in the circuit as shown in Fig. XVI-20.

The required capacitance of the condenser depends on the characteristics of the particular galvanometer that is used, and particularly on its resistance and the resistance of the shunts. The increase in current during the life of each mercury drop charges the condenser by the potential drop which it creates across the *net parallel* resistance, R_s, of the galvanometer and its

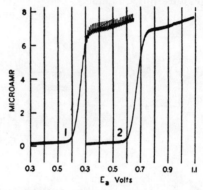

Fig. XVI-21. Damping effect of a condenser on galvanometer oscillations. 0.001 M cadmium chloride in 1 N potassium chloride: (*1*) without condenser; (*2*) with 2000 microfarad electrolytic condenser connected as shown in Fig. XVI-20.

shunts. When a mercury drop falls, the condenser discharges across R_s, and thus tends to maintain the current through the galvanometer until the succeeding drop has formed. It is evident that the "time constant" CR_s of the condenser-resistance combination (where C is the capacitance of the condenser and R_s is the resistance through which it discharges) must be at least as large as the drop time to achieve any significant damping. If, for instance, the drop time has a normal value of 3 sec. the value of CR_s should be at least 3 sec. Since CR_s is in the units of seconds when C is expressed in farads and R_s in ohms, this means that C has to be at least 3×10^{-3} farad (3000 microfarads) if R_s is 1000 ohms, and correspondingly larger or smaller if R_s is smaller or larger than 1000 ohms.

The value of R_s—and hence the required capacitance—depends on the setting of the Ayrton shunt (compare Fig. XVI-20). If we represent the setting of the Ayrton shunt, $i.$ $e.$, the fraction of the full sensitivity, by f, then

$$f = \frac{R_3}{R_2 + R_3} = \frac{R_3}{R_A} \tag{14}$$

and:

$$R_s = \frac{\{[R_g R_1/(R_g + R_1)] + (1 - f)R_A\}fR_A}{\{[R_g R_1/(R_g + R_1)] + R_A\}} \tag{15}$$

where R_g is the resistance of the galvanometer itself, and R_A is the total (constant) resistance of the Ayrton shunt ($= R_2 + R_3$). Since R_g and R_1 will ordinarily be much smaller than R_A, it is evident from the form of this relation that R_S will have a maximal value at some intermediate value of f, and will become smaller both when f is very small and when f approaches its maximum value of unity. It follows that a given condenser will be most effective at intermediate values of f. Lingane and Kerlinger verified this conclusion experimentally.

When the value of R_S is too small to permit effective condenser damping the additional required resistance of a few thousand ohms can be inserted between one side of the condenser and the movable contact of the Ayrton shunt as recommended by Stock and Fill.[18]

Condenser damping is feasible only when R_S (or R_S plus the auxiliary resistance) is relatively large, as otherwise the required capacitance is impractically great. This is objectionable because a large value of R_S introduces a significant iR drop in the circuit for which correction has to be made in evaluating half-wave potentials. Furthermore, at very large degrees of condenser damping the effective galvanometer period becomes so large that considerable recording lag is produced, which elongates the polarographic wave and causes the apparent half-wave potential to become larger than the true value. The resulting error becomes greater the greater the rate of change of the applied voltage.[19]

One must be alert to the fact that an electrolytic condenser is only a more or less good approximation to a pure capacitance; its d.c. resistance is not infinitely large and it may also generate small parasitic voltages. These imperfections are reflected in the recorded polarogram. They can be overcome to a great extent by the use of two equal condensers in *series* with opposed polarity (positive terminal of one condenser connected to positive

[18] J. T. Stock and M. A. Fill, *Trans. Faraday Soc.*, **40**, 502 (1944).
[19] P. Delahay, *Bull soc. chim. France*, [5], **15**, 527 (1948).

terminal of the other) as recommended by Philbrook and Grubb.[20] This arrangement cancels out parasitic voltages but the net capacitance of the series combination is only one-half the capacitance of each condenser. Philbrook and Grubb used this principle to improve the damping circuit of the Sargent-Heyrovsky Model XII polarograph.

Ideally a pure capacitance connected as in Fig. XVI-20 should have little or no effect on the diffusion current and Lingane and Kerlinger found that this was true with their particular circuit in which a galvanometer acted as the measuring element. However, Lingane[21] observed that the condenser damping circuit of the Sargent Model XX visible recording polarograph produced a very significant change in the apparent diffusion current, even though it did not alter the sensitivity of the recorder to a *steady* current.

In our opinion the practical applicability of condenser damping is limited by the objectionable features cited above. Rather than damp the original polarographic current it would appear to be more satisfactory practice first to amplify the undamped current with an electronic amplifier and then apply damping to the amplifier output. The circuit characteristics of the amplifier can be selected so that effective damping is obtained with a much smaller capacitance than when the raw signal is damped, and this enables one to avoid electrolytic condensers. It also avoids the introduction of a large iR drop in the polarographic circuit. This is essentially the principle used for damping in the new Model E Leeds and Northrup Electrochemograph.

5. USE OF A MICROAMMETER TO MEASURE POLAROGRAPHIC CURRENTS

By employing the foregoing principle of condenser damping a rugged microammeter can be used in place of a galvanometer to measure current in polarographic work.[22] When an instrument of fairly large internal resistance is used, the condenser can be connected directly across its terminals. We found that a microammeter (manufactured by Sensitive Research Instrument Corp., New York City) with a full scale of 3 microamp. and an internal resistance of 3500 ohms, with a 2000-microfarad condenser connected across its terminals, was very satisfactory. A variable shunt (0–99,999 ohm resistance box) was also connected in parallel with the microammeter and the condenser to vary its sensitivity and increase its range. With the proper condenser the oscillations of the indicating needle are practically completely eliminated.

[20] C. E. Philbrook and H. M. Grubb, *Anal Chem.*, **19**, 8 (1947).

[21] J. J. Lingane, *Ind. Eng. Chem., Anal Ed.*, **18**, 734 (1946).

[22] A. Neuberger, *Z. anal. Chem.*, **116**, 1 (1939).

The use of a condenser-damped microammeter is particularly convenient for amperometric titrations with the dropping electrode.

6. COMPENSATION OF INTERFERING DIFFUSION CURRENTS

Suppose that a certain reducible substance, B, is to be determined and that the solution also contains a more easily reducible substance, A, which is present in a much larger concentration. To obtain the small wave of the minor constituent B on the polarogram it is necessary to employ a relatively small sensitivity of the recording galvanometer, so that the large

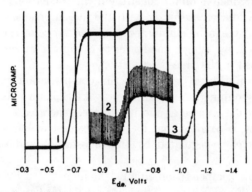

Fig. XVI-22. Compensation method for determining a small concentration of zinc in the presence of a larger concentration of cadmium. Solution consisted of 5×10^{-4} M zinc sulfate and 0.005 M cadmium sulfate in 1 N potassium chloride. Curve *1*, ordinary polarogram uncompensated; curve *2*, cadmium diffusion current compensated without condenser; curve *3*, compensated with a condenser.

wave of A is also obtained. Under these conditions the small wave of B is preceded by the larger wave of A, and it is too small for accurate measurement. This is demonstrated by curve *1* in Fig. XVI-22, obtained with a solution containing 0.005 M cadmium sulfate and only 5×10^{-4} M zinc sulfate in 1 N potassium chloride. The small wave of the zinc, preceded by the large wave of cadmium, is too small for accurate measurement.

In order to determine the minor constituent B (*e. g.*, Zn^{++}) without the necessity of a preliminary chemical separation Hohn[23] and Thannheiser and Willems[24] recommended that the interfering diffusion current of A (*e. g.*,

[23] H. Hohn, *Chemische Analysen mit dem Polarographen*, Berlin, 1937; *Z. Elektrochem.*, **43**, 127 (1936).

[24] G. Thannheiser and J. Willems, *Mitt. Kaiser-Wilhelm-Inst. Eisenforsch. Düsseldorf*, **21**, 65 (1939).

Cd^{++}) be compensated (reduced to zero) by sending an opposing current of equal magnitude through the galvanometer from an outside source. After the diffusion current of A is balanced out the sensitivity of the galvanometer can be increased so the wave of the minor constituent B becomes large enough for convenient measurement. This compensation method has heretofore not been very practical, and its application has been limited by the fact that the galvanometer oscillations retain about their same magnitude (in terms of microamperes) when the interfering diffusion current is balanced out; when the sensitivity is increased to record the wave of the more difficulty reducible minor constituent the oscillations become so very large that they interfere seriously with the measurement. It was found[25] that this difficulty can be eliminated, and the range of the compensation method increased, by using a condenser to damp the galvanometer oscillations as described in the preceding section.

Lingane and Kerlinger[25] employed the compensation circuit shown in Fig. XVI-23 in conjunction with a Heyrovsky-Shikata polarograph. The e.m.f. across the galvanometer and its shunts, generated by the interfering diffusion current, is balanced out by an opposing e.m.f. from the auxiliary 2-v. battery which is regulated by the rheostat R_2 and the variable resistance R_1.

The use of this compensation circuit is demonstrated by the typical example shown in Fig. XVI-22. After curve 1 in this figure was obtained in the usual way, the applied e.m.f. was set to 0.8 v. by manual adjustment of the bridge of the polarograph, so that the interfering diffusion current of the cadmium was obtained. The switch S_2 was then closed, and the compensating e.m.f. adjusted by regulating R_1 and R_2 until the galvanometer deflection was reduced approximately to zero. The sensitivity of the galvanometer was then increased by changing the setting of the Ayrton shunt from $f = 0.08$ to $f = 0.40$, and the wave of zinc was recorded starting at an applied e.m.f. of 0.8 v. Curve 2 was obtained after compensating the cadmium wave *without* the condenser in the circuit, whereas curve 3 was obtained with the condenser (2000 microfarads). Without the condenser (curve 2) the galvanometer oscillations are so large that the measurement of the wave height is difficult, but with the condenser (curve 3) the oscillations are greatly decreased and the wave height is more easily measurable.

This compensation technique is very attractive in principle, but its real utility in actual polarographic practice is questionable. Any tendency of the diffusion current to change with changing applied e.m.f. is greatly

[25] J. J. Lingane and H. Kerlinger, *Ind. Eng. Chem., Anal. Ed.*, **12,** 750 (1940).

magnified when the compensation method is used and the magnification of such imperfections distorts the magnified wave of the minor constituent. This effect severely limits the compensation technique to very well-defined waves. Even in a most favorable case, like that of cadmium and zinc, the magnification of imperfections becomes so pronounced when the ratio of major to minor constituent exceeds about 10 that the technique becomes useless. Mere magnification of a wave does not necessarily increase the accuracy with which it can be measured; a relatively small but

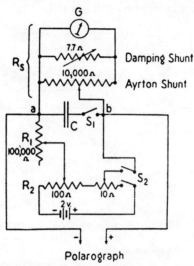

Fig. XVI-23. Compensation circuit, according to Lingane and Kerlinger, for balancing out an interfering diffusion current.

well-developed wave can be measured just as accurately as a magnified but greatly distorted one.

7. RESIDUAL CURRENT COMPENSATION

The residual current of a pure solution of an indifferent supporting electrolyte, that has been entirely freed from oxygen and other reducible impurities, is practically entirely a charging current or "condenser current." The properties of this condenser current are discussed in Chapter VII. The residual current interferes with the waves of very small concentrations of reducible substances, because with the large galvanometer sensitivity that it is necessary to employ when a very small concentration of a substance is to be determined, the slope of the residual current is quite large and tends to mask very small waves. In order to minimize the interference caused by the residual current, Ilkovic and Semerano[26] invented a circuit for automatically balancing out, or compensating, the residual current by sending a current of equal magnitude in an opposite direction through the galvanometer. Their circuit is shown schematically in Fig. XVI-24.

In this figure AB represents the bridge wire of the polarograph, and G is the galvanometer. The necessary condition that must be fulfilled in order that the residual current will be balanced out at all values of the applied

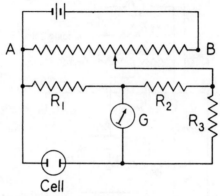

Fig. XVI-24. Circuit for compensating the residual current, according to Ilkovic and Semerano. The approximate optimum values of the various resistances are $R_1 = 1000$, $R_2 = 10$, and $R_3 = 75,000$ ohms. The exact values must be ascertained by trial and error, since they depend on the characteristics of the capillary that is used and the magnitude of the residual current.

e.m.f. is that that part of the potential drop across the terminals of the galvanometer that is due to the residual current is reduced to zero at all values of the applied e.m.f. This is approximated by introducing the resistances R_1, R_2, and R_3 into the circuit. In order to have no potential drop across the terminals of the galvanometer due to the charging current, the potential drop across R_3 must equal that across R_2. The potential drop across R_3 is equal to $i_c R_3$, where i_c is the charging current. The potential drop across R_2 at any value of the applied e.m.f., E_a, is given by $E_a[R_2/(R_1 + R_2)]$. Hence we have

$$i_c R_3 = E_a \frac{R_2}{R_1 + R_2} \tag{16}$$

[26] D. Ilkovic and G. Semerano, *Collection Czechoslov. Chem. Communs.*, **4**, 176 (1932).

as the necessary condition for compensation. The resistance R_2 should be small, and R_3 should be large, so that the potential drop between the cell and the sliding contact will be negligibly small. Furthermore, R_1 must be relatively large in order that the e.m.f. applied to the cell will not be affected by introducing R_1 into the circuit. Ilkovic and Semerano found the optimum values of these resistances to be $R_2 = 10$ ohms, $R_1 = 1000$ ohms, and $R_3 = 75,000$ ohms. The residual current increases almost linearly with the applied e.m.f. between about 0.3 and 1.5 v., and with the circuit shown in Fig. XVI-24 it is automatically balanced out at all values of E_a in this voltage range.

8. DIFFERENTIAL AND DERIVATIVE POLAROGRAPHY

Semerano and Riccoboni[27] devised the scheme shown in Fig. XVI-25 for obtaining differential polarograms.

Two dropping electrodes, as nearly identical in characteristics as possible, are connected in common to the negative side of the polarographic bridge, and each is placed in a separate polarographic cell. The way in which the recording galvanometer is connected into the circuit causes it to register the difference between the potential drops across resistances R_3 and R_4, and hence the difference between the currents that flow through the separate cells. By suitable adjustment of the various resistors, small differences in the characteristics of the two dropping electrodes can be compensated, and the galvanometer made to read zero when the solutions in the two cells are identical. This circuit is an electrochemical analogue of the electrical compensation technique.

The circuit was designed primarily for the determination of small amounts of one substance in the presence of much larger amounts of a more easily reducible substance, in which case a polarogram obtained in the ordinary manner would show such a large diffusion current of the major interfering constituent that the wave of the minor constituent would be more or less imperceptible. For this application the unknown solution is placed in one of the cells and the supporting electrolyte alone in the other. The applied e.m.f. is set to such a value that the large diffusion current of the interfering substance is obtained, and a solution of this substance is then added to the "compensating cell" until the galvanometer is restored to zero. When the galvanometer sensitivity is increased, and the polarogram recorded, only the wave of the minor constituent appears. It is unnecessary to remove dissolved air as the oxygen currents will be compensated.

---

[27] G. Semerano and L. Riccoboni, *Gazz. chim. ital.*, **72**, 297 (1942).

If it were possible to synchronize the drop formations exactly at the two electrodes this would be an elegant, generally useful technique. Actually, however, such synchronization is virtually impossible. Consequently the "compensated zero" undergoes rhythmic positive and negative shifts due to the periodic change in phase of the mercury drops, and this is reflected by a corresponding succession of nodes in the recorded polarogram.

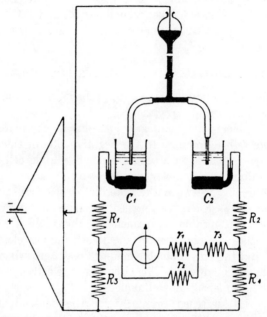

Fig. XVI-25. Semerano-Riccoboni circuit for differential polarography.

This beaded string effect can be minimized by using electrodes of very short drop time, but the Ilkovic equation then fails seriously.

The circuit shown in Fig. XVI-26 was devised by Heyrovsky[28] for obtaining the derivative $\Delta i / \Delta E$ of the current–voltage curve. It is comprised of two dropping electrodes (or better, streaming mercury electrodes) dipping in the same polarographic cell but connected across an end resistance in the polarograph bridge so that their potentials differ by a constant amount, ΔE, as the total applied e.m.f. is increased. According to Heyrovsky, the galvanometer placed in parallel with the two electrodes and their series resistors indicates the difference in current flowing in the two electrode circuits. The resulting recorded curve is a plot of $\Delta i / \Delta E$

---

[28] J. Heyrovsky, *Chem. Listy*, **40**, 222 (1946); *Analyst*, **72**, 229 (1947).

vs. E. Maxima appear at the half-wave potential of each substance in the solution, and the diffusion current plateaus are represented by minima. The heights of the maxima in the derivative curve are proportional to the concentrations of the respective substances. When used with dropping electrodes, the periodic phase shift of the dropping rates produces the same nodes observed with the Semerano-Riccoboni circuit, and to eliminate this nuisance Heyrovsky recommends the use of streaming mercury electrodes (see Fig. XVII-3 in Chap. XVII).

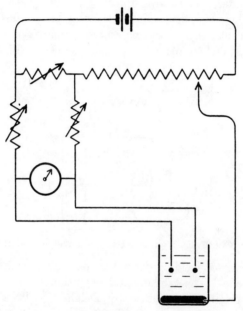

Fig. XVI-26. Heyrovsky circuit for derivative polarography.

Heyrovsky pointed out that substances whose reduction potentials are so close to the final current rise that a distinct wave does not appear on an ordinary polarogram can be detected unequivocally by the derivative technique, *e. g.*, sodium ion in the presence of a large excess of lithium ion. The circuit may also be useful for determining small amounts of a more difficulty reducible substance in the presence of more easily reduced major constituents.

A fundamental drawback to any derivative or differential technique that employs two dropping electrodes, even though their characteristics are closely matched, is that the drop times periodically go into and out of phase, and the derivative curve is distorted by the consequent periodic variation in the magnitude of the current oscillations. Heyrovsky recommended the use of two streaming mercury electrodes of constant area to overcome this difficulty (see Chap. XVII). Airey and Smales[29] devised a synchronization technique in which the two dropping electrodes are mounted together on an electromechanical vibrator which causes reproducible simultaneous disengagement of the drops. The latter authors also developed improvements in the Heyrovsky derivative circuit, and presented a thorough discussion of various fundamental aspects of both derivative and differential polarography.

The application of synchronized dropping electrodes in differential polarography has also been discussed by Stankoviansky.[30]

Leveque and Roth[31] employed the circuit shown in Fig. XVI-27 which

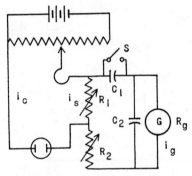

Fig. XVI-27. Derivative circuit of Leveque and Roth.[31]

has the advantage of yielding derivative polarograms with only a single dropping electrode. The fundamental operational principle of this type of circuit was originally discussed by Delahay.[32] Because of the high capacity electrolytic condenser C_1 (2000 microfarad) in *series* with the recording galvanometer G, the latter records the *rate of change* of the potential drop across R_1, and hence the rate of change di/dt of the electrolysis current as the applied e.m.f. is increased at a constant rate. Since the condenser C_1 does not pass *constant* current the galvanometer remains at zero both before and after a polarographic wave but deflects to a maximal value at the half-wave point.

The adjustable resistances R_1 and R_2 (whose sum is kept constant at 1200 ohms) constitute an Ayrton shunt for regulating the galvanometer

[29] L. Airey and A. A. Smales, *Analyst*, **75**, 287 (1950).

[30] S. Stankoviansky, *Chem. Zvesti*, **2**, 133 (1948).

[31] M. P. Leveque and F. Roth, *J. chim. phys.*, **46**, 480 (1949).

[32] P. Delahay, *Anal. Chim. Acta*, **1**, 19 (1947).

sensitivity. The condenser C_2 serves to damp the galvanometer oscillations; its optimum capacitance is not specified by Leveque and Roth but presumably it should be such that the time constant R_gC_2 (R_g being the internal resistance of the galvanometer) is of the order of the drop time. The current i_2 indicated by the galvanometer is given by

$$i_2 = C_1R_1(di_1/dt)(1 - e^{-t/RC_1}) \qquad (17)$$

where $R = R_1 + R_2 + R_g$, t is time, and i_1 is the electrolysis current. With a sufficiently small time constant RC_1 the exponential term in eq. 17 is relatively small and as a good approximation.

$$i_2 \cong C_1R_1(di_1/dt) \qquad (18)$$

When the e.m.f. applied to the dropping electrode cell is increased at a constant rate di_1/dt_1, and hence i_2, goes through a maximum near the half-wave potential. Because the value of i_1 at the half-wave potential is directly proportional to concentration of reducible ion, the maximal value of i_2 should be directly proportional to concentration. It should be emphasized that the maximal value of i_2 is also directly proportional to rate of application of applied e.m.f.; hence the sensitivity can be altered by varying dE/dt as well as by varying R_1 and R_2. Because its reproducible functioning depends on a uniform rate of application of the applied e.m.f., the polarographic bridge should be driven by a synchronous motor.

Using an ammoniacal solution containing cadmium and nickel Leveque and Roth demonstrated the utility of their circuit for determining a small amount of a substance in the presence of a much larger amount of a more easily reducible substance; with a hundred-fold excess of cadmium the small derivative maximum of the nickel was clearly developed immediately following the relatively huge cadmium maximum.

Since it requires only a single dropping electrode the Leveque-Roth circuit appears to be more convenient and practical than the Heyrovsky or Semerano-Riccoboni circuits. By simply placing a s.p.s.t. switch in parallel with C_1 the Leveque-Roth circuit can be used either for derivative polarography (switch open) or for conventional polarography (switch closed to short out C_1).

Lingane and Williams[32a] recently investigated the operational characteristics of the Leveque-Roth circuit in detail. They found that eq. 18 is valid as a limiting relation when the charging time of the condenser-galvanometer circuit and the galvanometer period are both relatively very

---

[32a] J. J. Lingane and R. Williams, *J. Am. Chem. Soc.*, **74**, 790 (1952).

small. The charging lag caused by a relatively large value of the time constant $C_1(R_1 + R_2 + R_g)$, and recording lag caused by a relatively long galvanometer period, both operate to decrease the height of the recorded derivative maximum. Because of these lags the recorded derivative curve is not symmetrical about the half-wave potential, and the potential at which the derivative peak occurs differs significantly from the half-wave potential. Because of the iR drop through the cell, which increases directly with increasing concentration, the height of the derivative maximum is not strictly proportional to concentration but becomes relatively too small as the concentration increases. In short, any factor which influences the slope of the c.v. curve itself will correspondingly affect the derivative maximum. For further details the original paper[32a] should be consulted.

Kanevskii[33] has described a differential polarographic technique which permits compensation of both electrolytic and non-Faradaic currents.

9. OSCILLOSCOPIC POLAROGRAPHY

One of the first applications of the cathode ray oscilloscope to polarographic measurements was made by Müller, Garman, Droz, and Petras.[34] The principle of their technique is indicated in Fig. XVI-28, where $OAHBC$ represents the ordinary polarographic wave. Provision is made for polarizing the dropping electrode with direct current in the ordinary way, and a small and adjustable sinusoidal alternating voltage is also superimposed on the cell. The magnitude of the superimposed alternating voltage is adjusted to correspond to the width of the wave as indicated in Fig. XVI-28. The alternating current component is applied to the vertical deflecting plates of a high-gain (3000 to 5000X) oscilloscope via a low primary impedance, high-gain transformer. The sweep frequency is synchronized with the 60-cycle applied alternating current to produce a Lissajous pattern whose vertical component corresponds only to the alternating current through the cell, the vertical amplitude being proportional to the slope of the polarographic wave. An ordinary dropping electrode is used. When the applied direct current voltage is adjusted exactly to the half-wave potential H, a perfectly symmetrical sinusoidal figure S appears, as shown in Fig. XVI-28, but very small displacements of the direct current voltage above or below the half-wave potential produce relatively large distortions of the figure.

The circuit is particularly useful for precise and rapid determinations of

[33] E. A. Kanevskii, *J. Applied Chem. U. S. S. R.*, **17**, 514 (1944).

[34] R. H. Müller, R. L. Garman, M. E. Droz, and J. Petras, *Ind. Eng. Chem., Anal. Ed.*, **10**, 339 (1938).

the reduction potentials of various substances in mixtures, and with refinements it should also be possible to employ it for quantitative purposes,
as with all other conditions constant the vertical dimension of the Lissajous
figure is a function of the magnitude of the diffusion current and hence of
the concentration.

Matheson and Nichols[35] developed a different technique based on the

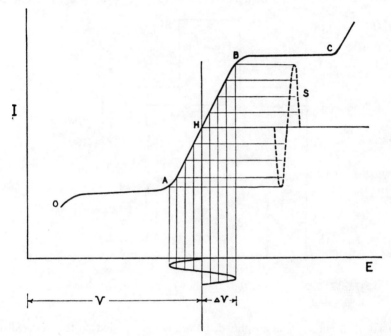

Fig. XVI-28. Principle of Müller-Garman-Droz-Petras oscilloscopic technique.[34]

application of a linear voltage sweep (30 cycles, 0–2.4–0 volts) to the dropping electrode using the circuit of Fig. XVI-29.

The dropping electrode cell is polarized from a voltage source consisting
of a 40-microfarad condenser, C, charged by a 45-v. battery through a
variable 20,000-ohm resistance, and discharged periodically by the motor-
driven, short-circuiting contactor S. By means of this arrangement the
e.m.f. applied to the cell is increased uniformly with time (linear voltage
sweep) from zero up to about 2.4 volts over a period of only a small fraction of a second (contact S open), and is then decreased to zero again for

[35] L. A. Matheson and N. Nichols, *Trans. Am. Electrochem. Soc.*, **73**, 193 (1938).

a new voltage sweep by the automatic closing of the contact S. The horizontal deflection of the cathode ray beam is controlled by the e.m.f. between the dropping electrode and the calomel reference electrode, which acts across the horizontal deflecting plates of the oscillograph, and varies periodically from zero up to 2.4 volts thirty times a second. The current through the cell controls the vertical deflection of the cathode ray beam by the potential drop which it creates across the resistance R. The po-

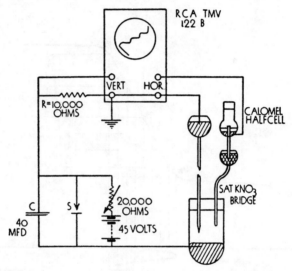

Fig. XVI-29 .Linear sweep cathode ray tube oscillograph circuit for polarographic measurements (according to Matheson and Nichols).

tential drop across R is amplified, before being applied to the vertical deflecting plates of the oscillograph.

When the frequency of the voltage sweep is sufficiently great the c.v. curve (oscillogram) appears on the viewing screen as a continuous curve, although it is actually a very rapidly moving spot of light. Matheson and Nichols obtained the best results with a linear voltage sweep of 30 cycles per second, from zero up to 2.4 v., with the contact S closed during one-half of each cycle.

When the usual drop time of 3 or 4 sec. is employed, a large number of voltage sweeps occur during the life of each mercury drop. Under these conditions, the c.v. curve which appears on the viewing screen changes its shape continuously during the life of each drop, because the image that appears is practically an instantaneous c.v. curve and the current at any instant is a function of the area of the drop. This is shown in Fig. XVI-30 which contains the first three traces on a new drop, obtained by Matheson and Nichols with a 60-cycle voltage sweep, and a drop time of 1 sec. A record of the successive traces was obtained by photographing the viewing screen. The total elapsed time for these three traces was only one twentieth of a second. It will be noted that the return traces (decreasing voltage) do not show the manganese wave. This indicates that the reduction of manganous ion is not reversible and the rate of the reverse reaction $Mn \rightarrow Mn^{++} + 2e$ is so small that the reaction does not proceed

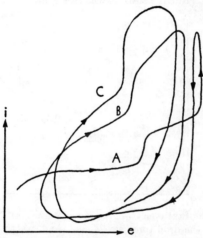

Fig. XVI-30. Oscillogram obtained by Matheson and Nichols with a 60-cycle voltage sweep and a drop time of 1 sec. Solution consisted of $0.002\ N$ manganous chloride in $0.1\ N$ lithium chloride.

to an appreciable extent during the rapidly decreasing voltage sweep. These curves exemplify the fact that the oscilloscopic technique is particularly valuable as a means of obtaining information about the rates of electrode reactions.

Matheson and Nichols found that the variation between successive traces can be eliminated by greatly increasing the dropping rate and synchronizing the number of drops per second with the frequency of voltage sweep. They obtained the c.v. curve shown in Fig. XVI-31 with a drop time of 1/30 of a second, exactly synchronized with the voltage sweep of 30 cycles per second. In this way only one trace is obtained per drop, and the c.v. curve appears as a stationary image on the viewing screen. It will be noted that the c.v. curve is very similar to the c.v. curves that are obtained in the usual way, except for the initial rapid rise in current at the start of the curve. This initial rise in current appears to be chiefly a charging current, and it is much larger in this type of measurement than in the ordinary method because of the rapidity with which the e.m.f. is applied. It will be observed that the general shapes of the waves are very much the same as those obtained by the classical method.

Matheson and Nichols found that the diffusion current of manganous ion, determined by this method, was not strictly proportional to concentration, but was relatively too large at small concentrations. However, the deviation from a linear relation was not great.

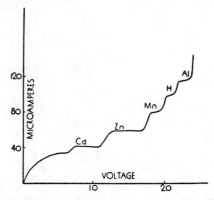

Fig. XVI-31. Stationary oscillogram obtained by Matheson and Nichols when the drop time was $\frac{1}{30}$ sec. and exactly synchronized with the 30-cycle linear voltage sweep. 0.0005 N CdCl₂, 0.001 N ZnCl₂, 0.001 N MnCl₂, 0.0005 N HCl, and 0.0005 N AlCl₃ in 0.1 N LiCl.

It will be noted that the half-wave potentials on the curve in Fig. XVI-31 are somewhat more negative than those observed by the ordinary method. For example, the half-wave potential of hydrogen is at about -2.0 v. (*vs.* the N.C.E.), whereas by the ordinary method it is at -1.4 v. *vs.* the N.C.E. The other half-wave potentials are also several tenths of a volt more negative than the values determined by the ordinary method.

The oscillographic method promises to be of value for studying slow electrode reactions. When the electrode reaction is slow, it is to be expected that the reduction potential should be shifted to a more negative value and that the height of the wave should be decreased, or no wave at all obtained. Matheson and Nichols concluded, from the curve in Fig. XVI-31, that these particular electrode reactions require not more than a few thousandths of a second to attain a steady state.

Boeke and van Suchtelen[36] described an oscillographic technique based on the simultaneous application of alternating and direct current voltages to a polarographic cell as in the method of Müller *et al.*, but employing the phase shift between current and voltage above and below the half-wave potential to produce characteristic oscilloscopic patterns which serve for the recognition of the half-wave potential.

An oscillographic polarograph based on the Boeke and van Suchtelen circuit has also been described by Prytz and Osterud.[37]

The Heyrovsky-Forejt circuit[38] shown in Fig. XVI-32 employs a Philips oscillograph Type GM 3156 for a sweep frequency up to 3000 cycles, and

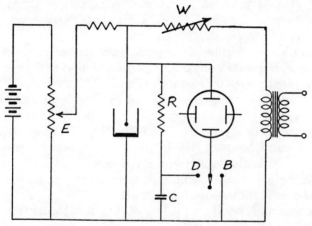

Fig. XVI-32. Oscilloscopic circuit of Heyrovsky and Forejt.

Type GM 3152 for a sweep frequency up to 150,000 cycles. A 100-v., 50-cycle sine wave or square wave alternating voltage is applied across both the cell, M, and a very large variable series resistance, W (1000 ohms to 2 megohms). The resistance, W, is made very large, so that most of the alternating current voltage drop occurs across it rather than the cell, which insures practically constant current impulses regardless of changes in the back e.m.f. of the cell. A direct current voltage is superimposed on the alternating current voltage across the cell by the potentiometer, E, and this direct current "bias" is adjusted so that the potential of the mercury microelectrode does not vary outside the limits of about 0 and

[36] J. Boeke and H. van Suchtelen, *Philips' tech. Rundschau*, **4**, 243 (1939); *Z. Elektrochem.*, **45**, 753 (1939).

[37] M. Prytz and T. Osterud, *Tids. Kjemi, Bergvesen Met.*, **1**, 27 (1941).

[38] J. Heyrovsky and J. Forejt, *Z. physik. Chem.*, **193**, 77 (1943).

−2 v. *vs.* the saturated calomel electrode during the alternating current cycle. The cell is connected at switch point B to the vertical plates of the oscilloscope, and the frequency of the time sweep is synchronized with that of the applied alternating current voltage, to produce a stationary potential–time figure on the screen.

The resistor, R (1000 ohms) and capacitor, C (0.05 microfarad), provide a means of obtaining the derivative of the potential–time curve when the switch is connected to point D. When thus connected, vertical deflection on the oscilloscope screen corresponds to the iR drop across resistance R, and its change with time depends directly on the rate of charging of the capacitor. This is maximal when dE/dt is maximal (midpoint of each branch of the potential–time curve), and minimal at the top of the potential–time curve where dE/dt is zero.

To avoid the complication of the periodically changing area of the dropping electrode, Heyrovsky and Forejt performed most of their experiments with the streaming mercury electrode (Fig. XVII-3 in Chap. XVII).

A typical potential–time trace observed by Heyrovsky and Forejt with supporting electrolyte solutions containing no depolarizing substances is illustrated schematically in Fig. XVI-33a; Fig. XVI-33b is the corresponding differential curve. The left branches of these curves correspond to cathodic polarization and the right branches to anodic polarization (decreasing applied voltage). Since 50-cycle alternating current was used, the time for each complete trace is 0.02 sec.

Any process which results in the flow of current at the mercury electrode (change in capacity or electrolytic reactions) produces a horizontal inflection (potential lag) in the potential–time figure. When the electrode reaction occurs very rapidly and reversibly (reduction of lead, cadmium, or thallous ions in dilute nitric acid, and reduction of biplumbite ion in alkaline media), the cathodic and anodic inflections occur at the same potential and the potential–time figure has the symmetrical shape shown in Fig. XVI-34a. If the reaction does not proceed reversibly, the anodic inflection occurs at a more positive potential than the cathodic one to produce the unsymmetrical type of figure shown by Fig. XVI-34b. Heyrovsky and Forejt observed this unsymmetrical type of oscillogram with zinc in potassium chloride, ammoniacal medium, and strongly alkaline medium, indicating that the reductions of zinc ion, tetrammino zinc ion, and zincate ion are not strictly reversible at the mercury electrode.

When the electrode reaction is very slow no inflections at all are observed. This was the case with the cadmium cyanide complex ion in 1 N potassium cyanide. Although the cadmium cyanide complex produces a normal polarographic wave by the conventional polarographic technique with the dropping electrode, the oscillograms show that its rate of reduction is so slow that no appreciable reduction occurs during the short in-

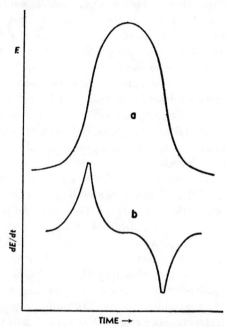

Fig. XVI-33. Types of oscilloscopic patterns observed by Heyrovsky-Forejt technique in absence of reducible substances.

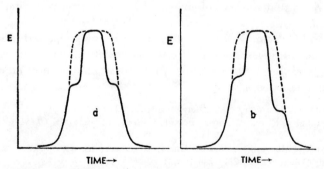

Fig. XVI-34. Heyrovsky-Forejt oscillographic patterns: (a) reversible electrode reactions; (b) irreversible reactions.

terval (0.01 sec.) of each cathodic voltage sweep. It is evident that this oscillographic technique provides a very delicate indication of the relative rates of electrode reactions.

Because the time lag at the inflection potential (width of the shoulder) increases with increasing concentration of the depolarizer, the Heyrovsky-Forejt technique can also serve for quantitative analysis. Heyrovsky and Forejt recommend the use of the derivative curve for this purpose. In its present state of development, the technique is neither as sensitive nor as precise as the classical polarographic method, but there is no evident limitation to further refinement.

Numerous examples of the kind of information obtainable with this circuit have been discussed by Heyrovsky and his collaborators.[39-41]

Bon and Reboul[42, 43] described an oscilloscopic method of studying current-time curves with the dropping electrode at constant potential.

A review of the principles underlying oscillographic polarography was presented recently by Randles.[44] The same author and Airey[45] described a new type of oscillographic circuit for practical polarographic analysis. The unique feature of this circuit is that a single voltage sweep is applied to each successive mercury drop during a 1- to 2-second period at a definite time during the drop life. An electronic time-delay circuit actuated by the sudden decrease in current as each drop falls is used to control the instant at which the voltage sweep begins. The stationary current-voltage figure which appears on the screen of the oscilloscope has the general characteristics of polarograms obtained by the classical method. The chief difference is the appearance of maxima resulting from the rather long time (1 to 2 sec.) of the voltage sweep. A closer correspondence to classical polarograms, and hence easier interpretation, can be achieved by employing a more rapid voltage sweep, e. g., 0.1 sec., at a late enough stage during the drop life so that the rate of change of electrode area with time is relatively small.

Breyer and Gutmann[46] and Randles[47] have recently reported theoretical and experimental investigations of electrode reactions with superimposed alternating and direct current fields which are of fundamental importance in oscillographic polarography.

[39] J. Heyrovsky, *Faraday Soc., Discussions,* **1,** 212 (1947).

[40] J. Heyrovsky, F. Sorm, and J. Forejt, *Collection Czechoslov. Chem. Communs.,* **12,** 11 (1947).

[41] A. Sevick, *Collection Czechoslov. Chem. Communs.,* **13,** 349 (1948).

[42] F. Bon, *Compt. rend.,* **222,** 286 (1946).

[43] G. Reboul and F. Bon, *Compt. rend.,* **224,** 1263 (1947).

[44] H. E. B. Randles, *Analyst,* **72,** 301 (1947).

[45] L. Airey, *Analyst,* **72,** 304 (1947).

[46] B. Breyer and F. Gutmann, *Australian J. Sci.,* **8,** 21 (1945); *Faraday Soc. Discussions,* **1,** 19 (1947).

[47] J. E. B. Randles, *Faraday Soc. Discussions,* **1,** 11 (1947).

Delahay[48] has discussed some fundamental aspects of oscilloscopic polarography and has designed a circuit which permits very high rates of potential change (5 to 1000 v. per second). In his circuit, like that of Heyrovsky and Forejt, the horizontal deflection on the c.r. tube is proportional to the alternating voltage applied to the cell and the current is registered as vertical deflection by means of the amplified iR drop across a resistor in series with the cell. A conventional dropping electrode is used. The alternating voltage applied to the cell has a saw-tooth pattern with a quiescent period between sweeps, and the frequency is adjustable from 5 to 1000 c.p.s. According to Delahay the quiescent period or "dead time" between the voltage sweeps allows for the complete re-oxidation of the reduced substance formed at the electrode surface during the preceding sweep. The anodic current from this re-oxidation decays completely to zero before the next sweep, and thus there is no distortion of the cathodic figure by the anodic current. The ratio of the quiescent period to the sweep period is adjusted from the order of unity at low frequencies (up to about 50 c.p.s.) to a much larger value at high frequencies (up to 1000 c.p.s.). The quiescent period must be relatively longer the higher the frequency in order to maintain sufficient time for complete re-oxidation. Provision is made for photographic recording on 35-mm. film, which is an evident improvement over earlier techniques. An exposure time of 20 sec. is used, so that 5 to 10 traces corresponding to various ages of successive drops are recorded. The waves are somewhat similar to ordinary polarographic waves except that they exhibit large peaks due to the rapid rate of voltage change. Only the largest peak, corresponding to the maximal area of the mercury drop, is used for measurement. The magnitude of this "maximal peak current" is about twenty times larger than the ordinary diffusion current, and it is directly proportional to the concentration of the reducible substance. The maximal peak current is influenced by the drop time, the frequency of the sweep generator, and the amplitude of the voltage sweep.

Delahay found that the maximal peak current I is expressible by the equation

$$I = Km^{2/3}t^{2/3}V^{1/2}C$$

where m and t have their usual significance; K is a constant peculiar to the substance reacting at the electrode and presumably is a function of the n-value of the electrode reaction, the diffusion coefficient, and tempera-

[48] P. Delahay, *J. Phys. & Colloid Chem.*, **53**, 1279 (1949); *J. Phys. Chem.*, **54**, 402 (1950).

ture; C is the concentration of the reducible substance; and V is the time rate of change of the voltage applied to the cell (not directly related to frequency because of the variable quiescent period but relatively greater the greater the frequency). Because the quantity $m^{2/3}t^{2/3}$ is directly proportional to the maximal area of the mercury drop, and the latter is independent of the pressure on the dropping electrode, the maximal peak current is independent of this pressure. The foregoing relation is valid only when V is smaller than about 50 v. per second; with larger rates of voltage change I becomes relatively too small apparently because diffusion control gives way to control by the rate of the electrode reaction itself.

Delahay observed that the addition of gelatin to a zinc solution greatly diminished the maximal peak current, and 0.05 per cent gelatin eliminated the peak entirely and produced an extended wave. Under these conditions the maximal current was no longer directly proportional to the maximal area of the mercury drops. Delahay concluded that gelatin decreases the rate of the electrode reaction.

In oscilloscopic polarography with alternating applied voltage, or when many voltage sweeps are applied during the drop life, the several current–voltage figures that appear on the oscilloscope screen reflect the increasing area of the electrode. Randles (loc. cit.) and Airey (loc. cit.) demonstrated that this can be overcome, and a single current–voltage figure corresponding closely to a conventional polarogram obtained, when only a single linear voltage sweep of short duration is applied to each drop during the last 0.1 to 0.5 sec. of its life. The voltage sweep is applied near the end of the drop life because the rate of change of area with time is smaller the older the drop. With these conditions the situation closely approximates what it would be if a solid spherical electrode of constant area were used. Quantitative interpretation of the current–voltage figure is thereby greatly facilitated, and the advantages of a mercury electrode whose area is constantly renewed are retained. The chief problem, of course, is the provision of an automatic means of timing the brief voltage sweep precisely so that it will always begin at the same age of the drop regardless of small inevitable variations of drop time from drop to drop. This has been solved most ingeniously by Snowden and Page,[49] by using the sharp decreased signal which results when the drop falls to actuate a time delay relay which instructs the sweep generator when to begin its next sweep.

The Snowden and Page circuit is shown schematically in Fig. XVI-35. (The original paper contains complete circuit diagrams and specifications of all components.) The sweep generator applies a linear voltage sweep

---

[49] F. C. Snowden and H. T. Page, Anal. Chem., **22**, 969 (1950).

from +0.5 to −2.5 v. *vs.* S.C.E. during the last 0.1 to 0.5 sec. of the drop life.   Compared to other oscilloscopic techniques the rate of change of applied voltage with time is relatively small (6 to 30 v. per second); this keeps the charging current from being interferingly large, and also minimizes the influence of the specific rate of the electrode reaction so that well-developed c.v. curves can be obtained with irreversible electrode reactions.   The current through the dropping ·electrode cell (which is of the conventional type with a drop time of 3 to 5 sec.) is measured by placing a resistor in series with the cell, amplifying the resulting iR drop by the "vertical amplifier," and applying the amplified signal to the vertical

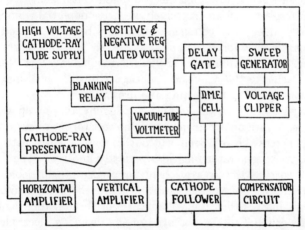

Fig. XVI-35. Snowden and Page oscillographic polarograph.[49]

plates of the cathode ray tube.   The sweep voltage applied across the cell is presented to the horizontal plates of the c.r. tube after amplification by the "horizontal amplifier," so that the single c.v. curve which appears on the screen shows increasing applied voltage from left to right on the abscissa and increasing current on the ordinate like a conventional polarogram.

Beginning at a time near the end of the drop life when the voltage sweep is being applied, the cycle of events is as follows.   When the drop falls the sharp decrease in the amplified iR drop across the resistor in series with the cell actuates the electronic time delay relay labelled "delay gate" which promptly switches the sweep generator off the cell.   Simultaneously the "delay gate" operates the "blanking relay" which switches the cathode of the c.r. tube to a voltage sufficient to displace the spot off the screen during the several second delay period.   This protects the screen from burning by the steady spot, and—by maintaining a dark screen between voltage sweeps—it facilitates photography of the image by eliminating the need for close synchronization of the camera shutter and voltage sweep. After a predetermined time (which can be adjusted up to 5 sec. with a precision of better than ±1 per cent) the "delay gate" deactivates the "blanking relay" and simultaneously switches on the sweep generator. The cycle is then repeated.

The function of the "voltage clipper" is to prevent the applied voltage from exceeding −2.5 v. *vs.* S.C.E. when the time of an occasional drop exceeds the average drop time, and thus to prevent the deterioration of the capillary orifice of the dropping electrode and consequent irregular dropping which results when an excessively negative potential is applied to the dropping electrode. The voltage sweep always begins at a fixed time after the beginning of drop formation, *e. g.*, at 2.80 sec. for an average drop time of 3.00 sec., and continues linearly until the potential of the dropping electrode reaches −2.5 v. The "voltage clipper" then maintains the potential constant at −2.5 v. until the drop falls.

Because part of the total voltage applied by the sweep generator is dissipated as a variable iR drop across the resistor in series with the cell, the voltage across the cell itself will not increase linearly with time even though the sweep generator functions perfectly linearly. The "compensator circuit" corrects this aberration by supplying an additional voltage to the circuit so that the voltage increase across the cell remains perfectly linear. This insures that the voltage axis of the c.r. tube figure will be directly proportional to the potential of the dropping electrode, prevents the apparent shift of the wave position with changing concentration (current) which otherwise occurs, and enables the instrument to measure half-wave potentials with a reproducibility of ±0.01 v. when a 5-inch c.r. tube is used.

The current–voltage figures obtained with this circuit correspond closely to conventional polarograms, and Snowden and Page state that the half-wave potentials agree with those observed by the conventional technique in the cases they studied. It is to be expected, however, that some discrepancy should be observed if the electrode reaction is very slow. The chief difference from conventional polarograms is the appearance of a rounded maximum at the top of the wave. This is simply due to the decay with time of the concentration of the electroactive substance. The situation corresponds to what would be observed if an e.m.f. were suddenly applied to a stationary spherical electrode of constant area, as discussed in Chapter II, and theoretically the current should decay to a constant steady-state value. Under the present conditions sufficient time is not available to attain the steady state, and hence the decay continues at a decreasing rate until the reduction potential of the next substance is reached.

Snowden and Page demonstrated that the magnitude of the maximum current is directly proportional to the concentration of the reducible substance, and concentrations could be determined with an accuracy of about ±2 per cent over the range from about 0.2 to several millimolar. For very small concentrations the finite width of the cathode ray trace is a limiting factor, but this is a trivial difficulty which doubtless can be overcome. These authors also demonstrated that the maxima could be eliminated by electrical integration of the curves before presentation to the c.r. tube, but as they point out this merely makes the curve more familiar in appearance and has no particular advantage.

Snowden and Page also demonstrated that the c.v. curve could be *differentiated* before presentation to the c.r. tube, to yield a derivative curve showing sharp peaks at the half-wave potentials instead of the usual plateaued waves.

In addition to performing all the functions of a conventional polarograph, the Snowden and Page polarograph is uniquely useful for following the rates of rapid reactions which involve polarographically determinable substances and the authors present several examples of this application.

CHAPTER XVII

The Dropping Mercury Electrode and Polarographic Cells

1. THE DROPPING ELECTRODE

The dropping electrode comprises essentially a glass capillary tube, vertically placed, from which mercury issues dropwise. The mercury is usually supplied from a levelling bulb under a pressure of 30 to 60 cm. The optimum characteristics of the dropping electrode are a drop time between about 2 and 5 sec., and rate of flow of mercury between about 1 and 3 mg. sec.$^{-1}$, under an applied pressure of 30 to 60 cm. of mercury.

It was shown in Chapter IV that the rate of mercury flow (mg. sec.$^{-1}$) is given approximately by

$$m = 4.64 \times 10^{9}(r^{4}h \, /l) \tag{1}$$

where h is the applied pressure (cm. of mercury), r is the internal radius (cm.) of the lumen of the capillary, and l is its length (cm.). From relations discussed in Chapter IV the drop time (sec.) is given by

$$t = 1000(2\pi r\sigma/mg) \tag{2}$$

where σ is the interfacial tension (dyne cm.$^{-1}$), and g is the gravitational constant (980.6 cm. sec.$^{-2}$). In most electrolytes σ is very nearly 400 dyne cm.$^{-1}$, and hence as a good approximation

$$t = 2600r/m = (5.5 \times 10^{-7} \, l)/r^{3}h \tag{3}$$

These equations emphasize the fact that the drop time depends directly on the length of the capillary but inversely on the third power of its radius, and consequently the radius is far more critical than the length in determining the capillary characteristics. Doubling the length only increases the drop time, and decreases m, by a factor of 2, but doubling the radius decreases the drop time by a factor of 8 and increases m by a factor of 16!

From eq. 3, a capillary 5 cm. long operating under a pressure of 40 cm. of mercury will have a drop time of 3 sec., and an m-value of 2.4 mg. sec.$^{-1}$, if $r = 0.0028$ cm. (diameter 0.056 mm.). To obtain drop times between 2 and 5 sec., with l between 5 and 10 cm. and h between 30 and 60 cm., the internal diameter must be in the range between 0.042 and 0.089 mm.

It is advantageous to employ a capillary which is relatively long rather than one of relatively small internal diameter, both because of more convenient placement in the cell and because clogging by dirt particles is more likely the smaller the bore of the capillary.

Fabrication. The dropping electrode capillaries may be prepared by hand drawing, starting with either soft glass or Pyrex capillary tubing of about 6 mm. outside diameter and 0.5 mm. bore. The bore of the tubing should be cleaned thoroughly and dried before drawing. A 20-cm. length of the tubing is heated over a length of about 1 cm. near its middle in a small flame and allowed to thicken until the lumen shrinks to a barely discernible line. It is then removed from the flame, allowed to cool for a second or two, and drawn out while held in a vertical position. The drawn portion should have a uniform diameter over a length of at least 10 cm., and its outside diameter should not be smaller than about 1 mm. or else it will be too fragile. The drawn section is cut, or melted asunder, to obtain two capillaries.

Following the original suggestions of Maas[1] and Siebert and Lange[2] it is now common practice to fabricate dropping electrodes with commerical capillary tubing of the proper bore. This is simpler and more satisfactory than the use of home-made capillaries. Suitable capillary tubing, with an outside diameter of about 6 mm. and a bore of approximately 0.05 mm., can be obtained as "marine barometer tubing" from the Corning Glass Works, Corning, N. Y., or from E. H. Sargent and Co., Chicago, Illinois. Thermometer-type tubing of suitable dimensions can also be obtained from the Nurenberg Thermometer Co., Cambridge, Mass.

As Müller[3] and Kolthoff and Kahan[4] have demonstrated, it is important that the end of the capillary be cut off "square" so that it makes an angle of very nearly 90° with the bore, i. e., that the flat end be horizontal to within about ±5°. When the flat end is not horizontal the mercury drops tend to adhere to the glass around the orifice, and correspondingly the drop size and drop time are erratic. A 5° tilt is readily apparent to the unaided eye.

---

[1] J. Maas, *De polarografische Methode met de druppelende kwikelectrode ten dienste van het pharmaceutische Onderzoek*, Amsterdam, 1937; *Collection Czechoslov. Chem. Communs.*, **10,** 42 (1938).

[2] H. Siebert and T. Lange, *Chem. Fabrik*, **11,** 141 (1938).

[3] O. H. Müller, *J. Am. Chem. Soc.*, **66,** 1019 (1944).

[4] I. M. Kolthoff and G. J. Kahan, *J. Am. Chem. Soc.*, **64,** 2553 (1942).

Assembly. The capillary may be connected by rubber pressure tubing to the stand tube or mercury reservoir. When the capillary is less than 5 cm. long we prefer to cement it into the end of a snugly fitting glass tube with Varno-Cement (Varniton Co., 5025 Washington Blvd., Los Angeles, Calif.), so that the assembly is long enough to fit conveniently into the polarographic cell. The cementing is done by inserting about 1 to 1.5 cm. of the capillary tubing into the end of glass tube of such a size that the capillary tube will just slip into it. The assembly is warmed over a small flame (or oven at 125° to 150° C.) and a piece of the Varniton cement is rubbed around the joint to form a melted ring. The seal is completed by pushing the capillary tubing about one centimeter further into the tube, with a rotary motion to spread the molten cement, taking care that the cement does not come in contact with the inner end of the capillary. After cooling the excess cement is scraped off with a knife. Varniton cement is especially suitable because it melts rather sharply below 100° C. to a mobile liquid which wets glass and flows readily into the annular space between the tubes, and it sets to a varnish-like solid which is brittle so that the excess is easily removed by scraping.

The simplest arrangement of the dropping electrode is to connect the capillary to the mercury reservoir (ordinary levelling bulb) by an 80- to 100-cm. length of thick-walled rubber tubing, as shown in Fig. XVII-1. The rubber tubing should be soaked for several hours in hot and fairly concentrated sodium hydroxide solution, to remove traces of sulfur and other surface impurities, and should then be washed thoroughly with pure water and carefully dried before use. Electrical connection to the mercury in the reservoir is effected by a platinum or tungsten wire sealed into the end of a soft glass tube, which is partly filled with mercury and held in place by the stopper of the reservoir. A bare nickel or iron wire may also be used.

In order to facilitate the adjustment and accurate measurement of the head of mercury, Lingane and Laitinen[5] employed the arrangement shown in Fig. XVII-2. The pressure on the dropping mercury is easily read from the height of mercury in the vertical stand tube, and is adjusted by raising or lowering the mercury reservoir.

A dropping electrode assembly with provision for automatically measuring the rate of flow of mercury is described in Chapter XVIII (Fig. XVIII-4).

In order to avoid contact of the mercury with rubber tubing, various authors have recommended the use of all-glass apparatus in which the capillary is sealed directly to the mercury reservoir, and the rate of mercury

---

[5] J. J. Lingane and H. A. Laitinen, *Ind. Eng. Chem., Anal. Ed.,* **11,** 504 (1939).

flow is regulated by increasing or decreasing the air pressure above the mercury in the reservoir.[6-9] Although we have used such all-glass apparatus, later experience has shown that it is needlessly complicated and unnecessary. The simple arrangements shown in Fig. XVII-1 and XVII-2

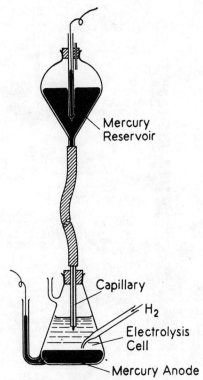

Fig. XVII-1. Simple arrangement of dropping electrode and electrolysis cell devised by Heyrovsky.

are entirely satisfactory, and no contamination from the rubber tubing need be feared when the tubing is properly cleaned and dried before use.

The dropping electrode must be mounted so that it is within $\pm 5°$ of the vertical. Greater degrees of tilt produce erratic dropping.

[6] J. J. Lingane and I. M. Kolthoff, *J. Am. Chem. Soc.*, **61**, 825 (1939).

[7] R. H. Müller, R. L. Garman, M. E. Droz, and J. Petras, *Ind. Eng. Chem., Anal. Ed.*, **10**, 339 (1938).

[8] M. von Stackelberg, P. Klinger, W. Koch, and E. Krath, *Tech. Mitt. Krupp*, **2**, 59 (1939).

[9] E. F. Mueller, *Ind. Eng. Chem., Anal. Ed.*, **12**, 171 (1940).

The dropping electrode is fairly sensitive to vibration, which causes erratic dropping, and the entire assembly should be mounted on a heavy support stand on a desk or bench that is vibration-free. In laboratories where vibration is severe it is advisable to mount the water thermostat

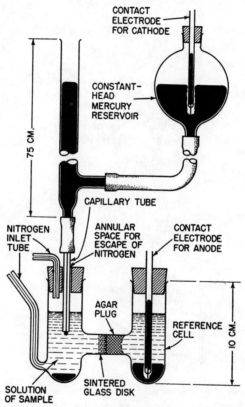

Fig. XVII-2. Cell employing a permanent external anode and arrangement of the dropping electrode according to Lingane and Laitinen.

and dropping electrode assembly on a special damping mount. Suitable vibration damping mounts may be purchased from Eberbach and Son, Co., Ann Arbor, and from Central Scientific Co., Chicago.

Maintenance. Because even traces of dirt or tiny particles will cause erratic behavior of the capillary, or clog it entirely, reasonable care must be exercised to prevent such contamination. *The cardinal rule is that the dropping electrode must never be allowed to stand in a solution when the mer-*

cury is not flowing. After use the dropping electrode should be withdrawn from the cell and the capillary washed thoroughly with a stream of distilled water from a wash bottle while the mercury is still issuing from the tip. The mercury reservoir is then lowered until the mercury flow *just stops* (not further), and the electrode is allowed to stand in the air.

As each mercury drop falls from the capillary the mercury thread momentarily retracts slightly up the lumen before the succeeding drop begins to form. This pumping of solution in and out of the end of the capillary tends to dirty it after long use. This can be prevented by making it a habit at the beginning of each period of use to immerse the capillary tip for a minute or so in 1:1 nitric acid (with the mercury flowing!) and then wash it thoroughly with pure water.

With these simple precautions a single capillary usually can be used for a year or longer.

Special Dropping Electrodes. The use of multiple-tip dropping electrodes (several capillaries joined to a common mercury reservoir) has been suggested by De Vries and Barnhart,[10] and by Gilvery, Hawkings and Thode,[11] as a means of increasing the diffusion current. From the Ilkovic equation the total current should obey the equation:

$$i_d = knD^{1/2}C(m_1^{2/3}t_1^{1/6} + m_2^{2/3}t_2^{1/6} + \cdots m_n^{2/3}t_n^{1/6}) \qquad (4)$$

Whether or not there is an appreciable gain in real accuracy by using multiple-tip electrodes is a moot question, because the residual current is also increased and the real accuracy depends on the difference between the two. However, multiple-tip electrodes may be useful as a means of eliminating current oscillations in certain types of polarographic measurements. For this purpose it would be necessary to use a large number of tips, *e. g.*, 25 or more, to insure that the various drops would always remain out of phase and that the contribution of each to the total current would be small. Bricker and Furman[12] reported unfavorable experience with multiple-tip electrodes.

In order to increase the size (average area) of the mercury drops at a single dropping electrode without increasing the dropping rate inordinately, Riches[13] suggested the use of a capillary with the radius at the orifice greater than the radius of the lumen higher in the tube. The electrode is

[10] T. De Vries and W. S. Barnhart, *Ind. Eng. Chem., Anal. Ed.*, **19**, 934 (1947).

[11] J. Gilvery, R. C. Hawkings, and H. G. Thode, *Canadian J. Research*, **B25**, 132 (1947).

[12] C. E. Bricker and N. H. Furman, *Anal. Chem.*, **20**, 1123 (1948).

[13] J. P. R. Riches, *Nature*, **157**, 520 (1946).

constructed by sealing a very short length of relatively large capillary tubing to the bottom of a conventional dropping electrode capillary. By proper choice of dimensions an electrode is obtained with a normal drop time of 3 to 4 sec. but a very large rate of mercury flow (6 to 7 mg. sec.$^{-1}$). Because of the correspondingly large $m^{2/3}t^{1/6}$ factor (4 to 5 mg.$^{2/3}$ sec.$^{-1/2}$) the diffusion current with this type of electrode is several times larger than with the conventional type. However, the residual current is also proportionately larger.

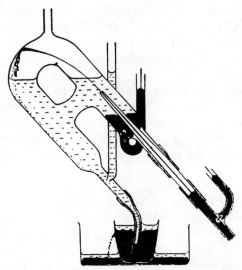

Fig. XVII-3. Heyrovsky-Forejt Cell with streaming mercury electrode.

Tsimmergakl[14] recommended an electrode similar to that of Riches but provided with an electromagnetic tapping device to dislodge the mercury drops. This technique is intended to obtain more uniform drop size than that obtainable by natural dislodgment of fully formed drops.

Enforced dislodgment of mercury drops from a conventional type of dropping electrode capillary has also been recommended by Skobets and Kavetskii.[15] They employ a small glass "hoe" attached to the dropping electrode in such a way that the blade is under the forming drop. When the growing drop contacts the blade it separates from the capillary orifice.

[14] V. A. Tsimmergakl, *Zavodskaya Lab.*, **15**, 1370 (1949). See also L. Airey and A. A. Smales, *Analyst*, **75**, 287 (1950).
[15] E. M. Skobets and N. S. Kavetskii, *Zavodskaya Lab.*, **15**, 1299 (1949).

It is claimed that this device eliminates current oscillations and maxima in the c.v. curves.

Streaming Mercury Electrode. To eliminate the effect of the periodic change in area of the classical type of dropping mercury electrode, Heyrovsky and Forejt[16] invented the streaming mercury electrode shown in Fig. XVII-3. The mercury jet issuing upward from the capillary tube remains coherent while in the solution and thus constitutes a cylindrical electrode whose surface is continuously renewed but which retains a constant area defined by the size of the capillary orifice (*ca.* 0.1 mm.) and the distance between the capillary tip and the surface of the solution (4 to 8 mm.). The jet electrode is supplied with mercury at about 50-cm. pressure from the usual type of levelling bulb reservoir. This ingenious electrode was intended primarily for oscillographic studies, but it has interesting possibilities in practical polarographic analysis, if it can be designed so that its area is more exactly defined and more reproducible than the present form, and so that it does not require such a large amount of mercury.

2. POLAROGRAPHIC CELLS

The classical type of polarographic cell originated by Heyrovsky and much used in the early days of polarography, is shown in Fig. XVII-1. A stationary pool of mercury on the bottom of the cell serves as the second electrode (usually the anode). When the mercury for the quiet electrode is added to a dilute chloride solution, sufficient mercurous chloride is formed by interaction of the mercury with chloride ions, hydrogen ions, and dissolved oxygen to saturate the solution with calomel before the air is removed. The quiet electrode thus acquires the potential of a calomel electrode corresponding to the particular chloride ion activity. The same principle applies when the solution contains iodide, bromide, hydroxide, and various other ions that form insoluble salts or complex ions with mercury. Since the current passing through the polarographic cell is very small, usually less than 10^{-4} ampere, the current density at the relatively large stationary electrode is correspondingly very small. Therefore, the potential of the quiet electrode remains constant during the electrolysis, and only the dropping electrode is polarized by the applied e.m.f.

With the internal mercury pool anode the *apparent* half-wave potential of a given substance will be in terms of the total e.m.f. applied to the cell, and it varies with the potential of the mercury anode. Consequently, to obtain meaningful values of half-wave potentials with such a cell the anode potential must be measured against a standard reference electrode

---

[16] J. Heyrovsky and J. Forejt, *Z. physik. Chem.*, **193**, 77 (1943).

(usually the saturated calomel electrode) at the end of each experiment. The measurement is made in the usual manner by placing a salt bridge from the reference electrode into the solution and measuring the e.m.f. between the anode and the reference electrode with a potentiometer. The measured anode potential is then subtracted from the apparent half-wave potential to obtain the true half-wave potential against the particular reference electrode. (Further details on the measurement of half-wave potentials are given in Chapter XVIII.)

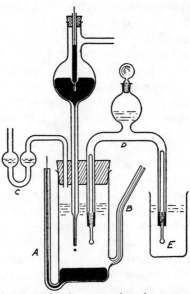

Fig. XVII-4. Arrangement for measuring the potentials of the dropping and quiet mercury electrodes without disturbing the electrolysis.[17]

The cell[17] shown in Fig. XVII-4 (50- to 100-ml. volume) is convenient when it is desired to measure the individual potentials of the dropping electrode and the quiet electrode against an external reference electrode during the course of an electrolysis. Mercury for the quiet electrode is poured into the cell until it rises into the capillary side tube A, and electrical connection is made by means of a platinum wire inserted into this side tube. This eliminates troublesome platinum–Pyrex seals. The capillary side tube B is for the introduction of nitrogen or hydrogen, and C is a gas outlet trap, containing either pure water or a little of the cell solution. The salt bridge[18] D may be filled with concentrated potassium

---

[17] J. J. Lingane and I. M. Kolthoff, *J. Am. Chem. Soc.*, **61**, 825 (1939).

[18] G. W. Irving, Jr., and N. R. Smith, *Ind. Eng. Chem., Anal. Ed.*, **6**, 480 (1934).

chloride or potassium nitrate solution, and the ground-glass plugs in the ends effectively prevent mixing of the bridge and cell solutions. The side arm of a calomel electrode, or other reference electrode, is immersed in the intermediate vessel E, so that the e.m.f. between this reference electrode and either the dropping electrode or the quiet electrode can be measured during the actual electrolysis. This is necessary when it is desired to measure the half-wave potential accurately in those instances when the solution does not contain ions that depolarize the quiet electrode, e. g., in potassium nitrate medium, because in such cases the potential of the quiet electrode changes during the electrolysis.

It is most convenient to insert the dropping electrode into a cell through an oversize hole in the stopper, which also serves as a gas outlet. Nitrogen or hydrogen is passed through the solution before the electrolysis to remove dissolved oxygen, and then over the surface of the solution during the recording of the polarogram.

Aside from the inconvenience of having to measure the anode potential separately, cells with a mercury pool anode are undesirable whenever the solution to be analyzed contains a substance whose oxidation potential is greater (more oxidizing) than that of the mercury in the particular solution. In such cases more or less reduction of the substance, e. g., ferric ion, $+6$ molybdenum or $+6$ tungsten in hydrochloric acid, etc., will occur while air is being removed and before the polarogram is recorded. If the supporting electrolyte is such that the mercuric or mercurous mercury formed by the oxidation remains in solution, e. g., 1 N or more concentrated hydrochloric acid, and thus produces a diffusion current nearly equivalent to that of the substance reduced, then no very large error develops. In many other cases, however, the oxidized mercury precipitates, e. g., as a mercurous halide, and consequently a large negative error results. This error can be minimized by deferring the addition of the anode mercury until after air has been removed from the solution and all is in readiness for recording the polarogram. It is better, however, to avoid this source of error entirely by employing a cell with a permanent external anode. Contact of the mercury and solution can also be minimized by collecting the mercury drops under a layer of chloroform contained in a small tube sealed onto the bottom of the cell.

Use of Silver or Lead Wire Anodes. The use of silver wire as a polarographic anode as a substitute for mercury has been recommended by Schwarz,[19] and Lingane.[20] By wrapping the silver wire as a helix directly on the dropping electrode as shown in Fig. 4 in Chapter XVIII a very

---

[19] K. Schwarz, *Z. anal. Chem.*, **115**, 161 (1939).

[20] J. J. Lingane, *Ind. Eng. Chem., Anal. Ed.*, **16**, 329 (1944); **18**, 429 (1946).

compact and convenient assembly is obtained. The area of the silver immersed in the solution may be as small as 1 cm.^{2} without significant polarization occurring with currents of the usual magnitude.

The solution must contain chloride ion, or some other ion which forms an insoluble silver salt, for the anode reaction $Ag + Cl^- \rightleftharpoons AgCl + e$. In any given chloride-containing medium the potential of the silver–silver chloride electrode is 0.046 v. more negative than the potential of a calomel electrode in the same medium.

The silver anode may be used in supporting electrolytes containing alkali or alkaline earth halides, hydrochloric acid, in acid, neutral, or basic tartrate or citrate solutions containing added chloride ion, sodium hydroxide, in solutions of the tetra-alkyl ammonium halides and hydroxides, etc. The silver anode cannot be used in ammoniacal solutions, in cyanide solutions, or, in general, whenever the solution contains substances which form soluble complex ions with silver, because in such cases the polarogram will show a diffusion current of the dissolved silver. A safe criterion in doubtful cases is to add a drop of 0.1 N silver nitrate solution to about 10 ml. of the solution in question, and if a precipitate forms (it need not be silver chloride) the silver anode may be used.

A lead wire anode is useful in certain solutions (such as ammonia) in which a silver anode cannot be used.

Cells with a Permanent External Anode. It is most convenient in practical analytical work to use a cell in which a reference electrode of constant known potential is employed as the second electrode (usually anode), instead of the pool of mercury on the bottom of the cell itself. With such an arrangement, the anode potential is constant and independent of the composition of the solution being analyzed, and the half-wave potentials on the polarogram are the characteristic potentials of the dropping electrode against the particular external anode that is employed. Hence no correction for the anode potential is required. Furthermore, this technique has the practical advantage of greatly decreasing the amount of mercury used in the measurements.

Cells employing a separate permanent anode have been described by Maassen[21] and Lingane and Laitinen.[22] Maassen used a test-tube-shaped vessel, containing 5 to 10 ml. of the solution to be analyzed which was provided with a diaphragm of porous ceramic material sealed into the wall of the tube near the bottom, as shown in Fig. XVII-5. This vessel is hung in an Erlenmeyer-shaped flask containing the reference electrode

---

[21] G. Maassen, *Angew. Chem.*, **50**, 375 (1937).

[22] J. J. Lingane and H. A. Laitinen, *Ind. Eng. Chem., Anal. Ed.*, **11**, 504 (1939).

solution, and a layer of mercury on the bottom of the flask as the permanent anode. A saturated calomel electrode is usually used as the external anode, in which case the outer vessel contains a saturated solution of potassium chloride that is also saturated with calomel. The porous diaphragm provides good electrolytic contact between the two solutions, but is tight enough to prevent streaming of one solution into the other.

Lingane and Laitinen recommended the H-cell shown in Fig. XVII-2. The solution to be analyzed (15 to 20 ml.) is placed in the left side of the cell, and the external anode in the right side. The solutions are separated by a sintered glass disc fused into the middle of the cross arm. In order

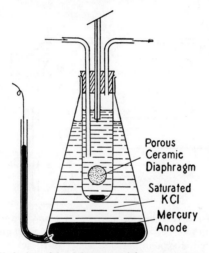

Porous
Ceramic
Diaphragm

Saturated
KCl

Mercury
Anode

Fig. XVII-5. Cell designed by Maassen with a permanent external anode.

to completely eliminate streaming of one solution into the other, and still maintain good electrolytic contact between the two halves of the cell, a plug of agar gel that is saturated with potassium nitrate or potassium chloride is also placed in the cross arm on the side of the reference anode. The internal resistance of this type of cell is of the order of only a few hundred ohms, when the ionic strength of the solutions is 0.1 M or greater. (The H-type cells may be purchased from E. H. Sargent and Co., Chicago, and from Leeds and Northrup Co., Philadelphia.)

The H-type cells are more generally useful than any other type for all kinds of polarographic measurements. They may easily be constructed in a variety of sizes to accommodate volumes as small as 1 ml. or as large as desired.

The agar gel is prepared by adding 100 ml. of cold water to 3 to 3.5 g. of granulated or finely cut agar. The mixture is heated on the steam bath (heating with a flame causes scorching!) and shaken or stirred until a homogeneous solution is obtained. Then 25 g. of solid potassium chloride is added and the solution is stirred until the salt dissolves.

The agar gel, heated to fluidity on the steam bath, is blown into the side arm of the cell as indicated in Fig. XVII-6. The side arm is filled completely with the molten agar, and is held in a vertical position until the gel solidifies. When a saturated calomel reference anode is used the agar gel is saturated with potassium chloride. If it is necessary to avoid chloride ion a mercury–mercurous sulfate reference anode in saturated potas-

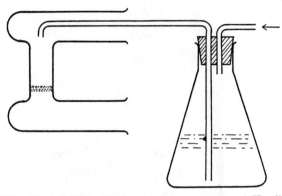

Fig. XVII-6. Transfer of molten agar gel to cross arm of H-cell. Pressure is applied by mouth to rubber tube connected to short inlet tube on Erlenmeyer flask. H-cell is kept in position shown until gel solidifies.

sium sulfate may be used, in which case the agar gel is prepared with about 1 M potassium nitrate (the agar does not solidify satisfactorily if potassium sulfate is used).

A saturated calomel electrode is generally used as the external anode. However, a mercurous sulfate electrode, with saturated potassium sulfate solution saturated with mercurous sulfate (potential about +0.40 v. *vs.* the S.C.E.), may be used when the half-wave potential of the substance under investigation is more positive than the potential of a saturated calomel electrode, or when, for one reason or another, chloride ion must be excluded from the analysis solution. A silver–silver chloride electrode of area equal to or larger than 1 cm.[2], immersed in a solution of potassium chloride, may also be used in place of the mercury electrodes.

If a mercury–mercurous sulfate electrode is used as the external anode, and the solution under investigation contains halide ions, or other ions which form very insoluble salts or very stable complex ions with mercury, a large negative current (opposite direction to a normal reduction current) is observed when the applied e.m.f. is zero and the cell is simply short-circuited. The combination of the dropping electrode and the mercurous sulfate reference electrode constitutes a galvanic cell:

$$\text{d.e./solution/K}_2\text{SO}_4 \text{ (satd.), Hg}_2\text{SO}_4\text{(s)/Hg}$$

When the solution contains chloride ion, or other ions that impart a more negative potential to a mercury electrode than sulfate ion, the potential of the dropping electrode is negative with respect to that of the mercurous sulfate electrode. Hence, when the cell is short-circuited a large negative current results, corresponding to a flow of positive electricity from left to right in the cell (anodic dissolution of mercury from the dropping electrode). The same effect is observed when a calomel anode is employed and the solution contains ions, such as cyanide or hydroxide ions, which impart a more negative potential to a mercury electrode than chloride ions. On the other hand, a spontaneous *positive* current (electroreduction at the dropping electrode) is observed when the equilibrium potential of the dropping electrode in the solution is more *positive* than that of the reference electrode. For example, this is the case when the solution contains ferric ion or other oxidizing agents.

Baumberger and Bardwell[23] recommended the use of a hydrogen electrode as reference electrode in a polarographic cell. The potential of this reference electrode can be varied over a wide range by changing the pH of the buffer solution used.

When the H-cell is not in use the left-hand compartment should be kept filled with saturated potassium chloride solution to prevent the agar plug from drying out. With this precaution the agar plug and reference electrode may be used for a long time before replacement is necessary.

Fears have been expressed that constituents from a preceding analysis solution which have diffused into the agar plug may diffuse back into the succeeding analysis solution and contaminate it. According to our experience the amount of such contamination is negligible. Diffusion is a remarkably slow process and if the analysis solution is not left in the cell any longer than necessary—and provided that the cell is washed out thoroughly with water between successive analysis solutions—the amount of diffusion into and out of the agar plug is negligibly small.

Incidentally, in washing out the H-cell it is permissible to tip it upside down and rinse it out as you would a beaker. The potential of the calomel

---

[23] J. P. Baumberger and K. Bardwell, *Ind. Eng. Chem., Anal. Ed.*, **15**, 639 (1943).

anode is not altered significantly by tipping the cell up and down. If desired, a stopcock can be sealed to the bottom of the cell for draining and washing.

The cell should be rinsed out with a small portion of the analysis solution before being filled with the solution. If desired, the cell can be dried before the analysis solution is put into it by rinsing it out with a small quantity of pure acetone, and then blowing air through for a minute.

The modified form of the H-cell shown in Fig. XVII-7 is a great con-

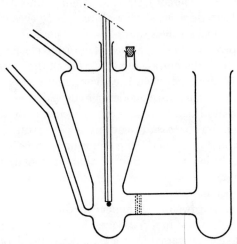

Fig. XVII-7. "Dilution cell" for measurements over wide concentration range; volume of test solution can be varied over ten-fold or larger range. A saturated calomel or other reference electrode is placed in right-hand compartment.

venience in checking the relation between diffusion current and concentration over a wide concentration range without having to prepare a whole series of solutions in volumetric flasks. The conical left-hand compartment for the analysis solution is fabricated from an inverted 125-mL. Erlenmeyer flask. It is possible to start with as little as 10 ml. of the supporting electrolyte solution alone in the bottom of the cone, and after measuring the residual current, to add many increments of an air-free standard solution of the substance in the same supporting electrolyte until the total volume is as large as 100 or 115 ml., *i. e.*, ten times the initial volume. This cell is also very useful in the frequent type of experiment in which a family of polarograms showing the influence of a systematic change in some variable, such as concentration of supporting electrolyte, or pH, or concentration of a complexing agent, etc., is recorded by adding increments of the appropriate solution to a relatively small original volume.

Carritt[24] recommended the modified H-cell shown in Fig. XVII-8 to avoid contamination of the test solution by constituents of the reference electrode (chloride ion or agar). The test solution is placed in the right-hand compartment and the inert gas is passed through the solution by way of the left-hand gas inlet tube and the inverted U connecting tube. When air has been removed the gas stream is passed over the surface of

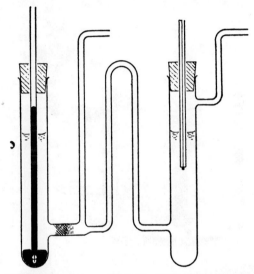

Fig. XVII-8. Carritt modified H-cell for preventing contamination of test solution by constituents of reference electrode.

the solution by means of the right-hand gas inlet, and the connecting U-tube is then filled by applying gentle suction to the left-hand gas tube. The long U-shaped connecting tube effectively prevents diffusion of chloride ion from the calomel electrode in the left-hand compartment into the test solution.

Beecher, Follansbee, Murphy, and Craig[25] recommended the H-cell shown in Fig. XVII-9, for the determination of the oxygen content of 1-ml. samples of biological fluids. The chief problem was transfer of the sample to the cell without contact with air (or any gas phase) which would

[24] D. E. Carritt, Ph.D. Thesis, Harvard University, 1947.
[25] H. K. Beecher, R. Follansbee, A. J. Murphy, and F. N. Craig, *J. Biol. Chem.*, **146,** 197 (1942).

alter its oxygen content. This is effected by first raising mercury reservoir 1 until the cell is completely filled with mercury. The sample fluid (preserved under mineral oil) is then drawn into the cell through the capillary side tube and stopcock by lowering the mercury reservoir.

The thermostated cell shown in Fig. XVII-10, with a capacity of 20 to 50 ml., was designed by Langer.[26] The external calomel electrode is contained in the outer vessel and electrolytic connection is made through

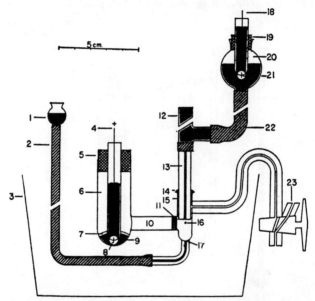

Fig. XVII-9. Beecher-Follansbee-Murphy-Craig cell especially designed for determination of oxygen in biological fluids.

the porous ceramic plug, P. The two-way stopcock serves for the introduction of an inert gas through tube J, and for removal of the solution.

Hume and Harris[27] advocated the use of a flexible salt bridge (rubber tubing) between the saturated calomel anode and polarographic cell proper as shown in Fig. XVII-11. When chloride ion must be excluded from the test solution the auxiliary inset tube D, filled with the same solution as in the cell and closed with an agar plug, is used. When 6-mm. or larger rubber tubing is used and the total length of the bridge does not exceed about 50 cm., the resistance will not be greater than about 600 ohms.

[26] A. Langer, *Ind. Eng. Chem., Anal. Ed.*, **17**, 454 (1945).
[27] D. N. Hume and W. E. Harris, *Ind. Eng. Chem., Anal. Ed.*, **15**, 465 (1943).

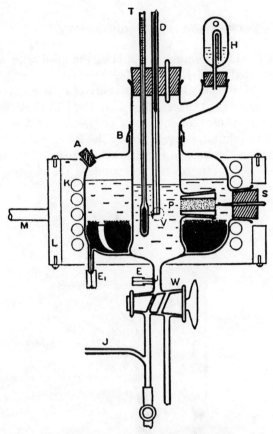

Fig. XVII-10. Thermostated polarographic cell designed by Langer.

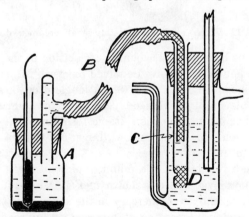

Fig. XVII-11. Hume and Harris method of making electrolytic contact between reference electrode and test solution.

The glass tube C which terminates the bridge is filled with a 3 per cent agar gel in saturated potassium chloride.

Micro Cells. Majer[28] made a special study of cells suitable for micro-polarographic analysis. The cell shown in Fig. XVII-12 is convenient for use with volumes of solution from a few tenths of a milliliter up to about 1 ml. The solution is contained in the lower, narrow tube, and a layer of mercury in the bottom serves as the anode. The upper half of the cell is widened for convenience in mounting the stopper that carries the dropping electrode.

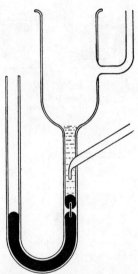

Fig. XVII-12. Micro cell for moderately small volumes of solution.

For the analysis of very small volumes of solution in the presence of air (or when sulfite is used to remove dissolved oxygen), Majer employed the simple devices shown in Fig. XVII-13. A single drop of solution can be electrolyzed by placing it on a large layer of mercury, which serves as the anode. The other arrangement is suitable for electrolyzing from 0.05 to about 0.2 ml. of solution. The narrow, drawn-out type of capillary must be used to fit into the narrow tube.

To electrolyze a few tenths of a milliliter of solution in the absence of oxygen, Majer employed the cell shown in Fig. XVII-14. The solution is placed directly on the anode mercury in the small inset tube A, and air is removed by prolonged passage of nitrogen or hydrogen through the

28 V. Majer, *Mikrochemie*, **18**, 74 (1935).

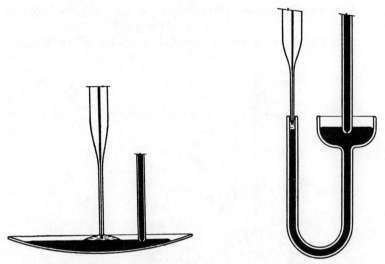

Fig. XVII-13. Simple devices for electrolyzing very small volumes of solution in the presence of air (according to Majer).

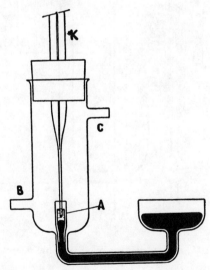

Fig. XVII-14. Cell for electrolysis of a very small volume of solution in the absence of air (Majer).

surrounding mantle. Majer also designed a cell in which volumes of solution as small as 0.005 ml. can be electrolyzed.

The cell in Fig. XVII-15 was recommended by Langer[29] for the analysis

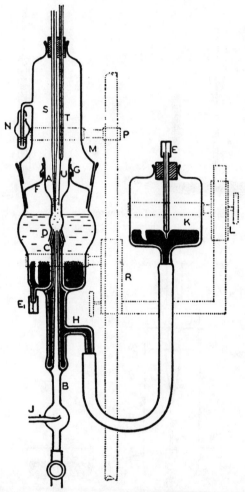

Fig. XVII-15. Langer cell for polarographic microanalysis.

of a few milliliters of solution, and for amperometric titrations on a micro scale. Electrolytic connection between the test solution in the inner cup and the calomel electrode surrounding it is made through the ground joint at C. The inert gas used to remove dissolved air is admitted via tubes J

29 A. Langer, *Ind. Eng. Chem., Anal. Ed.*, **17**, 454 (1945).

and *B*. The end of the capillary inlet tube at *D* can be closed by a layer of mercury by raising the mercury reservoir, *K*, slightly. After analysis the solution may be drained out of the cell *via* tube *B* and the lower stopcock.

Temperature Control. Because the diffusion current generally increases by 1.5 to 2.0 per cent per degree it is important that polarographic cells be so designed that the temperature of the test solution can be controlled. This can be accomplished either by providing the cell with a jacket through which thermostated water is circulated, or, more commonly, by simply immersing the cell in a water thermostat. For most purposes control to within a few tenths of a degree suffices. A large beaker filled with water, whose temperature is regulated by manual addition of hot or cold water as required, serves adequately in many cases. An automatic, electrically heated water thermostat is more convenient, of course, when many measurements are to be made.

Another technique is simply to measure the temperature of the test solution (not merely the room temperature) at the time that the polarogram is recorded and to correct the observed diffusion current back to a standard temperature by means of the known temperature coefficient. The temperature coefficient of the diffusion current of the particular substance being determined is evaluated experimentally by preliminary measurements over the appropriate temperature range, usually from about 15° to 30° C.

We recommend that all measurements be made at 25° C., since this is the generally accepted practice.

CHAPTER XVIII

Common Operations in Polarographic Analysis

In this chapter certain operations common in practical polarographic analysis are discussed, together with some practical hints that may help the beginner to avoid certain pitfalls. On paper polarographic analysis is deceptively simple, but, since the characteristics of polarographic waves are influenced by many factors, its successful practical application demands a good appreciation of the underlying theory. The reader is therefore strongly urged to familiarize himself with at least the main theoretical fundamentals discussed in Part One before attempting to perform practical analyses.

1. RÉSUMÉ OF FACTORS THAT GOVERN THE DIFFUSION CURRENT

A detailed discussion of the various factors that influence the diffusion current, and the technique of measuring it, will be found in Chapter IV.

The fundamental equation for the diffusion current is

$$i_d = knD^{1/2}Cm^{2/3}t^{1/6}\left(1 + \frac{aD^{1/2}t^{1/6}}{m^{1/3}}\right) \tag{1}$$

where k is theoretically equal to 607, and a is 39, at 25° C., n is the number of electron equivalents per molar unit of the electrode reaction, D is the diffusion coefficient (cm.^{2} sec.$^{-1}$) of the reducible or oxidizable substance, C is its concentration in millimoles per liter, m is the rate of mercury flow from the dropping electrode in mg. sec.$^{-1}$, and t is the drop time in seconds.

This relation is valid only when the limiting current is diffusion controlled, and to achieve this condition the concentration of the supporting electrolyte must be maintained at least fifty times larger than the concentration of the reducible or oxidizable substance.

The diffusion coefficient depends on: (a) the kind and concentration of supporting electrolyte, and (b) the temperature. The nature of the supporting electrolyte influences D, and hence the diffusion current, because it determines the actual ionic state of the electroactive substance, e. g., complex formation in the case of metal ions, formation of undissociated acids and bases at different pH values, etc. Changes in the concentration of a particular supporting electrolyte usually have only a minor influence provided that the concentration is at least fifty times greater than that of the reducible or oxidizable substance.

In most cases diffusion currents increase by 1 to 2 per cent per degree increase in temperature. Therefore, temperature control is an important factor.

The quantities m and t are properties of the particular dropping electrode capillary, and are very nearly independent of the nature of the supporting electrolyte. The temperature coefficient of m is $+0.3$ per cent per degree. Small changes in temperature, $i.\,e.$, $\pm10°$, have no appreciable influence on the drop time.

The optimum range of drop times is 2 to 4 sec. With very rapid dropping rates (t less than about 1.5 sec.) the diffusion layer at the electrode surface is disturbed by stirring and it becomes difficult to obtain reproducible results.

The quantity $m^{2/3}t^{1/6}$ changes with the potential of the dropping electrode, due chiefly to the change in drop time. This effect is especially marked at potentials more negative than about -1.0 v. $vs.$ S.C.E. In comparing diffusion currents at two different potentials the values of the ratio $(t_1/t_2)^{1/6}$ must be taken into account.

Even relatively small amounts of certain capillary-active substances may markedly change (usually decrease) the drop time. The same is true of certain maximum suppressors.

With other conditions constant the drop weight mt remains nearly constant as the pressure on the dropping mercury is varied, $i.\,e.$, with different heights of the mercury reservoir. In other words, m is very nearly a linear function of the pressure, and t varies inversely with the pressure. Consequently, the quantity $m^{2/3}t^{1/6}$, and hence the diffusion current, is very nearly directly proportional to the square root of the pressure on the dropping mercury.

2. MEASUREMENT OF HALF-WAVE POTENTIALS

Detailed discussions of the factors which govern half-wave potentials, and the thermodynamic significance of half-wave potentials in various types of electrode reactions, will be found in Chapters XI and XII.

When the classical type of cell with a mercury pool anode is used the apparent half-wave potential will only be in terms of the total e.m.f. applied to the cell, and is therefore dependent on the potential of the mercury pool anode and is not uniquely characteristic of the reaction at the dropping electrode. To obtain significant values of half-wave potentials with such cells the mercury pool anode potential must be measured against a standard reference electrode, and the value obtained must be subtracted from the apparent half-wave potential. It is almost universal practice in polarography to express half-wave potentials with reference to the saturated calomel electrode (S.C.E.).

A better practice is to employ one of the types of cells described in Chapter XVII with a permanent anode of constant potential. The H-type cell with a saturated calomel anode is especially convenient.

The observed half-wave potential is always larger than the true value because of the iR drop through the cell. Therefore polarographic cells should be designed to have a low resistance (not greater than about 1000 ohms). In no case should high-resistance calomel reference electrodes of the type commonly used with glass electrode pH meters be used as anodes in a polarographic cell, since such electrodes commonly have a resistance as large as 10,000 ohms or even greater. When for some special reason it may be necessary to use a high-resistance cell, the resistance should be measured and the appropriate iR correction should be subtracted from the apparent half-wave potential.

The cell resistance can be measured with the usual type of a.c. Wheatstone bridge. It may also be determined by measuring the apparent half-wave potentials at several widely different concentrations of some substance whose true half-wave potential is known to be independent of concentration. The apparent half-wave potentials will be greater (more negative for a cathodic reaction and more positive for an anodic reaction) than the true value by the respective quantities $i_{1/2}R$, where $i_{1/2}$ is the current at the half-wave point. A plot of the apparent half-wave potentials on the abscissa against the half-wave currents on the ordinate will be a straight line whose slope is equal to the reciprocal of the cell resistance.

With some commercial polarographs, especially those that employ a condenser-resistance combination for damping, the recorder lag is so great that the apparent half-wave potentials are erroneously too large to a very significant extent. With instruments whose polarizing bridge can be driven in both the forward and reverse directions the error resulting from recorder lag can be circumvented by recording the polarogram first in the forward direction and then in the reverse direction, i. e., "backing down" the wave. The apparent half-wave potential with reversed or decreasing polarization will be *smaller* than the true value by exactly the same amount as it is too *large* with forward or increasing polarization, and the arithmetic mean of the two values is the true half-wave potential. If the instrument is not designed for both forward and reverse polarization true half-wave potentials can be measured with it only by operating the polarizing bridge manually and thus allowing time for the recorder to indicate true current values.

Meites[1] described a precise technique for measuring half-wave potentials which employs linear interpolation of potential values obtained at 1-mv. intervals in the immediate vicinity of the half-wave point.   Before interpolation the separately determined values of the residual current are subtracted from the observed current at points along the wave and on the diffusion current plateau to obtain the true currents due to the substance in question.   The potential values at 1-mv. intervals near the half-wave point are then interpolated to the half-wave current by assuming that E is a linear function of i, which is certainly valid over the 1-mv. potential differences used.   The apparent half-wave potential thus obtained is then corrected for the ohmic potential drop through the cell by subtracting the value $i_d R/2$ where i_d is the diffusion current (in amperes if the correction is to be expressed in volts) and R is the measured cell resistance.   Meites concluded that this technique yields half-wave potentials precise to ± 0.2 mv. when the current measurements are made with manual apparatus.

3. STANDARDIZATION OF THE DROPPING ELECTRODE

Direct Comparison Method.   Fundamentally every quantitative polarographic analysis is based on an empirical comparison of the diffusion current observed with the "unknown" with that obtained with a known concentration of the substance in question under identically the same conditions.   The most important conditions that must be maintained constant in the comparison are: (1) composition of the supporting electrolyte; (2) characteristics of the dropping electrode, i. e., constant m and t values; (3) temperature; and (4) concentration of maximum suppressor.   The quantitative influence of all these factors on the diffusion current, the various techniques of measuring the diffusion current, and the correction for the residual current or "blank" of the supporting electrolyte alone, have been discussed in Chapter IV.

The most direct comparison technique is to record the polarogram of a "known" at the same time that the "unknown" polarogram is recorded. Maximal accuracy results when the concentration of the comparison standard is about the same as that of the unknown.   The comparison solutions may be prepared from standard stock solutions of the substances being determined.   Care should be observed to synthesize the comparison solution under exactly the same conditions as the known.

[1] L. Meites, *J. Am. Chem. Soc.*, **72**, 2293 (1950).

In the analysis of complex materials, such as traces of metals in certain alloys, it is sometimes advisable to add to the comparison solution approximately the same amounts of the other substances that are present in the unknown. Whether or not this is necessary can be determined by systematically investigating the effect of the substances in question on the polarographic characteristics of the substance to be determined.

Although it is not necessary to know the exact capillary characteristics (m and t) in this comparison method, it is, of course, essential that the characteristics of the dropping electrode remain constant during the comparison. A convenient check on this constancy may be obtained by measuring the drop times in each case, and if these are constant it may be safely concluded that the capillary characteristics are constant.

Another advantage of the direct comparison method is that the temperature need not be controlled at any fixed value *provided that it is exactly the same for the unknown and the comparison standard.* In this connection one may not assume that constant room temperature (air temperature) means that the two solutions will be at the same temperature, or even at the ambient temperature. Solutions in glass vessels must stand for many hours before they actually attain the ambient temperature. In order to assure constancy of temperature the cells should be immersed in a large vessel containing water at room temperature.

Comparison with Standard Samples. When dealing with the analysis of alloys and other complex materials the recommendation of Taylor[2] that a standard sample be used as the comparison standard is highly commendable. The standard sample should have a composition that closely approximates in all respects the composition of the samples being analyzed. The various standard samples of alloys, ores, ceramic materials, etc., issued by the National Bureau of Standards, Washington, D. C., serve excellently as comparison standards in many instances. These samples are also invaluable as "knowns" to test the reliability and accuracy of a new method.

Empirical Calibration Curves. When a large number of samples is to be analyzed it may be convenient to calibrate the particular dropping electrode empirically with various known concentrations of the substance in question. Obviously, one must be sure that the dropping electrode retains constant characteristics, and it is also essential that the temperature be controlled at a fixed value (preferably 25° C.). A calibration curve (usually a straight line) may then be constructed showing diffusion current or wave height as a function of concentration, from which the concentratio ∶

---

[2] J. K. Taylor, *Anal. Chem.*, **19**, 368, 478 (1947).

of an unknown may be read.   Alternatively the diffusion current quotient, i_d/C, determined with the known concentrations may be used to compute the concentration of the unknown from its observed diffusion current.

A typical set of such calibration polarograms obtained with copper in ammoniacal medium is shown in Fig. XVIII-1, in which curve 1 is the residual current of the supporting electrolyte alone.   The diffusion current data from these polarograms are assembled in Table XVIII-1.   The constancy of the diffusion current quotient, i_d/C, in the last column shows that the diffusion current (after correction for the residual current) is a

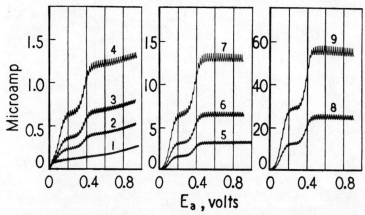

Fig. XVIII-1. Calibration polarograms of various concentrations of copper in 2 N NH₄Cl–2 N NH₄OH, with 0.01 per cent tylose, at 25° C. Concentration of copper was: (1) none, (2) 0.0393, (3) 0.0780, (4) 0.1585, (5) 0.489, (6) 0.990, (7) 1.97, (8) 3.83, (9) 8.43 millimoles per liter.

linear function of concentration over a 200-fold concentration range.   The diffusion current data are plotted in Fig. XVIII-2.

In the great majority of cases the limiting current is diffusion controlled and hence is found to be a linear function of concentration.   There are some instances, however, especially when dealing with catalyzed electrode reactions, where the limiting current is not a linear function of concentration.   It is in these cases, of course, that the empirical calibration curve is most useful.

Method of Standard Addition.   This method, which appears to have been originated by Hohn,[3] is very convenient for an occasional analysis. The polarogram of the unknown solution is first recorded, and then a known volume of a standard solution of the substance in question is added

---

[3] H. Hohn, *Chemische Analysen mit dem Polarographen.*   Berlin, 1937 (pp. 51–52).

to the unknown solution in the cell and a second polarogram is obtained. From the increase in the diffusion current caused by the known addition, the original concentration can be computed.

Let V = the original volume of the unknown solution in the cell, v = the

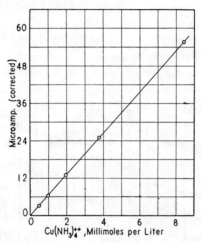

Fig. XVIII-2. Calibration curve for copper in ammoniacal medium; data from Fig. XVIII-1 and Table XVIII-1.

TABLE XVIII-1

CALIBRATION DATA FOR COPPER IN AMMONIACAL MEDIUM

Various concentrations of cupric sulfate in 2 N NH$_4$Cl–2 N NH$_4$OH plus 0.01 per cent tylose at 25° C.   Air removed from solutions with nitrogen. h = 72.0 cm., t_i = 4.0 sec., $m^{2/3}t^{1/6}$ = 1.65 mg.$^{2/3}$sec.$^{-1/2}$.   Diffusion currents (total double wave) measured at a potential of −0.6 v. with respect to the saturated calomel electrode.

CuSO$_4$, millimolar	i_d, microamp.		i_d/C, microamp. mmole^{-1} liter
	Obs.	Corrected	
0	0.180[a]	—	—
0.0393	0.436	0.256	6.52
0.0780	0.700	0.520	6.66
0.1585	1.238	1.058	6.67
0.489	3.24	3.06	6.26
0.990	6.55	6.37	6.44
1.97	13.18	13.00	6.60
3.83	25.2	25.0	6.53
8.43	56.0	55.8	6.63
Av...			6.54 ± 0.10

[a] Residual current of supporting electrolyte alone.

volume of standard solution added, C_1 = the original concentration of the substance, $C_{std.}$ = the concentration of the standard solution, ΔC = the increase in concentration due to the standard solution, i_1 = the original diffusion current, and Δi = the increase in the diffusion current. We then have the following relations:

$$C_1 = \frac{i_1}{k} \tag{2}$$

$$\Delta C = \frac{\Delta i}{k} = \left(\frac{v}{V+v}\right) C_{std.} - \left(1 - \frac{V}{V+v}\right) C_1 \tag{3}$$

$$k = \frac{\Delta i(V+v)}{v(C_{std.} - C_1)} \tag{4}$$

$$C_1 = \frac{i_1 v C_{std.}}{\Delta i(V+v) + i_1 v} \tag{5}$$

For maximum precision the amount of standard solution added should be sufficient just about to double the original wave height. The amount to add can be estimated readily from the value of the original diffusion current, after a little experience has been gained with a given capillary.

Lingane and Kerlinger[4] employed this method in the determination of traces of nickel impurity in cobalt salts. They obtained the polarograms shown in Fig. XVIII-3. Curve *1* was obtained with a solution prepared by dissolving a 3.00-g. sample of reagent quality $CoSO_4 \cdot 7H_2O$ in about 50 ml. of water in a 100-ml. volumetric flask, adding 2 ml. of 12 N hydrochloric acid, 5 ml. of pure pyridine (13 M), 5 ml. of 0.2 per cent gelatin, and diluting to the mark. Exactly 75 ml. of this solution was transferred to a polarographic cell and curve *1* was recorded. Then 4.00 ml. of a 9.24×10^{-3} M nickel chloride solution was added and curve *2* was obtained.

The original diffusion current of the nickel impurity was 1.97 microamp. and the increase due to the standard addition was $3.95 - 1.97 = 1.98$ microamp. Hence from eq. 5 the original concentration of nickel was:

$$C_1 = \frac{1.97 \times 4 \times 9.24 \times 10^{-3}}{(1.98 \times 79) + (1.97 \times .4)} = 4.43 \times 10^{-4} \, M$$

This corresponds to 0.087 per cent Ni, or 0.42 per cent $NiSO_4 \cdot 7H_2O$, in the sample of cobaltous sulfate.

Internal Standard Method. This method, which was suggested by

[4] J. J. Lingane and H. Kerlinger, *Ind. Eng. Chem., Anal. Ed.*, **13**, 77 (1941).

Forche,[5] is based on the fact that the relative diffusion currents obtained with equal concentrations of various substances, *i. e.*, the relative diffusion current constants, are independent of the particular capillary that is used, provided that the nature and concentration of the supporting electrolyte and the temperature are kept constant. Therefore when the relative diffusion current constants of a number of different substances are accurately known, one of the substances can be used as an internal standard to calibrate a given capillary for the determination of all the others. For

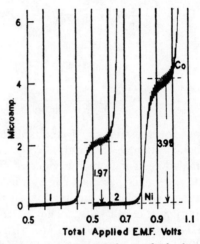

Fig. XVIII-3. Application of the method of standard addition in the determination of traces of nickel in cobalt salts: (1) Original wave of nickel impurity obtained with a solution of cobaltous sulfate in a supporting electrolyte containing pyridine. (2) After addition of standard nickel solution.

example, the relative diffusion current constants of thallous, lead, cadmium, and zinc ions have been accurately determined in 0.1 N potassium chloride as supporting electrolyte at 25° C., and the thallous ion can be used as internal standard in the determination of the other three metals. From the measured diffusion current of a single known concentration of thallous ion obtained with the capillary in question, the diffusion current constants of the three other metals with this particular capillary can be computed. The outstanding advantage of this method is that only a single standard solution is required, instead of a separate standard solution for each substance to be determined.

As a variant of this method a known *weight* of the standard substance,

[5] E. Forche, *Polarographische Studien*, Leipzig, 1938; *Mikrochemie*, **25**, 217 (1938).

in the form of a known volume of a standard solution, may be added to the sample after the latter has been weighed out and before it is brought into solution. It is then not necessary to adjust the sample solution to an exactly known volume before it is polarographed. Representing the wave height of the pilot substance by i_1 and that of the unknown by i_2 it is evident that:

$$i_1/i_2 = I_1 C_1 / I_2 C_2 \tag{6}$$

where I is the diffusion current constant $607 n D^{1/2}$. Since for each substance $C = w/MV$, where w is the weight of the substance, M is its molecular or atomic weight, and V is the volume of the solution, it follows that:

$$i_1/i_2 = I_1 w_1 M_2 / I_2 w_2 M_1 \tag{7}$$

and hence the ratio of the wave heights depends only on the ratio of the weights and is independent of volume. Since I_1, I_2, M_1, M_2, and w_1 are known, w_2 may be calculated from the observed value of i_1/i_2. The ratio I_1/I_2 is independent of the characteristics of the particular dropping electrode, and hence these need not be known. Since the temperature coefficients of I_1 and I_2 will usually be nearly the same, the ratio I_1/I_2 is also nearly independent of temperature over a small range in the vicinity of room temperature, so that exact temperature control is not necessary.

Absolute Method Employing Diffusion Current Constants. Lingane[6] pointed out that quantitative polarographic analysis can be placed on a quasi-absolute basis, and that time-consuming comparison calibrations can be entirely eliminated, by direct application of the Ilkovic equation:

$$i_d = 607 n D^{1/2} C m^{2/3} t^{1/6} \text{ (at } 25°) \tag{8}$$

The quantity $607 n D^{1/2}$ is constant for a given substance in a given supporting electrolyte at a constant temperature $(25°)$, and is independent of the concentration and characteristics of the dropping electrode provided that the drop time is greater than about 1.5 sec. Lingane proposed the name "diffusion current constant" and the symbol I for this constant. Because of inadequate data for diffusion coefficients in the various supporting electrolytes used in polarographic measurements it is not possible to calculate I-values that are sufficiently accurate for practical analysis, but they can be determined experimentally with known concentrations and measured values of m and t by the relation:

$$I = i_d / C m^{2/3} t^{1/6} \tag{9}$$

---

[6] J. J. Lingane, *Ind. Eng. Chem., Anal. Ed.*, **15**, 588 (1943).

Once the I-value of the substance in question has been established it can then be used in eq. 9 to compute the concentration in an unknown case from the observed value of i_d and the measured values of m and t for the dropping electrode used. The measurement of the rate of mercury flow m, and the drop time t, is much simpler and quicker than the recording of comparison polarograms, and in addition no standard solution of the substance being determined is required.

As discussed in Chapter IV the linear relation between i_d and $m^{2/3}t^{1/6}$ predicted by the Ilkovic equation is not strictly obeyed, and I changes slightly with different capillary characteristics. However, with capillaries whose drop time is between about 1.5 and 9 sec. the maximum variation of I amounts to only about 4 per cent, and with capillaries whose drop times are in the normal range from 2 to 4 sec. the variation of I is only about 2 per cent or smaller. Furthermore, it is a simple matter in an actual analysis to employ a dropping electrode whose characteristics $(m^{2/3}t^{1/6})$ are close to those of the dropping electrode originally used to determine the I-value, and when this is done the uncertainty due to the small variation of I with capillary characteristics usually will be smaller than 1 per cent. Hence eq 9 is amply accurate for most practical analyses.

More exact results are obtainable by using the modified relation[7, 8]

$$I = \frac{i_d}{Cm^{2/3}t^{1/6}(1 + 39D^{1/2}t^{1/6}m^{-1/3})} = 607nD^{1/2} \qquad (10)$$

which has been discussed in Chapters II and IV. The diffusion current constant defined by this equation is truly independent of capillary characteristics. The use of this equation requires a knowledge of D, and this can be evaluated with sufficient accuracy from the approximate relation:

$$D \cong \sqrt{i_d/607nCm^{2/3}t^{1/6}}$$

Diffusion current constants for a number of common metal ions in several different supporting electrolytes are shown in Table 10 in Chapter IV. Diffusion current constants for other elements are quoted, whenever available, in the special chapters on the various elements.

To facilitate the practical application of the diffusion current constant method Lingane recommended the dropping electrode assembly shown in Fig. XVIII-4, with which m is measured automatically.[8a] Three tungsten contacts are sealed into the stand tube and connected to a self-starting

[7] J. J. Lingane and B. A. Loveridge, *J. Am. Chem. Soc.*, **72**, 438 (1950).

[8] H. Strehlow and M. von Stackelberg, *Z. Elektrochem.*, **54**, 51 (1950).

[8a] J. J. Lingane, *Ind. Eng. Chem.*, *Anal. Ed.*, **16**, 329 (1944).

electric clock or equivalent electrical timer as shown.   The resistor is placed in the circuit to minimize sparking at the tungsten–mercury contacts, and it should be as large as possible.   The exact value must be determined

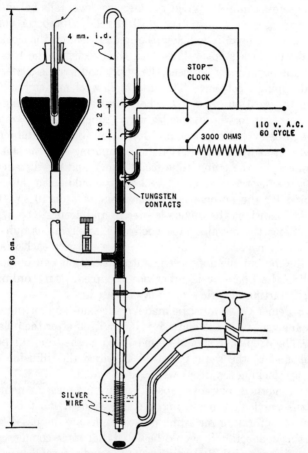

Fig. XVIII-4. Cell for rapid routine analysis with device for automatic measurement of m according to Lingane.[8a]

by trial with the particular clock used, and it must not be so large that the clock lags appreciably (more than about 1 sec.) on starting.   (Because of the danger of inadvertently grounding the "hot" side of the a.c. line this circuit presents a shock hazard and it is safer to use the mercury contacts only to operate low-voltage d.c. relays which in turn control the electric clock.)

To measure m the mercury reservoir is raised so that the mercury level in the stand tube is slightly above the uppermost tungsten contact, and the screw clamp on the rubber connecting tube is then closed tightly. (A glass stopcock, lubricated lightly with silicone grease, may be used in place of the screw clamp.) When the mercury level falls below the upper contact the short circuit across the clock is relieved and the clock starts. When the mercury level falls below the middle contact the clock circuit is opened and the clock stops. The clock thus registers the time required for the volume of mercury between the upper and middle contacts to flow from the dropping electrode. The rate of flow of mercury is then computed from the relation $m = k/t$, where t is the clock reading (seconds) and k is a constant for the particular stand tube. The apparatus is calibrated, $i.$ $e.$, k is evaluated, once and for all by weighing the mercury delivered over a measured time interval and comparing with the clock reading.

The diameter of the stand tube ($ca.$ 4 mm.), and the distance between the two upper tungsten contacts (1 to 2 cm.), should be so chosen that the time required for the automatic measurement of m is 10 to 20 minutes. Under these conditions the device is precise and accurate to 0.2 per cent or better. Since the m-value of a good capillary remains quite constant it is usually only necessary to measure m once or twice each working day, and since the measurement proceeds automatically it can be done during periods when the operator is otherwise occupied. Any ordinary, inexpensive, self-starting electric clock may be used.

The measurement of m must be made in the same supporting electrolyte used in an analysis, or in the analysis solution itself after the polarogram is recorded. The drop time should be measured at the time the polarogram is recorded, and at the same potential at which the diffusion current is measured, by clocking ten drops with a stop watch.

Since this method employs absolute current measurements (microamperes) the particular measuring instrument used must be calibrated. Techniques of calibrating recording polarographs are discussed in Chapter XVI. In this connection it should be noted that some commercial polarographs are equipped with damping circuits (usually a condenser-resistance combination) for damping the current oscillations. With some instruments these samping devices produce a false shift in the average of the oscillations, and in such cases the calibration factor obtained with steady direct current does not apply to actual current measurements with the dropping electrode. The prospective purchaser of a polarograph should request specific information on this point from the manufacturer before deciding on a particular instrument.

In the case of polarographs employing photographic recording the dimensions of the photo paper will depend to some extent on the method used to dry the paper after development, *i. e.*, on the final moisture content of the paper. Hence, the calibration should be done by placing "current marks" on the paper at the time of polarogram is recorded. These marks are recorded by momentarily opening the shutter of the camera first with the galvanometer beam in its zero position and then after the galvanometer has been deflected with a known current as described in Chapter XVI.

4. PRELIMINARY SEPARATION TECHNIQUES

Although it is possible in many cases to eliminate interferences by proper choice of supporting electrolyte (complex formation, pH, etc.) some preliminary separations are usually necessary in the analysis of complex materials, especially in trace analysis. All of the various separation techniques of classical analytical chemistry are, of course, applicable in polarographic analysis; of these, precipitation, extraction, and electrolytic separation methods are most commonly used.

In those instances where the interfering substance produces a wave well in advance of the substance to be determined, the removal of the interfering substances usually does not have to be perfectly complete, but only complete enough so that the concentration of the interfering substance is decreased to the same order of magnitude as that of the substance to be determined, or somewhat smaller. When the interfering substance produces a wave which actually coincides with that of the substance being determined, the separation of the interfering substance must, of course, be complete.

Precipitation Separations. When the interfering substance is removed by precipitation it usually is not necessary to filter off the precipitate. In many instances the precipitation may be made in a volumetric flask, the mixture diluted to the mark, and a portion of the supernatant solution taken for the polarographic analysis. The volume occupied by the precipitate is usually small enough to be neglected. Centrifugation may also be applied. For example, in the determination of small amounts of other metals in ferro-alloys and steels the bulk of the iron may be removed by precipitation as the hydrous oxide with ammonia, barium carbonate suspension, pyridine, etc. Some practical procedures are described in Chapter XXXV.

When precipitation methods are used one must always be alert to possible loss by coprecipitation of the substance to be determined. For example, metals like copper, nickel, zinc, manganese, and especially cobalt, tend to coprecipitate with hydrous ferric oxide when the latter is precipitated by ammonia, and a very serious loss may result when small amounts of these metals are being determined in ferro-alloys. By using a pyridine–pyridinium ion buffer (pH *ca.* 5.5) to precipitate the hydrous ferric oxide the coprecipitation of nickel and copper is completely avoided. In sulfide separations one must reckon with postprecipitation phenomena. For example, very little zinc is coprecipitated with cupric sulfide in 0.5 *N* sulfuric acid medium, but when the precipitate is allowed to stand in contact with the mother solution zinc appears in the precipitate in increasing amounts with time. A detailed discussion of coprecipitation phenomena has been given by Kolthoff and Sandell.[9]

It is sometimes possible to correct empirically for errors due to coprecipitation by standardizing a given procedure with synthetic samples or standard samples whose composition closely approximates in all respects the samples being analyzed. For example, Spalenka[10] recommended this principle to correct empirically for the coprecipitation of copper with hydrous aluminum oxide when the latter is precipitated by ammonia in the course of the analysis of aluminum alloys (see Chapter XXXV). Since such a procedure is entirely empirical its success depends very greatly on rigid control of the precipitation conditions.

Electrolytic Separations (Constant Current). In contrast to precipitation methods, electrolytic separations of metals do not require the introduction of large amounts of reagents, which may complicate subsequent polarographic analysis. Furthermore, possible loss of minor constituents by coprecipitation is avoided.

Electrolytic separations may be performed with either platinum or mercury cathodes. Electrolytic separation with a mercury cathode by the classical "constant current" technique has long been recognized as a very advantageous procedure for separating large amounts of such metals as iron, copper, nickel, and others which are deposited on or in mercury from acid solutions, from such elements as vanadium, uranium, titanium, aluminum, tungsten, and others which are not deposited. A good discussion of practical applications of constant current electrolytic separations with the mercury cathode in connection with the analysis of steel and other ferro-alloys has been given by Lundell, Hoffman, and Bright.[11] Application of this technique in connection with the polarographic determination of vanadium in steel has been described by Lingane and Meites,[12] and Johnson,

[9] I. M. Kolthoff and E. B. Sandell, *Textbook of Quantitative Inorganic Analysis*, Macmillan, New York, 1943.

[10] M. Spalenka, *Z. anal. Chem.*, **128**, 42 (1947).

[11] G. E. F. Lundell, J. I. Hoffman, and H. A. Bright, *Chemical Analysis of Iron and Steel*, Wiley, New York, 1931 (p. 47). See also G. E. F. Lundell and J. I. Hoffman, *Outlines of Methods of Chemical Analysis*, Wiley, New York, 1938 (p. 94); and J. A. Maxwell and R. P. Graham, *Chem. Revs.*, **46**, 471 (1950).

[12] J. J. Lingane and L. Meites, *Ind. Eng. Chem., Anal. Ed.*, **19**, 159 (1947).

Weaver, and Lykken[13] developed a "unitized" mercury cathode assembly which is especially useful for electrolytic separations prior to polarographic analysis.   Optimum conditions for the removal of iron, copper, zinc, nickel, cobalt, chromium, lead, tin, and molybdenum by constant current electrolysis with the mercury cathode have been studied by Parks, Johnson, and Lykken.[14]

Ordinarily electrolytic separations are used to remove large amounts of interfering metals, leaving the elements to be determined in solution. Recently Furman and Bricker[15] utilized the opposite principle of separating micro amounts of the metals to be determined leaving the large amounts of the major metallic constituents in solution.   The small amounts (ca. 0.1 to 2 mg.) of the metals to be determined are electrolytically deposited from 100 ml. of a dilute sulfuric acid solution on a small (2.5 ml., area ca. 10 cm.^{2}) mercury cathode, using a current density of about 0.08 amp. cm.$^{-2}$ for 8 to 15 hours.   The electrolysis cell is in the form of a cylinder (10 cm. high and 4.5 cm. wide) provided with a stopcock in the bottom for the withdrawal of the mercury, and a platinum–10% iridium wire serves as anode.   After electrolysis, the cathode mercury is drained into a silica combustion boat, which is then placed in an electrically heated combustion tube and the mercury is distilled off in a current of nitrogen.   The residue is dissolved in appropriate solvent acids and the solution is examined polarographically and colorimetrically for the various metals.   The method is especially suitable for the determinations of traces of metallic impurities, such as iron, copper, lead, cadmium, and zinc in pure compounds of uranium, barium, beryllium, calcium, magnesium, and sodium.

Instead of distilling off the mercury it should be possible to remove the deposited metals by electrolysis, using the amalgam as anode.   By controlling the potential of the amalgam anode, according to the techniques described below, selective and successive removal of the various metals ought to be possible.   Another possible method for determining the metals deposited in the amalgam is to employ the amalgam as a dropping amalgam electrode, whereby anodic waves of the dissolved metals are obtainable.[16, 17]

Controlled Potential Electrolytic Separations.   In the classical constant

---

[13] H. O. Johnson, J. R. Weaver, and L. Lykken, *Ind. Eng. Chem., Anal. Ed.*, **19**, 481 (1947).

[14] T. D. Parks, H. O. Johnson, and L. Lykken, *Anal. Chem.*, **20**, 148 (1948).

[15] N. H. Furman and C. E. Bricker, *Report No. MDDC-691*, Feb. 17, 1947, United States Atomic Energy Commission, Document Sales Agency, P. O. Box 62, Oak Ridge, Tenn.

[16] J. J. Lingane, *J. Am. Chem. Soc.*, **61**, 976 (1939).

[17] J. Heyrovsky and M. Kalousek, *Collection Czechoslov. Chem. Communs.*, **11**, 464 (1939).

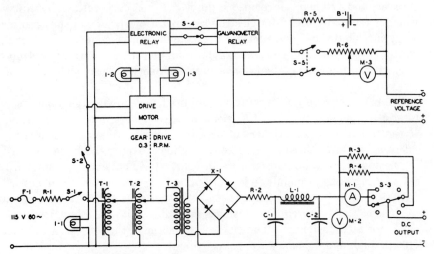

Fig. XVIII-5. Circuit of the Lingane-Jones potentiostat.

current technique separations are achieved only by virtue of the fact that hydrogen ion is reduced less readily than the metals plated out but more readily than certain other metals, and the latter thus remain in solution because the cathode potential is automatically limited by hydrogen discharge. Lingane[18] demonstrated that the inherent advantages of electrolytic separations can be more fully utilized, and much more selective separations achieved, by employing the technique developed by Sand[19] for electrogravimetric analysis, whereby the cathode potential against an external reference electrode is carefully controlled by appropriate adjustment of the total e.m.f. applied to the cell.

To eliminate the tedium of manually controlling the cathode potential instruments have been designed by Hickling,[20] Caldwell, Parker, and Diehl,[21] Lingane,[22] Penther and Pompeo,[23] Heyd, Ohmart, and Hites,[24] Lamphere and Rogers,[25] and Allen[26] which perform this function automatically.

The circuit of the Lingane-Jones potentiostat is shown in Fig. XVIII-5 and the assembled instrument is shown in Fig. XVIII-6. The first Variac transformer T-1 provides a convenient means of manually controlling the input to the automatically operated Variac T-2 to provide the optimum d.c. output range for a particular electrolysis experiment. The motor-operated Variac is followed by a stepdown transformer T-3, a full-wave selenium rectifier X-1, and a conventional inductance-capacitance filter circuit to smooth the rectified d.c. A voltmeter M-2 across the output indicates the total voltage applied to the cell and the electrolysis current is read on a multirange ammeter M-1. High precision is not required of either of these meters, and ordinary panel-type instruments with an accuracy of the order of ± 2 per cent are adequate.

The control circuit comprises an ordinary radio-type potentiometer R-6

[18] J. J. Lingane, *Ind. Eng. Chem., Anal. Ed.*, **16**, 147 (1944); **18**, 429 (1946); *Faraday Society Discussions*, **1**, 203 (1947); *Anal. Chim. Acta*, **2**, 584 (1948).

[19] H. J. S. Sand, *Trans. Chem. Soc.*, **91**, 373 (1907).

[20] A. Hickling, *Trans. Faraday Soc.*, **38**, 27 (1942).

[21] C. W. Caldwell, R. C. Parker, and H. Diehl, *Ind. Eng. Chem., Anal. Ed.*, **16**, 532 (1944). See also H. Diehl, "Electrochemical Analysis with Graded Cathode Potential Control," G. F. Smith Chemical Co., Columbus, Ohio, 1948.

[22] J. J. Lingane, *Ind. Eng. Chem., Anal. Ed.*, **17**, 332 (1945); *Anal. Chem.*, **21**, 497 (1949). J. J. Lingane and S. L. Jones, *Anal. Chem.*, **22**, 1169 (1950).

[23] C. J. Penther and D. J. Pompeo, *Anal. Chem.*, **21**, 178 (1949).

[24] J. W. Heyd, P. E. Ohmart, and C. E. Hites, Laboratory Report of Monsanto Chemical Co., 48-12-65, Dec. 20, 1948.

[25] R. W. Lamphere and L. B. Rogers, *Anal. Chem.*, **22**, 463 (1950).

[26] M. J. Allen, *Anal. Chem.*, **22**, 804 (1950).

powered by a 1.5-v. dry cell to provide the reference voltage, which is read directly on voltmeter *M-3*, a Weston Model 30 galvanometer relay, and a dual electronic relay to control the reversible shaded-pole motor which drives the Variac autotransformer.

When the potential of the working electrode against the reference electrode (usually a saturated calomel electrode) differs from the opposing reference voltage the galvanometer relay makes contact right or left and activates the double electronic relay, which in turn causes the motor to operate Variac *T-2* in the appropriate direction either to increase or decrease the total voltage applied to the cell until the potential of the working electrode returns to the value of the reference voltage. Because the reference voltage is read directly on a meter the control circuit requires no preliminary adjustment or calibration before use, and the reference voltage can be changed instantly during the course of an electrolysis by merely readjusting potentiometer *R-6*.

The control sensitivity depends primarily on the sensitivity of the Weston galvanometer relay. This instrument has a rated sensitivity of ±15 microamp. per millimeter, and an internal resistance of 1100 ohms, corresponding to a voltage sensitivity of approximately ±16 mv. per millimeter. By adjusting the contacts to minimal clearance the net sensitivity can be adjusted to somewhat better than ±10 mv. when the resistance in the control circuit does not exceed about 1000 ohms. Most of the resistance in the control circuit occurs in the salt bridge between the reference electrode (usually a saturated calomel electrode) and the electrolysis solution, and it is a simple matter to design the salt bridge so that the total resistance in the control circuit amounts to only a few hundred ohms. A control sensitivity smaller than about ±10 mv. is usually of little practical value, and control to ±50 mv. is adequate for most purposes.

The d.c. power output is approximately 30 watts, corresponding to a maximum current output of about 7.5 amp. at 4 v., or to a maximum output voltage of about 30 with smaller currents.

By connecting the control circuit directly across the cell electrodes the instrument can be used to perform an electrolysis at a constant total applied e.m.f. It can also be used for electrolysis at constant current by connecting the control circuit across a standard resistance in series with the electrolysis cell, which thus maintains a constant iR drop across the resistance and hence a constant current.

Figure XVIII-7 shows a simple cell that is convenient for controlled potential electrolytic separations with the platinum cathode. An ordinary 250-cc. beaker serves as electrolysis vessel. The usual type of cylindrical electrodes of heavy platinum gauze are used, with the inner electrode functioning as anode.   The cathode is 5 cm. in diameter and 5 cm. high with a total area of *ca*. 160 cm.^{2}; the anode is 2.4 cm. in diameter and 5 cm. high with a total area of 75 cm.^{2}.   A helical platinum wire anode is also satisfactory.   Very efficient stirring is essential and it is provided con-

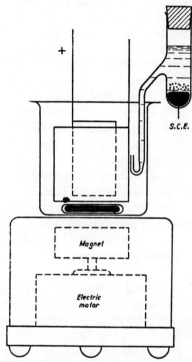

Fig. XVIII-7. Cell for controlled potential electrolytic separations with the platinum cathode.[27]

veniently by a magnetic stirrer, comprising a soft iron bar sealed in a glass tube which is caused to rotate at high speed by a rotating Alnico magnet placed beneath the beaker.   (This stirring apparatus is obtainable from A. H. Thomas Co., Philadelphia, catalogue number 9235-R.)

A saturated calomel reference electrode is used (S.C.E. in Fig. XVIII-7) and its tip must be placed as close as possible to the outside surface of the cathode.   The observed cathode potential is related to the true potential by:

$$E_{obs.} = E_{true} + iR \qquad (10)$$

where iR is the ohmic potential drop in the solution between the cathode surface and the tip of the salt bridge from the reference electrode. By placing the tip of the salt bridge very close to the cathode, and on the outside of it, iR is kept negligibly small.

In controlled potential electrolysis the current decreases (usually exponentially with time) as the electrolysis proceeds, and finally attains a constant minimal value which indicates that the electrolysis is complete. When the particular electrode reaction proceeds with 100 per cent current efficiency the current finally decreases to zero, and in such cases the amount of metal deposited can be computed by Faraday's Law from the quantity of electricity passed as measured by a coulometer in series with the cell.[27]

It has been shown[28] that controlled potential electrolytic separations are most advantageously performed with a mercury cathode, rather than platinum, because the optimum potential and other conditions are easily ascertained from the known polarographic characteristics of the metals concerned. With the mercury cathode it is possible to obtain sharp separations of metals whose reduction potentials differ by only 0.2 v., such as copper from bismuth and bismuth from lead in an acidic tartrate solution (pH = 4.5), or lead from cadmium in a neutral chloride medium. The optimum potential for a given separation is a value corresponding to the diffusion current plateau of the metal plated out but well below the potential at which the wave of the more difficulty reducible metal ion begins.

Figure XVIII-8 shows the cell recommended by Lingane for controlled potential separations with the mercury cathode. It has a capacity of about 75 ml. and the area of the mercury pool cathode is about 15 cm.^{2}. The mercury–solution interface is kept in rapid motion by the motor-driven glass propellor, which is essential to obtain rapid deposition. The tip of the salt bridge from the saturated calomel reference electrode is placed so that it just touches the mercury surface when the latter is stirred. The anode is a wire of an appropriate metal wrapped as a helix on the stirrer shaft. For many purposes a platinum wire anode may be used, but when the solution contains metals (such as bismuth) which are easily oxidized on the platinum anode a silver wire anode is employed. When a silver wire anode is used the solution must contain chloride ion for the anode reaction $Ag + Cl^- \rightleftharpoons AgCl + e$.

The analysis of a mixture of copper, bismuth, lead, and cadmium described by Lingane serves as a good example of the general procedure.

[27] J. J. Lingane, *J. Am. Chem. Soc.*, **67**, 1916 (1945); *Anal. Chim. Acta*, **2**, 584 (1948).
[28] J. J. Lingane, *Ind. Eng. Chem., Anal. Ed.*, **16**, 147 (1944).

The optimum supporting electrolyte in this case is one containing 0.5 M total tartrate with the pH adjusted to 4.5.   The half-wave potentials are: Cu − 0.09 v., Bi − 0.23 v., Pb − 0.48 v., and Cd − 0.64 v. *vs.* S.C.E.

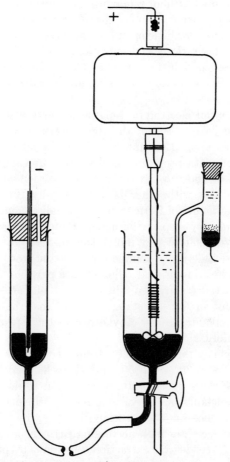

Fig. XVIII-8. Cell for controlled potential separations with the mercury cathode.[28]

Copper is determinable from a polarogram of the original solution regardless of the relative amounts of the other metals present.   The solution is then placed in the mercury cathode cell, and copper is removed by controlled potential electrolysis at −0.15 ± 0.02 v. *vs.* S.C.E., and a small sample is taken and polarographed to determine bismuth.   The potential is then increased to −0.38 ± 0.02 v. to remove bismuth, and a small sample of the residual solution is polarographed to determine lead. Finally, the potential is increased to -0.55 ± 0.02 v. to remove lead, and the residual solution is polarographed for cadmium. The complete analysis may thus be performed without removing the solution from the electrolysis cell. When a potentiostat is used the electrolytic separations proceed automatically so that very little operator time is required. In this example the most unfavorable ratio of concentrations was assumed, *i. e.*, that the concentrations decreased in the order of Cu > Bi > Pb > Cd. With more favorable relative concentrations fewer separations would, of course, be required.

Controlled potential electrolytic separations may also be made with a platinum cathode using a cell of the type shown in Fig. XVIII-7. This technique has been applied advantageously in the analysis of copper-base alloys.[29] The complete procedure is described in Chapter XXXV.

Separations of Metals by Extraction. Extraction of aqueous hydrochloric acid solutions with ether is an especially useful technique for separating large amounts of ferric iron from small amounts of many other metals as a preliminary step in the polarographic analysis of ferro-alloys. With 6 to 8 M hydrochloric acid, molybdenum, thallium, gold and gallium are also extracted practically completely with the iron. Tin, antimony, arsenic, germanium, iridium, and tellurium are partially extracted.[30] Vanadium is also partially extracted when present in the $+5$ state, but not at all when present in the $+4$ state.[30a] Swift[31] has shown that isopropyl ether has several advantages over ethyl ether for the extraction of iron from 6 to 8 M hydrochloric acid.

Dithizone (diphenylthiocarbazone) forms complexes with metals of atomic numbers 25 to 30, 46 to 50, and 79 to 83, which are extractable from aqueous solutions by chloroform or carbon tetrachloride. Because the instability constants of the various metal-dithizone complexes differ considerably, and since the stability (and hence extractability) of a given metal dithizonate decreases with decreasing pH over a certain range, it is possible to obtain considerable extraction selectivity by proper adjustment of the pH of the aqueous phase. Selective extractions are also obtained by adding appropriate complex-forming reagents. Excellent discussions of

---

[29] J. J. Lingane, *Ind. Eng. Chem., Anal. Ed.*, **18**, 429 (1946).

[30] See G. E. F. Lundell, J. I. Hoffman, and H. A. Bright, *Chemical Analysis of Iron and Steel*, Wiley, New York, 1931 (p. 41).

[30a] J. J. Lingane and L. Meites, *J. Am. Chem. Soc.*, **68**, 2443 (1946).

[31] E. H. Swift, *A System of Chemical Analysis*, Prentice-Hall, New York, 1939 (p. 292).

dithizone and other extraction methods have been given by Sandell,[32] and Flagg.[33]

One of the first applications of dithizone extractions in combination with polarographic analysis was made by Stout, Levy, and Williams[34] in connection with the determination of traces of zinc in plants, and their procedure is described in Chapter XXIX under zinc. Kolthoff and Matsuyama[35] have utilized dithizone extraction in the polarographic determination of small amounts of zinc and lead in aluminum alloys. Their procedure is described in detail in Chapter XXXV.

5. REMOVAL OF DISSOLVED AIR (OXYGEN)

Since oxygen is so easily reduced at the dropping electrode it is usually necessary to remove dissolved air from the analysis solution to prevent the oxygen wave from interfering with that of the substance being determined. Most commonly air is removed by bubbling hydrogen, nitrogen, or—in acid media—carbon dioxide through the solution. The flow of the inert gas is then directed over the surface of the solution during the actual recording of the polarogram. The time required depends on the rate of gas flow, the solution volume, and the geometry of the particular cell; it is usually of the order of 10 to 15 minutes.

In most cases removal of the last traces of oxygen is not necessary, and it is usually possible to employ commercial nitrogen or hydrogen from high-pressure cylinders without special purification. A large Kipp generator charged with pure (arsenic-free) granulated zinc and approximately $6 N$ hydrochloric acid is a convenient source of the relatively small volumes of hydrogen required in polarographic work, and the gas so prepared is of relatively high purity and need only be washed with water to remove traces of hydrochloric acid.

Heyrovsky[36] recommended the preparation of pure hydrogen by "internal electrolysis" in a cell consisting of a large layer of zinc amalgam short-circuited to a large platinum electrode.

When necessary the last traces of oxygen can be removed from nitrogen or hydrogen by passing the gas through finely divided copper turnings

---

[32] E. B. Sandell, *Colorimetric Determination of Traces of Metals*, Interscience, New York, 1950 (p. 87 *et seq.*).

[33] J. F. Flagg, *Organic Reagents Used in Gravimetric and Volumetric Analysis*, Interscience, New York, 1948.

[34] P. R. Stout, J. Levy, and L. C. Williams, *Collection Czechoslov. Chem. Communs.*, **10**, 129 (1938).

[35] I. M. Kolthoff and G. Matsuyama, *Ind. Eng. Chem., Anal. Ed.*, **17**, 615 (1945).

[36] J. Heyrovsky, *Polarographie*, Springer, Vienna, 1941 (reprinted by Edwards, Ann Arbor, Michigan, 1944), p. 22.

packed in a combustion tube and heated to 400–450°C. in a tubular electric furnace. Hydrogen, nitrogen, or carbon dioxide can be freed from small amounts of oxygen very conveniently by passage through a wash bottle containing a solution of chromous sulfate in about 1 N sulfuric acid. The chromous solution is prepared by filling the wash bottle about one-fourth full of pure granulated zinc that has been amalgamated with about 1 per cent of mercury and then adding an approximately 0.1 M solution of chromic sulfate in about 1 N sulfuric or hydrochloric acid.

Meites and Meites[37] recommend the use of a vanadous sulfate solution for removing traces of oxygen from nitrogen, and they describe a very convenient method of preparing and regenerating the solution.

An excellent discussion of the techniques of preparing very pure hydrogen has been given by Clark.[38]

The quality of commercial nitrogen and hydrogen is so high these days that the assembly of elaborate purification trains usually is a waste of time, except in very exceptional cases.

When the analysis solution contains volatile constituents, $e.\ g.$, ammonia, the gas used to sweep out dissolved air should be equilibrated with the volatile substance by passing it through a wash bottle containing some of the same solution (or an exactly similar solution) before passing it into the polarographic cell. This preliminary equilibration is, of course, especially important when the substance being determined is volatile.

When a cell with an internal mercury pool anode is used, and the solution contains a large concentration of chloride ion, appreciable reduction of the dissolved oxygen can occur before the latter is removed:

$$Hg + 2Cl^- + O_2 + 2H_2O \rightleftharpoons HgCl_2 + H_2O_2 + 2OH^-$$

This same type of reaction occurs whenever the solution contains substances which form stable complexes or very slightly soluble compounds with mercury, and it is especially pronounced in solutions containing cyanide ion or iodide ion.[39, 40] The soluble mercuric complexes which are thus formed in the solution contribute to the diffusion current. In cyanide and chloride media the hydrogen peroxide formed also produces its characteristic wave. Furthermore, if the solution is originally neutral and unbuffered the hydroxide ion formed in the above reaction may raise the pH

[37] L. Meites and T. Meites, *Anal. Chem.*, **20**, 984 (1948).

[38] W. M. Clark, *The Determination of Hydrogen Ions*, Williams and Wilkins, Baltimore, 1928.

[39] I. M. Kolthoff, *Ind. Eng. Chem., Anal. Ed.*, **14**, 197 (1942).

[40] C. S. Miller, Ph.D. Thesis, University of Minnesota, 1940.

to such a point that precipitation of the hydroxides of metals can occur. These interfering effects can be circumvented by removing the dissolved oxygen from the solution before bringing it in contact with the mercury anode, or better by employing a cell with an external anode.

Sulfite ion in neutral and alkaline solution rapidly reduces dissolved oxygen

$$2SO_3^{--} + O_2 \rightleftharpoons 2SO_4^{--}$$

and, as originally suggested by Hohn,[41] this reaction may be utilized to remove dissolved oxygen from polarographic solutions. For this purpose sufficient solid sodium sulfite to produce a sulfite ion concentration of 0.05 to 0.1 M is dissolved in the solution, and reduction of the oxygen usually is complete in 5 minutes or less. Since in solutions of pH smaller than about 6 hydrogen sulfite ion and sulfurous acid produce reduction waves at the d.e., the use of sulfite ion to remove dissolved oxygen is limited to solutions of pH greater than about 7.

The oxygen-sulfite reaction is inhibited by some substances and one must be on the alert for such effects. For example, in solutions of sodium hydroxide containing lead (plumbite ion) the oxygen-sulfite reaction is so slow that it cannot be used to remove dissolved oxygen.[42] In a great many cases it does serve efficiently and is much more convenient than sweeping with an inert gas.

6. PRECAUTIONS REGARDING GELATIN AS A MAXIMUM SUPPRESSOR

Various substances which have the ability to eliminate maxima and aid in the production of well-developed waves have been discussed in Chapter X. Of these gelatin is one of the most commonly used and it is generally quite satisfactory provided certain precautions are observed. The first of these is that only freshly prepared solutions should be used; the use of old, decomposed solutions frequently has a deleterious influence on wave characteristics. Usually a 0.1 or 0.2 per cent aqueous solution is prepared by treating a weighed amount of granulated gelatin with cold water and finally heating on the steam bath with thorough stirring until solution is complete. It is possible to add certain preservative agents to retard bacterial decomposition, but since the solutions are so easily prepared we recommend that they be prepared freshly every few days as needed.

In using gelatin it is important not to employ a greater concentration than is actually required. Ordinarily a concentration of 0.005 per cent,

---

[41] H. Hohn, *Chemische Analysen mit dem Polarographen*, Berlin, 1937.
[42] J. J. Lingane, *Ind. Eng. Chem., Anal. Ed.*, **18**, 431 (1946).

or at most 0.01 per cent, is adequate. The use of larger concentrations can decrease wave slopes, distort the wave form, and decrease the diffusion current markedly. For example Meites[43] observed that addition of 0.01 per cent gelatin to an alkaline tartrate solution of copper nearly obliterates the copper wave. Taylor and Smith[44] reported a similar observation with lead in alkaline tartrate medium, and many other examples could be quoted. These effects very probably reflect the formation of gelatin-metal complexes, and/or phenomena associated with the adsorption of gelatin on the surface of the mercury drops.

The various effects produced by gelatin and other maximum suppressors have been systematically discussed by Meites, Meites, and Colichman.[45] According to these investigators the effects fall into six classes according to the type of influence on half-wave potentials and diffusion currents, whether they cause division of an originally single wave into two parts, and whether they influence the degree of reversibility of the electrode reactions.

7. MERCURY POISONING

Because of its appreciable vapor pressure (0.0013 mm. at 20°), and the fact that it is highly toxic, reasonable precautions should be observed when working with mercury. According to Jacobs[46] the maximal safe concentration of mercury vapor is about 0.1 mg. per cubic meter of air, and air saturated with mercury vapor at 20° contains about 15 times this quantity. It is evident that the toxic limit can easily be exceeded in poorly ventilated laboratories in which droplets of mercury have been allowed to accumulate in crevices in floors and desks or otherwise carelessly handled. Methods of determining the concentration of mercury vapor in air are described by Jacobs (loc. cit.).

---

[43] L. Meites, J. Am. Chem. Soc., **71,** 3269 (1949).

[44] J. K. Taylor and R. E. Smith, Anal. Chem., **22,** 495 (1950).

[45] L. Meites, T. Meites, and E. L. Colichman, J. Am. Chem. Soc., **72,** 3686 (1950). E. L. Colichman, ibid., **72,** 4036 (1950).

[46] M. B. Jacobs, Analytical Chemistry of Industrial Poisons, Hazards, and Solvents, 2nd Ed., Interscience, New York, 1949 (p. 224).

CHAPTER XIX

Voltammetry with Solid Microelectrodes

1. STATIONARY PLATINUM MICROELECTRODES

Various investigators have reported current–voltage curves that show limiting currents in electrolysis experiments using stationary electrodes in unstirred solutions. As early as 1897 Salomon[1] described c.v. curves obtained with solutions of silver, mercurous, and cupric ions, using stationary electrodes of the respective metals. Although definite diffusion currents were obtained the conditions of diffusion near the electrodes were not well defined, and the curves are difficult to interpret. Glasstone[2] and Glasstone and Reynolds,[3] found a proportionality between the diffusion current and concentration in the electroreduction of ferricyanide, ferric ion, permanganate, quinone, cadmium ion, and cupric ion, and in the electrooxidation of ferrocyanide, ferrous ion, iodine, hydroquinone, and hydroxylamine. These experiments were performed using a small platinum wire electrode in unstirred oxygen-free solutions at room temperature without temperature control. Wilson and Youtz[4] studied the oxidation of ferrous iron to ferric iron using a cylindrical carbon anode of relatively large area separated by means of a porous cup from the cathode, which was a large hollow carbon cylinder. The concentration of ferrous ion was high (0.03 M to 0.25 M) and the diffusion currents consequently were much greater than those observed by Glasstone and Reynolds. Even in this unfavorable case, the diffusion current was found to be approximately proportional to the concentration of ferrous iron.

The measurements reported in the literature are, however, accurate only to about ± 5 per cent in the best cases, and are not comparable in accuracy with those made with the dropping mercury electrode. For analytical purposes, and accuracy of ± 0.5 to ± 1 per cent in the current readings is desirable. Laitinen and Kolthoff[5] determined the reproducibility of diffusion

---

[1] E. Salomon, *Z. physik. Chem.*, **24**, 55 (1897); **25**, 365 (1898).

[2] S. Glasstone,. *Trans. Am. Electrochem. Soc.*, **59**, 277 (1931).

[3] Glasstone and G. D. Reynolds, *Trans. Faraday Soc.*, **29**, 399 (1933).

[4] R. E. Wilson and M. A. Youtz, *Ind. Eng. Chem.*, **15**, 603 (1923).

[5] H. A. Laitinen and I. M. Kolthoff, *J. Phys. Chem.*, **45**, 1061 (1941).

currents obtained under well-defined diffusion conditions with a platinum wire microelectrode and checked the proportionality between diffusion current and concentration with a view to possible analytical applications. These authors used a manual apparatus. In most experiments, the current was measured by determining the potential drop across a standard 9999-ohm resistance in series with the cell (see Chapter XVI). A galvanometer used to measure the current gave exactly the same results, and may be preferred since the approach to the steady current state may be followed directly, and any fluctuations in the current are immediately apparent. A microammeter may also be used for the current measurements. The electrodes used consisted of a platinum wire 4 mm. long and 0.5 mm. in diameter sealed in the end of a glass tube and suspended in the solution.

Technique of Measurements. The attainment of a steady current state with a stationary platinum microelectrode depends upon reaching a state of uniform and reproducible convection in the solution immediately surrounding the microelectrode. It is therefore necessary to perform the experiments in a solution maintained at a constant temperature to avoid thermal convection, and under conditions that prevent any mechanical disturbances, such as vibrations from the thermostat stirring motor. The experiments of Laitinen and Kolthoff were run with the cell in a water thermostat regulated to $\pm 0.01°$, with the stirrer mounted on wall brackets to prevent vibration. The absence of mechanical disturbances was shown by measuring the diffusion current both with the thermostat stirrer in operation and shut off. Identical results were obtained in all cases whether the stirrer was in operation or not.

In most cases, it is necessary to remove dissolved oxygen from the solutions, since oxygen is reduced to hydrogen peroxide on a platinum electrode at sufficiently negative potentials. In certain cases, such as the oxidation of ferrocyanide or ferrous ions, the removal of dissolved oxygen is unnecessary, since the entire current–voltage curve occurs in a region of potentials so positive that the reduction of oxygen does not interfere. Tank nitrogen is usually sufficiently free of oxygen to be used without purification. A stream of nitrogen is bubbled through the cell solution for about 30 minutes, and is shut off and the solution allowed to stand until stirring has ceased before the current–voltage curve is determined.

At each value of the applied e.m.f., the electrolysis is allowed to proceed until the current has reached a steady value. In most cases, two to three minutes is sufficient, although in certain cases of irreversible electrode reaction, a considerably longer time is required for a steady current state. The applied e.m.f. is carefully and slowly increased to reach the next desired point on the curve, in order to cause a minimum of disturbance of the diffusion state near the electrode, and to prevent even a momentary discharge of gaseous hydrogen or oxygen on the electrode surface. The current–voltage curves were found to be entirely reproducible in either direction if care was taken to prevent the formation of gas bubbles on the electrode surface.

In the case of metal deposition on a platinum surface, the metal will, of course, enter solution at any potential more positive than the null potential of the metal in the solution of its ions, and to this extent the current–voltage curve depends on the direction of change of the applied e.m.f.

(a) Other Types of Stationary Electrodes

A vibrating platinum microelectrode has been designed by Harris and Lindsey[6] which vibrates at a constant frequency of 100 cycles per second with an amplitude considerably greater than its linear dimensions. With this electrode, reproducible polarograms were obtained free from irregularities due to external vibration and were smoother than polarograms obtained with a dropping mercury electrode. This type of electrode can be adapted to obtain polarograms with small volumes of solution where other mechanisms (such as rotating) would be too bulky.

Müller[7] has constructed an apparatus in which the solution under study flows through a constricted tube containing a small platinum wire electrode having an area of only 0.3 mm.^{2} (called "by-passed" electrode). Under the proper conditions the limiting currents are a linear function of the concentration of the reacting substance and of the logarithm of the rate of flow. With this apparatus the system ferric–ferrous chloride was found to be reversible, but the system quinone–hydroquinone was irreversible. These results are similar to those found with the stationary platinum electrodes. The by-pass electrode may be adapted for studies in biological systems where the electrode may be inserted into the blood stream. The electrode may also have industrial use in the continuous measurement of concentrations of electroactive materials in a fluid circulating at a constant rate or measurement of the rate of flow if the concentration is known.

Using a flow method, Giguère and Lauzier[8] developed a method for the continuous determination of oxygen dissolved in water.

A "dipping electrode" has been designed by Lyalikov and Karmazin.[9]

---

[6] E. D. Harris and A. J. Lindsey, *Nature*, **162**, 413 (1948).

[7] O. H. Müller, *J. Am. Chem. Soc.*, **69**, 2992 (1947).

[8] P. A. Giguère and L. Lauzier, *Can. J. Research*, **B23**, 223 (1945).

[9] Yu. S. Lyalikov and V. I. Karmazin, *Zavodskaya Lab.*, **14**, 138–143 (1948).

A platinum needle surrounded by an open-end glass tube is immersed in the solution and a gas is led through the tube and allowed to escape in bubbles. The needle comes in contact with the solution every time a gas bubble escapes and thus is intermittently and alternately dipped and isolated from the solution. Linearity was observed between the magnitude of the current and the concentration for lead, cadmium, and cupric solutions. This electrode was also applied to the determination of cations in fused salts,[10] e. g., cadmium, copper, nickel in potassium nitrate, and silver.[11]

Solid electrodes sometimes give irreproducible currents as electrolysis proceeds due to changes in the surface of the electrode. In order to minimize these effects, Miller[12] employs two platinum wire electrodes in conjunction with a reference electrode. One of the wire electrodes is periodically "renewed" by being short-circuited to the anode, while the other is being used as a polarized cathode. A polarization period of 0.5 to 1 sec. is used. Miller claimed that this technique is suitable for the determination of metals less noble than mercury and for polarographic studies with fused electrolytes.

Morris[13] adapted this same technique to the use of two rotating electrodes in solution using an electronic control as a switch.

Olson, Brackett, and Crickard[14] applied an alternating potential to a stationary platinum microelectrode. This alternating potential had the form of a square wave with interposed shorting periods between the negative and positive pulses. The frequencies found best suited for use were 5 to 10 cycles per minute. The instantaneous current passing through the cell was measured near the end of each negative pulse applied to the platinum microelectrode. By stepwise increase of the magnitude of the square wave voltage, current–voltage curves were obtained similar to those obtained with the dropping mercury electrode. The height of the diffusion current was found to be proportional to the concentration of oxygen and of lead. Olson et al. claim that the method has the advantage of utilizing simple stationary platinum electrodes with as good or improved stability as compared to those methods requiring moving electrodes, constant flow, or recessed electrodes. A day-to-day stability of ±1 per cent was observed

---

[10] Yu. S. Lyalikov and V. I. Karmazin, *Zavodskaya Lab.*, **14**, 144–148 (1948).

[11] Yu. S. Lyalikov and R. I. Glazes, *Zavodskaya Lab.*, **15**, 909–911 (1949).

[12] S. D. Miller, *Trudy Vsesoyuz. Konferents Anal. Khim.*, **2**, 551 (1943).

[13] C. J. O. R. Morris, *Analyst*, **72**, 298 (1947).

[14] R. A. Olson, F. S. Brackett, and R. G. Crickard, *J. Gen. Physiol.*, **32**, 681–703 (1949).

for 10^{-3} M lead solution. For these reasons the method should be useful for biological determinations *in situ*.

The use of solid microelectrodes in conjunction with oscillographic polarography has been described by Randles[15] and Airey.[16] A linear potential sweep of 1 to 2 sec. duration was applied periodically every 7 to 10 sec. to a stationary microelectrode in the polarographic cell. The current during the sweep is observed oscillographically as a function of the potential applied to the cell. A current maximum is observed when reduction occurs. The height of this maximum is proportional to the concentration of the reducible species. Between voltage sweeps the potential of the microelectrode is returned to positive potentials for a length of time sufficient for the metals that have been plated out during the previous sweep to be redissolved and normal diffusion conditions to be restored at the electrode surface (about 10 sec.). Platinum and amalgamated platinum and silver electrodes have been used as electrodes. The amalgamated electrodes have the advantage of being usable up to potentials as negative as -2.1 (Airey), but of course their use at positive potentials is limited.

(b) Use of a Silver Wire Electrode

Instead of platinum electrodes of silver, copper,[17] and of amalgams of these metals[16] have been recommended.

(c) Automatic Recording

Rogers *et al.*[18] and Skobets and Kacherova[19] investigated the automatic recording of polarograms with stationary and rotating platinum electrodes. With stationary electrodes current maxima were obtained when the voltage was continuously increased. These current maxima are due to the fact that the voltage change is more rapid than the rate at which a steady state of diffusion equilibria can be set up at the electrode.

Skobets, Turov, and Ryabokon[20] have found that these current maxima may be eliminated by using operating temperatures of 50° to 60° C. It is claimed that it is possible to analyze substances such as zinc and cadmium to concentrations of 10^{-6} to 10^{-7} M by using a bath thermostated at 60° C.

---

[15] J. E. B. Randles, *Trans. Faraday Soc.*, **44**, 327 (1948); *Analyst*, **72**, 301 (1947).

[16] L. Airey, *Analyst*, **72**, 306 (1947).

[17] D. Lydersen, *Acta Chem. Scand.*, **3**, 259 (1949).

[18] L. B. Rogers, H. H. Miller, R. B. Goodrich, and A. F. Stehney, *Anal. Chem.*, **21**, 777 (1949).

[19] E. M. Skobets and S. A. Kacherova, *Zavodskaya Lab.*, **13**, 133–137 (1947).

[20] E. M. Skobets, P. P. Turov, and V. D. Ryabokon, *Zavodskaya Lab.*, **15**, 912–914 (1949).

Rotating electrodes do not show these maxima but Rogers *et al.*[18] have observed a second type of maxima with the use of silver ion in 0.1 *M* potassium nitrate. These maxima of the second type are attributed to a brief discharge of hydrogen.

The effect of the rate of change of potential on the current–voltage curve of silver with stationary electrodes was also investigated by Rogers *et al.* No effect was observed on the half-wave potential but sometimes faster rates of polarization produced larger diffusion currents. The height of the diffusion current was found to be roughly proportional to the area of the electrode, but large errors might be obtained if one attempts to predict the size of the diffusion current of an electrode by comparing its area with that of a second electrode.

Rogers found a linear relationship between concentration and the diffusion current for the reduction of silver ions at stationary platinum electrodes using a continuously changing voltage, but the precision is not as good as with the dropping mercury electrode. It was also found that a ten-fold increase in the concentration of silver ion (all other factors being constant) shifts the half-wave potential by 0.056 v., in good agreement with the theoretical shift of 0.059 v. For the reduction of ferric iron in 0.1 *N* hydrochloric acid no change in half-wave potential with concentration of reducible ion is to be expected. Actually, an increase of 0.006 v. for a hundred-fold decrease in the concentration of ferric iron was observed.

The effect of stirring a solution when using stationary electrodes is to increase the diffusion current and remove the maxima common to the application of a continuously changing voltage to the stationary electrodes. The range of the diffusion current plateau also becomes less and in some cases is not observed at all.

2. EXAMPLES OF CURRENT–VOLTAGE CURVES OBTAINED WITH THE STATIONARY PLATINUM WIRE ELECTRODE[21]

Deposition of Metal Ions. Typical current–voltage curves obtained in the deposition of silver, copper, thallous, and lead ions from 0.001 *M* solutions in 0.1 *N* potassium chloride (0.1 *N* potassium nitrate in the case of silver) are shown plotted in Fig. XIX-1.

A region of constant diffusion current is obtained in each case, followed by a rising current due to hydrogen evolution. The difference in hydrogen overvoltage on the various freshly deposited metal surfaces is clearly indicated by the differences in the potentials at which the final unlimited rise in current occurs. It may be mentioned that the nature of the hydrogen

---

[21] H. A. Laitinen and I. M. Kolthoff, *J. Phys. Chem.*, **45**, 1061 (1945).

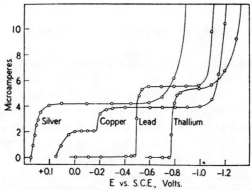

Fig. XIX-1. Typical current–voltage curves of 0.001 M solutions of silver, copper, thallous, and lead ions, obtained with a stationary platinum microelectrode.

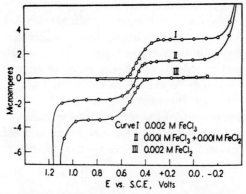

Curve I 0.002 M FeCl$_3$
    II 0.001 M FeCl$_3$ + 0.001 M FeCl$_2$
    III 0.002 M FeCl$_2$

Fig. XIX-2. Cathodic, anodic, and composite cathodic-anodic curves of ferric and ferrous ions, obtained with a stationary platinum microelectrode.

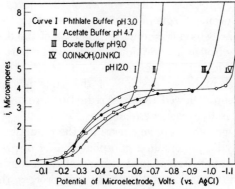

Curve I Phthlate Buffer pH 3.0
    II Acetate Buffer pH 4.7
    III Borate Buffer pH 9.0
    IV 0.01 NaOH, 0.1 N KCl
        pH 12.0

Fig. XIX-3. Oxygen waves obtained with a stationary platinum microelectrode in various air-saturated solutions.

405

evolution curve is determined not only by the hydrogen ion concentration and the hydrogen overvoltage of the metal surface, but also by the buffer capacity of the medium, since the discharge of hydrogen ion results in a region of comparatively alkaline solution near the electrode surface unless the solution is well buffered. With the above metals the diffusion current (after correction for the residual current) was found proportional to the concentration. The concentration range studied was between 2×10^{-4} and 2×10^{-3} M.

Oxidation and Reduction Reactions in Which the Oxidized and Reduced Forms Are Both Soluble in the Liquid Phase. Examples of this type of reaction are the oxidation of ferrocyanide and ferrous ions, the reduction of ferricyanide and ferric ions, etc.

Figure XIX-2 shows a set of current–voltage curves obtained in the case of ferrous and ferric iron, separately and in a mixture. A linear proportionality between diffusion current and concentration was found. A similar proportionality was found in the cases of ferricyanide (cathodic current) and ferrocyanide (anodic current) when enough indifferent salt was present to eliminate the migration current.

Current–voltage curves for *oxygen* reductions in various buffer solutions, in 0.01 N sodium hydroxide, and in 0.1 N potassium chloride saturated with air, are shown in Fig. XIX-3. It is striking that although the net electrode reaction

$$O_2 + 2e + 2H^+ \rightarrow H_2O_2$$

involves hydrogen ions, there is no pronounced pH effect on the potential at which oxygen reduction begins or on the shape of the current–voltage curve. The small differences in the shapes of the curves are probably to be attributed to specific effects of the ions constituting the various buffer systems. A similar behavior is found in the case of the dropping mercury electrode where hydrogen ions do not appear to take part in the potential determining reaction, but changes in the shape of the reduction curve are found if two different buffer systems of the same pH are investigated. Laitinen and Kolthoff showed that the reduction product of oxygen on a platinum surface is hydrogen peroxide.

A typical set of current–voltage curves for the reduction of quinone and the oxidation of hydroquinone in a phosphate buffer of pH 7.0 is shown in Fig. XIX-4. Although well-defined regions of diffusion currents are obtained for both the oxidation and the reduction process, the shapes of the curves show pronounced deviations from those predicted theoretically.

Skobets and Atamanenko[22] studied the anodic oxidation of organic com-

---

[22] E. M. Skobets and N. N. Atamanenko, *Zavodskaya Lab.*, **15**, 1291 (1949).

pounds using automatic recording. Hydroquinone, pyrocatechol, and ascorbic acid were found to give well-defined waves. Substances which undergo destructive oxidation (resorcinol, oxalic acid, ethanol, and formic acid) give curves with a peculiar fairly sharp maximum followed by a continuous rise. Interesting and exact studies on the anodic oxidation of substituted p-phenylenediamines at the stationary electrode are described by Julian and Ruby.[23]

Current–Voltage Curves for Hydrogen Evolution. Since the potential region in which current–voltage curves can be obtained with platinum microelectrodes is always restricted in the negative potential direction by

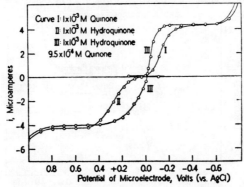

Fig. XIX-4. Typical current–voltage curves of quinone and hydroquinone, and their mixture, obtained with a stationary platinum microelectrode.

the evolution of hydrogen, the electrolysis of solutions of weak and strong acids in appropriate in different solutions was investigated.

Figure XIX-5 shows current–voltage curves obtained in the electrolysis of 0.001 N hydrochloric acid in 0.1 N potassium chloride using bright and platinized platinum microelectrodes of approximately the same geometrical area (projected area). Well-defined diffusion current regions were obtained in both cases, but the diffusion current was not found to be proportional to the concentration of hydrochloric acid in either case.

The formation of hydrogen bubbles on the platinum surface and the consequent decrease in effective electrode area with increasing current probably accounts for the decreasing value of the diffusion current constant i_d/C with increasing concentration of hydrochloric acid.

A somewhat more steeply rising curve, occurring at a potential about 0.1 v. more positive, is obtained with a platinized electrode than with the

[23] D. B. Julian and W. R. Ruby, *J. Am. Chem. Soc.*, **72**, 4719 (1950).

bright electrode, clearly indicating the hydrogen overvoltage on the latter. This difference in potential, however, cannot be regarded as a quantitative measure of the overvoltage of the bright platinum electrode, since the platinized electrode has a zero overvoltage only at the null point, *i. e.*, at zero current.

In the electrolysis of a very weak acid, the diffusion current is determined by the rate of diffusion of the undissociated acid rather than by the diffusion of hydrogen ions. For a given concentration of solution, a weak acid should therefore give a much smaller diffusion current than a strong acid, since the diffusion coefficient of a weak acid molecule in general is much smaller than that of hydrogen ions. This behavior is illustrated in

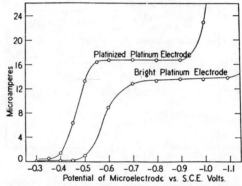

Fig. XIX-5. Current–voltage curves of hydrogen evolution from 0.001 N hydrochloric acid in 0.1 N potassium chloride, with bright and platinized platinum wire microelectrodes.

Fig. XIX-6 which shows the current–voltage curves obtained in the electrolysis of 0.001 N acetic acid in 0.1 N potassium chloride, and in 0.1 N sodium acetate and 0.1 N potassium chloride. The diffusion currents obtained were 3.3 and 3.0 microamp., respectively, as compared with 13.5 microamp. with the same concentration of hydrochloric acid. The current obtained in the presence of a large excess of sodium acetate may be taken as an indication of the rate of diffusion of undissociated acetic acid molecules, since under these conditions the acetic acid is present almost entirely in the undissociated form. The current of 3.3 microamp. obtained in the absence of sodium acetate is partly due to the diffusion of hydrogen ions from dissociated acetic acid.

General Characteristics of Current–Voltage Curves Obtained with the Stationary Platinum Microelectrode. From the above review it appears that the stationary electrode can be of use in analytical work, the accuracy being of the order of 1 per cent when proper care is taken in the measurements. It should be emphasized that the diffusion current increases about 4 per cent per degree increase of temperature, while the temperature coefficient in the case of the dropping electrode and also of the rotating electrode is about 2 per cent per degree. Laitinen and Kolthoff also found that the diffusion current of silver ions increased markedly with the electrolyte content of the solution. For example, with solutions of 0.001 M silver nitrate they found the following values of i_d : in 0.1 N KNO$_3$, 3.80; in 0.2 N KNO$_3$, 3.85; in 0.5 N KNO$_3$, 3.95; in 1 N KNO$_3$, 4.20 microamp.

It is of interest to compare diffusion currents obtained with various

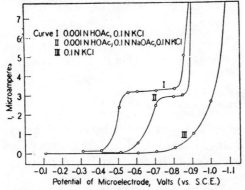

Fig. XIX-6. Current–voltage curves of hydrogen evolution from acetic acid, obtained with a bright platinum wire microelectrode.

substances at the same temperature, and to consider the thickness of the diffusion layer around the electrode. If it is assumed that the steady state of current is reached when a diffusion process occurs through a diffusion layer of constant effective thickness* in all cases, it is possible to derive simple equations for the diffusion currents of various substances and for the shapes of the current–voltage curves.

The total flow, f, of a diffusing substance having a diffusion coefficient D, through a diffusion layer of effective thickness l, to an electrode of

---

* The effective thickness of a diffusion layer is defined as the thickness of a hypothetical diffusion layer in which the concentration gradient of diffusing substance is constant throughout the layer and equal to that of the actual diffusion layer at the electrode surface. The flux of diffusing material and, therefore, the current are determined only by the concentration gradient *at the electrode surface*, and are therefore the same in the actual and hypothetical cases.

area A is given by Fick's First Law of diffusion, which becomes

$$f = (AD/l)\ (C - C_0)\ \text{moles sec.}^{-1} \tag{1}$$

where C is the molar concentration of diffusing material in the bulk of the solution and C_0 is the concentration at the electrode surface.

The current due to the electrode reaction is

$$i = nF_y f = (AD/l)\ nF_y(C - C_0) \tag{2}$$

where n is the number of electrons involved in the electrode reaction and F_y is the faraday.

When a diffusion current is reached, C_0 becomes vanishingly small and eq. 2 becomes

$$i_d = (AD/l)\ nF_y C \tag{3}$$

For a given electrode, and assuming that l is a constant in all cases, we have

$$i_d = knDC \tag{4}$$

Equation 4 predicts a proportionality between diffusion current and concentration, which should hold only if the effective diffusion layer thickness is a constant independent of the concentration of diffusing material. This appears to be the case.

For various electrode reactions, the diffusion current at the same *equivalent* concentration of diffusing substance should be proportional to the diffusion coefficients, while in the case of the dropping electrode i_d is proportional to the square root of D. A comparison of the calculated and experimental values of the diffusion current quotient (the diffusion current observed with a solution containing one millimole per liter of electro active substance) for various ions at 25° C. in solutions containing 0.1 N indifferent electrolyte, is given in Table XIX-1.

It is seen from the table that there is a fair agreement (± 5 per cent) between the observed diffusion current quotients and those calculated from that of the thallous ion, assuming a proportionality between the diffusion current constant and the diffusion coefficient. This indicates that the effective diffusion layer thickness is at least approximately constant for various electrode processes. The effective diffusion layer thickness l calculated from eq. 3 for the electroreduction of thallium and lead ions and electrooxidation of ferrocyanide ions was found to be 0.25 mm. This is a quite plausible value.   The change of the thickness l with the temperature is given by:

$$l_t = l_{25} \cdot \frac{D_t}{D_{25}} \cdot \frac{(i_d)_{25}}{(i_d)_t} \tag{5}$$

Actually, Laitinen and Kolthoff found that l decreased slightly with increasing temperature but became constant at 30° C. or above.

Polarization phenomena are responsible for the fact that the calculated shapes of the c.v. curves obtained with the stationary electrode differ considerably from the theoretical shapes which are calculated on the as-

TABLE XIX-1

RELATION BETWEEN DIFFUSION CURRENT AND DIFFUSION COEFFICIENT AT A STATIONARY PLATINUM MICROELECTRODE

| Substance | D^0, cm.^{2} sec.$^{-1}$ | microamp./millimole/liter | | |
		Calcd.	Obsd.	Diff., per cent
Tl$^+$	2.00×10^{-5}	$(5.35)^b$	(5.35)	—
Ag$^+$	1.65	4.41	4.24	-3.9
Cu^{++}	0.72	3.85	3.92	1.8
Pb^{++}	0.98	5.24	5.48	4.6
Fe(CN)$_6^{---}$	0.89	2.38	2.28	4.2
Fe(CN)$_6^{----}$	0.74	1.98	2.04	3.0
O$_2$	2.38^a	—	12.8	—

^{a} Calculated from diffusion current.
^{b} Comparison standard.

sumption that concentration polarization is the only kind of polarization which occurs.

3. ROTATED PLATINUM WIRE MICROELECTRODES

Measurements with the stationary electrode involve the disadvantage that is is necessary to wait for at least two minutes at each value of the applied e.m.f. until a steady state of current is reached.   Laitinen and Kolthoff[24] eliminated this disadvantage by working with a rotating electrode.

Many investigators have studied current–voltage curves obtained in electrolysis experiments using either rotating platinum microelectrodes or microelectrodes of various metals in stirred solutions.   Nernst and Merriam[25] were the first to describe current–voltage curves obtained with a

[24] H. A. Laitinen and I. M. Kolthoff, *J. Phys. Chem.*, **45**, 1079 (1941).
[25] W. Nernst and E. S. Merriam, *Z. physik. Chem.*, **52**, 235 (1905).

rotating platinum microelectrode. They observed constant regions of diffusion current, which were proportional to the concentration of the electroactive substance in the electroreduction of iodine, bromine, chlorine, silver ion, and permanganate ion, in an excess of indifferent electrolyte. In other cases, such as the electroreduction of dichromate, chlorate, ferricyanide, and persulfate ions, and the electrooxidation of ferrocyanide, ferrous, and stannous ions, a much smaller current was observed than was expected and no well-defined diffusion current regions were observed. Fresenius[26] observed diffusion currents with dilute solutions of hydrochloric acid in 0.1 N potassium chloride using a small rotating platinized platinum cathode and a large platinized platinum anode. Goldschmidt[27] studied the electroreduction of nitrobenzene in 0.1 N sodium hydroxide in 65 per cent alcohol at various electrodes in stirred solutions. No well-defined diffusion current regions were observed. Åkerberg[28] investigated the electrooxidation of oxalic acid in the presence of sulfuric acid at a platinized platinum anode in stirred solutions. Although he did not determine current–voltage curves it appears from his data that definite diffusion current regions proportional to the oxalic acid concentration would be expected in a strongly acid medium. Russ[29] and Haber and Russ[30] studied the reduction of nitrobenzene, paranitrophenol, and quinone, and the oxidation of hydroquinone, using relatively large electrodes of various metals in stirred solutions. No diffusion current regions were observed in these experiments, due to the large size of the electrodes and the relatively great concentrations used. In each case, the potential of the electrode was found to be a linear function of the logarithm of the current. This relationship indicates the variation of the speed of the electrode reaction as a function of the potential, since under the experimental conditions the current was not determined by the rate of diffusion. A similar type of investigation has recently been carried out by Rosenthal, Lorch, and Hammett[31] on the kinetics of the electrode reactions of the quinone–hydroquinone system, using very rapidly rotating electrodes. It was found that a speed of stirring could be reached beyond which there was no further effect on the current. Under these conditions the current appears to be determined only by the rate of the electrode reaction itself, and it was strongly influenced by the catalytic properties of

[26] L. R. Fresenius, *Z. physik. Chem.*, **80**, 481 (1912).

[27] H. Goldschmidt, *Z. Elektrochem.*, **7**, 263 (1900).

[28] T. Åkerberg, *Z. anorg. allgem. Chem.*, **31**, 161 (1902).

[29] R. Russ, *Z. physik. Chem.*, **44**, 641 (1903).

[30] F. Haber and R. Russ, *Z. physik. Chem.*, **47**, 257 (1904).

[31] R. Rosenthal, A. E. Lorch, and P. Hammett, *J. Am. Chem. Soc.*, **59**, 1795 (1937).

the electrode surface. Brunner[32] studied the oxidation of iodide and the reduction of iodine in a 1 N potassium chloride solution containing a small concentration of hydrochloric acid using a platinum electrode in a stirred solution. Diffusion current regions corresponding to the reduction of iodine to iodide ion, and the oxidation of iodide ion to iodine and to hypoiodite were observed. Brunner[33] also observed diffusion currents due to hydrogen evolution on a platinized platinum cathode.

A state of confusion exists in the literature concerning the effect of the rates of stirring of solutions on the rates of reactions at a solid–liquid interface. Nernst and Merriam found that the diffusion current increased with the 0.6th power of the rate of rotation of the microelectrode. Brunner found that the diffusion current of hydrogen ions with a stationary electrode in a stirred solution increased with the two-thirds power of the rate of rotation of the stirrer. On the other hand Jablczynski[34] reported that for rapid heterogeneous reactions, the rate varied with the 0.85th power of the rate of stirring, while Van Name and Edgar[35] gave the power to be 0.80. Roller[36] is of the opinion that an exponent of 0.8 is to be expected for all cases in which the chemical reaction at the solid–solution interface is rapid. His conclusion does not appear to be justified in cases where constant diffusion current regions are observed. Here the rate of the electrode reaction is certainly much more rapid than the rate of diffusion, and smaller values of the exponent are observed.

A more detailed discussion of the work of Laitinen and Kolthoff[37] is given below. They used two types of rotating microelectrodes.

Electrode A. This is a microelectrode consisting of a platinum wire about 3 mm. long and 0.5 mm. in diameter, sealed in the side of a 10-mm. bulb on the end of a piece of 6 mm. soft glass tubing. The tubing was mounted in an ordinary cone-drive laboratory stirring motor which rotated the electrode at a speed of about 600 r.p.m. Electrical connection to the electrode was made by means of a piece of copper wire inside the glass tubing, sealed with a small piece of Wood's metal to the platinum wire and connected to the cone-drive shaft of the motor. The top of the cone-drive shaft was drilled to form a small cup into which a drop of mercury was

[32] E. Brunner, *Z. physik. Chem.*, **56**, 321 (1906).

[33] E. Brunner, *Z. physik. Chem.*, **47**, 56 (1904).

[34] K. Jablczynski, *Z. physik. Chem.*, **64**, 748 (1908).

[35] R. G. Van Name and G. Edgar, *Am. J. Sci.*, **29**, 237 (1910); *Z. physik. Chem.*, **73**, 93 (1910).

[36] P. S. Roller, *J. Phys. Chem.*, **39**, 221 (1935).

[37] H. A. Laitinen and I. M. Kolthoff, *J. Phys. Chem.*, **45**, 1079 (1941).

introduced. A copper wire connection to the mercury drop formed an excellent electrical contact. No provision was made to remove dissolved oxygen, and therefore the application of electrode A was limited to cases in which oxygen did not interfere. It was found that the speed of rotation could be maintained very constant during a single experiment lasting 30 minutes to one hour, but that reproducible results could not be obtained from one day to the next. This type of electrode is very suitable for amperometric titrations in which the presence of oxygen does not interfere.

Electrode B. This is a rotating electrode, enabling a very constant and reproducible speed of rotation to be maintained in a system from which air can be removed, is shown in Fig. XIX-7. The electrode consists of a platinum wire 3.2 mm. long and 0.5 mm. in diameter on one side of an iron shaft. Two flanges on each side of the electrode protect it from mechanical damage or bending when the electrode is inserted into the rubber stopper. A mercury seal device is used to prevent the entrance of air, and also serves to make electrical contact to the electrode. The entire iron shaft is coated with several layers of ceresin wax for electrical insulation, and the wax is carefully scraped away from the platinum surface. One application of a thick coating of wax was found to last indefinitely and to provide good protection from corrosion and excellent electrical insulation. The bearing surfaces of the shaft consist of two 1/2-inch portions of the brass cover section, with a one-inch portion in the middle machined away from the shaft to decrease friction. The bearing surfaces are placed above the mercury seal to prevent any oil from the bearings from reaching the solution in the electrolysis cell.

In the experiments of Laitinen and Kolthoff the electrode was rotated by means of a *synchronous* electric motor rotating at exactly 1800 r.p.m. The synchronous motor was made from an ordinary split-phase 1/4 horsepower motor by accurately machining four slots 3/8 inch wide and 1/16 inch deep at exactly 90-degree intervals, into the rotor. The slots served to lock the motor into synchronism with 60-cycle alternating current, so that it rotated at exactly 1800 r.p.m. with light loads. A small pair of gears served to reduce the speed to 600 r.p.m. A flexible shaft was attached with a strong rubber connection to the gear shaft. The other end of the flexible shaft was provided with a flattened end to fit the slot in the top of the rotating electrode shaft. By these means the motor could be mounted in a horizontal position on a shelf conveniently removed from the thermostat.

All measurements were made with the electrolysis cell mounted in a water thermostat at 25° C., regulated to ±0.02°.

Another electrode assembly (Fig. XIX-8) which is also useful in amperometric titrations has been described by Stock.[38] A small hole A is blown in the upper part of the electrode stem B and allows emergence of

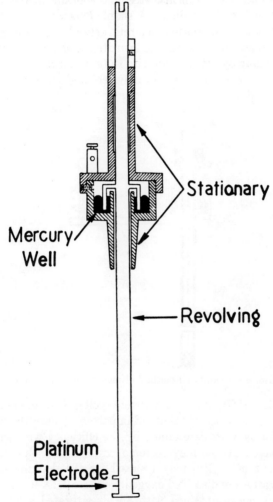

Fig. XIX-7. Rotated platinum microelectrode
(according to Laitinen and Kolthoff).

the copper wire which makes contact with the inner end of the platinum wire by the agency of a bead of mercury. The emerging end of the copper

[38] J. T. Stock, *Metallurgia*, **36**, 51 (1947).

wire is bent over and gripped within the bore of steel sleeve C by rubber D. The latter is cut from pressure tubing and holds the sleeve in position upon the electrode stem.   Well E is also steel and contains mercury, into which the lower end of the sleeve dips.   A shank F is welded to the well and enables the latter to be supported on a retort stand by means of a bosshead, a sleeve G of rubber tubing serving to insulate the shank from the bosshead. Connection is made by attaching a wire to terminal H.   To avoid rusting, all portions of the steel work not actually required for contact purpose are coated with cellulose enamel.

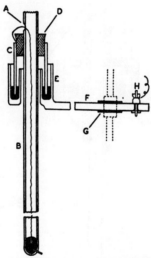

Fig. XIX-8. Sleeve and well method of making electrical connection.[38]

The Reduction of Oxygen.   The current–voltage curves of oxygen reduction on rotating microelectrodes are of importance, since the limit of practical application is often determined by the efficiency with which the last traces of dissolved oxygen may be removed from the solution.   Also, the diffusion current of oxygen may be used for the determination of very small concentrations of dissolved oxygen.   Figure XIX-9, curve I, shows a current–voltage curve obtained with an air-saturated solution of 0.1 N potassium chloride using electrode B.   Curve II was obtained after bubbling unpurified tank nitrogen through the solution for ten minutes.   The tremendously increased currents obtained with the rotating electrode are evident from the fact that a diffusion current of 61 microamp. for an air-saturated solution was obtained with the rotating microelectrode as compared with a diffusion current of 3 microamp. with a stationary microelectrode of equal area.

The removal of oxygen by bubbling unpurified tank nitrogen through the solution at the rate of about 4 bubbles per second is shown by the following data. After 5 minutes the diffusion current was 50 per cent of the original value; after 15 minutes, 14 per cent; after 30 minutes, 2.3 per cent; after 60 minutes, 1.3 per cent. Further bubbling did not appreciably lower the current. The removal of dissolved oxygen by reaction with sulfite[39] was found to be efficient and rapid. To 100 ml. of air-saturated 0.1 N potas-

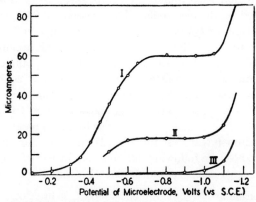

Fig. XIX-9. Current–voltage curves of oxygen obtained with the rotated platinum microelectrode: curve I, 0.1 N potassium chloride solution saturated with air; curve II, unpurified tank nitrogen bubbled through the solution for ten minutes; curve III, after adding 0.1 g. of sodium sulfite to 100 ml. of the solution.

sium chloride solution 0.1 g. of sodium sulfite was added, and the current–voltage curve determined after allowing the solution to stand for 10 minutes. No detectable amount of oxygen remained in solution. The current—voltage curve is shown in Fig. XIX-9, curve III.[40]

The reduction of oxygen on a silver-plated electrode was also investigated. It appeared that oxygen is reduced at a less negative potential at the silver surface than at the platinum surface. However, the freshly plated silver surface had a lower hydrogen overvoltage than the bright platinum surface, so that the evolution of hydrogen also occurred at less negative

---

[39] J. Heyrovsky, "Polarographie," in W. Böttger, *Physikalische Methoden der analytischen Chemie* (Vol. 3), Leipzig, 1936. H. Hohn, *Chemischen Analysen mit dem Polarographen*, Berlin, 1937.

[40] Cf. I. M. Kolthoff and H. A. Laitinen, *Science*, **92,** 150 (1940).

potentials on the silver surface. Actually, the diffusion current region was less well defined with the silver-plated electrode.

The Reduction of Bromine. In this case the diffusion current is reached at potentials at which oxygen is not yet reduced. The c.v. curve, therefore, can be determined in the presence of oxygen, which is of great practical advantage. Laitinen and Kolthoff found that i_d was proportional to the concentration, between 2.5×10^{-5} and 1×10^{-4} M; measured at $E = +0.200$ v. (vs. S.C.E.).

The Deposition of Silver Ion. A drifting current and no constant diffusion current region were found. This appeared to be due to the silver crystals deposited on the electrode. The presence of 0.01 per cent of gelatin in the solution produced well-adhering coatings of silver of finely crystalline structure. In the presence of these small amounts of gelatin, constant and reproducible diffusion currents were obtained with silver nitrate. In a medium of constant potassium nitrate concentration the diffusion current was found to be directly proportional to the silver ion concentration over a concentration range between 6×10^{-5} and 4×10^{-4} M silver nitrate. The diffusion current was found to be greatly dependent upon the potassium nitrate (or nitric acid) concentration in the solution. This is illustrated by the following data obtained with 10^{-4} M silver nitrate at different concentrations of indifferent electrolyte:

Nitrate concentration M	0.01	0.02	0.05	0.10	0.20	0.50	1.00
i_d microamp.	5.10	5.17	5.35	5.85	6.36	5.82	5.65

This variation of the diffusion current with changing indifferent electrolyte concentration cannot be attributed, except in a small part, to a variation of the diffusion coefficient of the silver ions. The main effect seems to be a change of the diffusion layer thickness with varying salt concentration due to secondary effects such as the changing viscosity of the medium. A change in the nature of the surface of the plated silver may also cause a change in the current by changing the effective electrode area. Since the diffusion layer thickness is only of the order of 0.02 mm., small surface irregularities would cause appreciable effects. The diffusion current of silver ions must be determined in the absence of oxygen.

The Oxidation of Ferrocyanide Ion. The appearance of a horizontal diffusion current region on a current–voltage curve requires the electrode reaction to be rapid in comparison with the rate of diffusion. With a rotating electrode the current density is increased tremendously for a given solution as compared with a stationary electrode, and it is therefore necessary to determine for each particular case whether current–voltage curves with well-defined diffusion current regions can be obtained. An example of the difficulties which may be encountered is that of the oxidation of ferrocyanide ion, which gave perfectly constant diffusion current regions with the stationary platinum wire microelectrode.

A solution of 5×10^{-4} M potassium ferrocyanide in 0.1 N potassium chloride was electrolyzed in the presence and absence of dissolved oxygen, using electrode B. In both cases only a very small current was observed when the potential of the microelectrode was made more positive, until a potential was reached at which oxygen evolution began. Oxygen evolution was allowed to proceed for a few minutes, after which the potential was made less positive. Now a fairly well-defined diffusion current region due to the oxidation of ferrocyanide was obtained for a few minutes, after which the current began to decrease with time. These results appear to indicate that the electrode reaction involves an intermediate substance formed during the evolution of oxygen. A possible mechanism is that proposed by Klemenc[41] and by Glasstone and Hickling[42] for various anodic processes. They suggest the formation of neutral hydroxyl, OH, which reacts with ferrocyanide to give ferricyanide and hydroxyl ions.

A definite salt effect on the shape of the current–voltage curves was observed. With increasing potassium chloride concentration, a more reversible behavior was obtained with the current rising more steeply with increasing potential.

The temperature coefficient of the diffusion current of ferrocyanide ion was found to be 2.5 per cent per degree over the temperature range 20° to 30° as compared with the value of 4 per cent per degree found with the stationary platinum wire microelectrode. The value of 2.5 per cent per degree would be expected on the basis of the change of the diffusion coefficient with temperature. Therefore, it may be concluded that the effective diffusion layer thickness remains practically constant with the rotating electrode for small temperature changes, while with the stationary electrode the effective diffusion layer thickness decreases with increasing temperature.

The rotated platinum electrode is of limited applicability and will find use only in specific cases, for example, in the determination of dissolved oxygen, bromine, iodine, chlorine, and silver even when present in traces.

Skobets and Kacherova[43] use the rotated electrode in the determination of mercury, lead, cadmium, and zinc in a mixture of the four. They also recommend the electrode for electrolysis studies in nonaqueous solutions and fused salts.

---

[41] A. Klemenc, *Z. physik. Chem.*, **A185**, 1 (1939).
[42] S. Glasstone and A. Hickling, *Chem. Revs.*, **25**, 407 (1939).
[43] E. M. Skobets, *et al.*, *Zavodskaya Lab.*, **14**, 131 (1948); *Chem. Abstr.*, **42**, 466 (1948).

Kolthoff and Leussing[44] use the rotated electrode to advantage in ammoniacal solutions containing sulfite. The sulfite removes the oxygen and the determinations need not be carried out in an inert gas. The diffusion current of thallium (I) was found proportional to the concentration. Cupric copper in ammoniacal medium containing sulfite gives two waves, the first wave corresponding to the reduction of cupric to cuprous and the second wave of cuprous to copper. The first wave is of special analytical importance; it is entirely reproducible and can be used in the determination of traces of copper, e. g., in distilled water. The reduction of cupric copper by sulfite in ammoniacal medium is slow. Cuprous copper gives an anodic wave under the above conditions. When an ammoniacal cupric copper solution which contains sulfite is allowed to stand, the anodic wave develops slowly. Thus, the rate of formation of cuprous copper can be studied amperometrically. It is expected that ammoniacal cupric copper solutions can be used advantageously in amperometric titrations with the rotated platinum electrode as indicator electrode.

Many strong oxidizing agents like ceric sulfate and chromic acid do not yield well-developed diffusion currents; this is due to polarization phenomena. Ceric sulfate in 2 N sulfuric acid gives a smeared-out wave; the current increases with increasing negative potential. Apparently the transfer of an electron to the ceric cerium is not extremely rapid, and the current is not entirely diffusion controlled.

Marks and Bannister[45] recommend rotating platinum electrodes in the control of water chlorination. Solutions of chloramines and hypochlorous acid were electrolyzed at varying pH values. A limiting current was found under favorable conditions even at the low chlorine concentrations that exist in drinking water when the electrode area was sufficient. Hypochlorous acid solutions yield a diffusion current in a potential range where chloramine is not yet reduced. Amperometric methods were found useful for continuous recording of chlorine residuals, even though limiting currents are not always found.

---

[44] I. M. Kolthoff and D. L. Leussing, *Z. anorg. Chem.*, **262**, 160 (1950).
[45] H. C. Marks and G. L. Bannister, *Anal. Chem.*, **19**, 200 (1947).